HOUSEHOLD EQUIPMENT

BOOKS IN HOME ECONOMICS

HOUSEHOLD EQUIPMENT. By *Louise Jenison Peet* and *Lenore E. Sater.*

ECONOMICS OF HOUSEHOLD PRODUCTION. By *Margaret G. Reid.*

FOOD PREPARATION. By *Marion Deyoe Sweetman.*

MANUAL FOR FOOD PREPARATION STUDY. By *Florance B. King.*

EXPERIMENTAL COOKERY FROM THE CHEMICAL AND PHYSICAL STANDPOINT. By *Belle Lowe.*

FOOD PREPARATION STUDIES. By *Alice M. Child, Kathryn Bele Niles,* and *Agnes M. Kolshorn.*

FOOD PREPARATION RECIPES. By *Alice M. Child* and *Kathryn Bele Niles.*

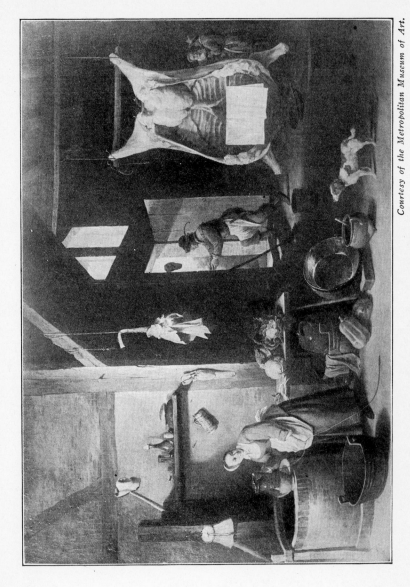

FIG. 1.—*Frontispiece*—A Dutch Kitchen. David Teniers the Elder, Flemish School, 1582-1649.

HOUSEHOLD EQUIPMENT

BY

LOUISE JENISON PEET, Ph.D.

Head of Household Equipment
Iowa State College

AND

LENORE E. SATER, M.S.

Assistant Professor of Household Equipment
Iowa State College

NEW YORK

JOHN WILEY & SONS, Inc.

London : CHAPMAN & HALL, Limited

1934

34-17062

Printed in the U. S. A.

THE HADDON CRAFTSMEN, INC.
CAMDEN, N. J.

The equipment does the work, but the hand gets the credit.
　　　　　　　　　　　　　　　—PERSIAN PROVERB.

PREFACE

This book is the outgrowth of lectures given during the past few years to students in the Home Economics Division of Iowa State College. Such a course in equipment, the writers believe, should find a place in every general home economics curriculum. During the last twenty years an increasing number of household appliances has appeared, and some special training is essential if the homemaker is to select an appliance wisely and use it intelligently. In the text, points of selection and methods of operation and care are stressed. Brief summaries are given at the end of each chapter.

It has seemed best in a textbook of this scope to limit the discussion for the most part to equipment commonly found in the kitchen and laundry. This eliminates certain appliances which have not been widely adopted as yet in the average home. Chapters on home lighting, heating and ventilating, and plumbing have also been included, since the care of these fixtures is frequently the duty of the housewife, and their efficient regulation and upkeep affect not only the budget but often to an important degree the health and happiness of the family.

The construction of many types of equipment is based on fundamental scientific laws, and these laws must be understood if the operator is to use the appliance with greatest efficiency. Although some knowledge of physics is a prerequisite to the course in equipment, students often fail to apply the principles learned, and it has seemed best to include a short summary of such physical, chemical, and other scientific facts as have direct bearing on the subject matter under discussion.

Illustrative material has been included whenever it seemed to aid in bringing out the meaning of the context, but it is expected that the text will be supplemented by suitable classroom demonstration and laboratory experiments. It is planned to follow this book in the near future with a manual of laboratory exercises.

The reference material is merely suggestive and by no means all-inclusive. With a very few exceptions no reference has been made to the many popular or semi-popular articles which appear from month to month in the homemaker's columns of magazines. Much valuable material is often obtainable from manufacturers of household appliances, but in this case has been omitted unless of a purely educational nature.

The authors wish to express their cordial appreciation to all those to whom they are indebted for suggestions and help. Special thanks are due our colleague, Professor Vivian Brashear, for permission to use material on kitchens and non-electrical small equipment; Professors F. E. Johnson, William Kunerth, R. A. Norman, R. W. Breckenridge, and Olive Settles; Messrs. Charles H. Roe of the Electrical Testing Laboratories and R. M. Conner of the American Gas Association Testing Laboratory; and Miss Iris Ashwell, who read all the manuscript.

When not otherwise specified, indebtedness for permission to use illustrative material is acknowledged at the end of each chapter.

CONTENTS

CHAPTER   PAGE

    I. KITCHENS 1

   II. MATERIALS USED IN HOUSEHOLD EQUIPMENT......... 26

  III. FUNDAMENTALS OF ELECTRICITY.................... 39

  IV. FUELS 52

   V. THE ELECTRIC RANGE............................. 56

  VI. GAS 82

 VII. THE GAS RANGE................................... 91

VIII. COAL, GASOLINE, AND KEROSENE RANGES............ 107

  IX. SMALL EQUIPMENT, ELECTRICAL.................... 120

   X. SMALL EQUIPMENT, NON-ELECTRICAL 135

  XI. REFRIGERATION 165

 XII. LAUNDRY PROCEDURE.............................. 195

XIII. ELECTRICAL CLEANING EQUIPMENT................. 224

XIV. HOME LIGHTING 238

 XV. HOME PLUMBING 272

XVI. HEATING AND VENTILATING....................... 288

CHAPTER I

KITCHENS

The term "equipment" is generally used for those appliances provided in the kitchen and laundry of the home in distinction to the "furnishings" of the other rooms of the house. Equipment implies action in addition to use.

A study of equipment includes the selection, operation, care, and arrangement of appliances. Since selection will depend upon the arrangement which is possible or pleasing, the arrangement of the kitchen may be considered first. This arrangement will not be exactly alike for every home, for the kitchen should express individuality the same as other rooms in the house, and it is doubtful if a wholly standardized kitchen is desirable except in large apartment houses or in small homes for the low or moderate wage earner. That such homes are in the majority is indicated by Whitten and Adams' study of families in 73 cities which showed that 61 per cent of the families had incomes averaging $2,000 or less, and paid rents under $35 a month. Of added significance is the fact that between 40 and 50 per cent of families live in rented houses. If the situation found in Arkansas by Carter is generally true, that a tenant family changes residence every three years, then kitchens of general design will undoubtedly more nearly fit the needs of the various occupants. Unfortunately "as in other crafts which are handed down from generation to generation, methods of building have been regulated too much by tradition and usage, and too little by reason and logic."[1]

The housekeeper, and she as a rule is the mother, spends an average of 45 to 50 per cent of her working hours in the kitchen. The most efficiently arranged and, therefore, undoubtedly the best-arranged kitchen is one that is so planned that the maximum amount of work may be done by the worker with a minimum amount of effort. The equipment used in the kitchen is arranged around three work centers: the preparation, cooking and serving, and clearing

[1] McDonald, John R. H. Modern Housing. p. 15.

1

away centers. The location of these three centers depends upon the size of the kitchen, its shape, and the position and number of openings.

Work centers.—Of the three operations, experiment has shown that the preparation of food takes more time and attention than the other two; clearing away, with the attendant dish-washing and replacing of dishes and utensils in their respective cupboards, claims second place in amount of time required; and cooking and serving ranks third. The equipment should be so arranged that the work of the more time-demanding centers may not be sacrificed to the less time-demanding. This arrangement is the more difficult because the sink and refrigerator are common to more than one center.

Equipment in work centers.—In the preparation center are the preparation cabinet or table, with storage cupboards for needed staple supplies and utensils, a refrigerator for perishables, bins for fruits and vegetables, and the sink. The cooking and serving center contains the range, with a shelf or cupboard for the utensils and serving dishes used primarily at the range, and some kind of a serving table. This table may be either stationary or movable. The clearing away center has a stack table with garbage receptacle, sink and drainboard, refrigerator for left-overs, and cabinets for the clean dishes.

Preparation center.—The supplies used in meal preparation are delivered at the back door or service entrance; so the preparation center should be close to this entrance. A shelf by the door where the delivery clerk may place the supplies prevents tracking across the kitchen. Owing to shortness of time it is sometimes necessary to leave the preparation table in a somewhat upset condition while the meal is being served and eaten. There is, therefore, an added advantage in having this center away from the dining room door. A place near the rear entrance is also the logical location for the refrigerator, when the ice-type refrigerator is used, although it is more convenient if the refrigerator may be iced through an outside opening. A mechanical refrigerator may be placed nearer the dining room door. Built-in air coolers may be used for the more bulky, less perishable foods, which do, however, need to be kept cooler than the average kitchen temperature permits.

Cooking and serving center.—To shorten the work of serving, the cooking and serving center should be near the dining room unless a coal or wood range is used. Whenever possible a coal or wood range is placed near the door to cellar or outside, to save steps and eliminate dirt in the bringing in of fuel and the removal of ashes.

When there is a breakfast nook or a table in the kitchen where the breakfast or other occasional meals are eaten, it should be at the

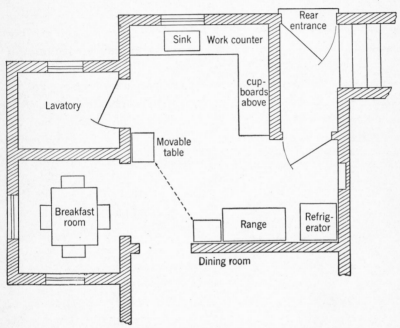

FIG. 2.—In this arrangement the breakfast alcove does not interfere with the general routing.

same end of the kitchen as the dining room to keep the general routing the same, but not necessarily between the kitchen and dining room. Such a location may increase the number of steps taken when meals are served in the dining room. (Fig. 2.)

Clearing away center.—The stack table for dishes returned from the dining room is preferably near the dining room door. When a cart has been used in serving the meal, it may be used to bring the dishes back to the stack table. To the left of the stack table is the sink with one or two drainboards, or without a drainboard if such an arrangement is preferred. A single drainboard should be at the left of the sink, unless the housekeeper is left-handed. Utensil and china cabinets may be built at either side of the sink or even above it. When the cabinet is above the sink, the sink should project at least 6 inches beyond the cabinet and there should be a clearance of 22 inches between the bottom of the sink and the cabinet; with the cabinet shelves 8 inches apart, dishes may be placed on the first three shelves without the use of a stool and without uncomfortable stretching. Such a location for the cabinet reduces walking to a minimum.

When the china is to be kept in a cupboard at one side of the sink the side chosen is a matter of personal preference. If the cupboard is at the left of the sink, the dishes may be placed in the cupboard as they are wiped without extra steps; if at the right of the sink, some steps must be taken, and probably some extra handling will be required, but the china may be nearer the dining room when needed again for the table. Some investigators suggest building the dish cabinet on a party wall between kitchen and dining room, with openings into both rooms. This undoubtedly saves steps in setting the table, but many homemakers find that such built-in cupboards detract from the appearance of the dining room and prefer to keep all but perhaps some unusually lovely pieces of china in the kitchen. When the kitchen is carefully arranged, it is doubtful if the difference in amount of energy used in the two cases is worth considering.

Routing.—A right-handed person uses fewest movements if she washes her dishes from right to left. The dishes are stacked to the right of the dish pan, are placed in the pan and washed, set on the drainboard to the left of the pan, and wiped and placed on a table to the left of the drainboard.

In the preparation and cooking and serving centers, one may work from right to left or left to right with equal convenience so long as the processes end at the dining room door, but it has been found that maximum efficiency is attained if the work is progressive with little or no retracing of steps. Since the clearing away center is arranged for work from right to left, the work carried on in the other centers would seem to fit in with this arrangement most satisfactorily if also routed from right to left. Actual experiment has proved this to be the case. The floor plan in Fig. 3 shows how a minimum of steps is taken in routing the meal from refrigerator and supply cupboard to preparation table, to stove, to serving table, to dining room, to stack table, sink, and back to cupboards. Equipment is placed close together wherever possible to give a continuous working surface.

A study of the relationship between the location of two pieces of equipment and the number of steps required to pass between them indicates that more steps are usually necessary between two

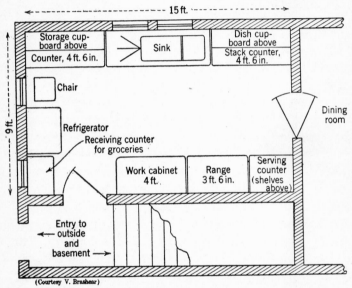

Fig. 3.—A minimum of steps is taken in this kitchen.

adjacent pieces of equipment against the same wall and between two pieces of equipment on opposite walls, even when the clearance space is not over five feet, than when two pieces of equipment are adjacent on adjoining walls.

Circular work center.—Dr. Lillian Gilbreth, well-known home engineer, acted as consulting engineer in the planning of a practical kitchen for the Herald Tribune Institute of New York and also for the Brooklyn Borough Gas Company. In both cases a circular work space was found to eliminate all unnecessary motions. The steps taken in the circular space to prepare, bake, and serve a typical product were reduced to less than one-sixth the number previously used for the same operation. This increase in efficiency was obtained by grouping equipment in such a way that the worker might stand or sit in the center and reach all the necessary supplies and utensils. Floor plans show the steps taken in a kitchen arranged without thought, and in the one scientifically planned for efficiency.

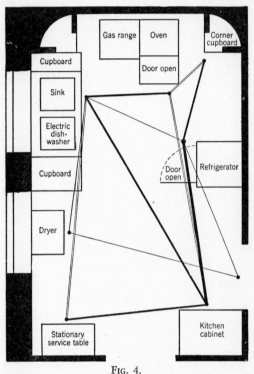

Fig. 4.

Contrast the steps taken in a haphazardly arranged kitchen with

(Figs. 4 and 5.) The number of operations carried on was reduced from 97 to 64, and the number of steps taken from 281 to 45. It is not surprising that investigation has proved that the homemaker in the haphazardly arranged kitchen walks as many as five miles a day.

Small equipment.—Work may be made easier in any kitchen by having small equipment near the place where it is to be used; vegetable brushes and paring knives at the sink; bowls, measuring cups, egg beaters, spoons, and a spatula on a shelf or in a cabinet at the food preparation table; skillets and saucepans with their covers, and salt and pepper shakers at the range; serving dishes near the serving table. The serving table is a good location for the bread box and slicing knife. Duplication of equipment may occur in some cases, but these small appliances are so relatively inexpensive that it is advisable to purchase several of them if possible.

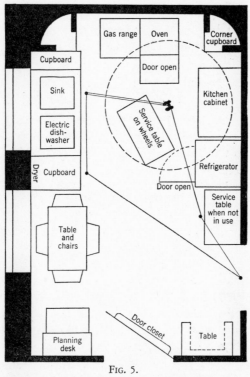

FIG. 5.
steps taken in a scientifically planned kitchen.

Shape.—Kitchens are usually square or rectangular, but sometimes they are irregular in shape. The rectangular type seems to permit the most efficient arrangement, except for the very small kitchen. Equipment is customarily placed against the walls. When the central clearance between the pieces of equipment is 5 feet, one or even two adults may work without troublesome interference and with a minimum of unnecessary steps. Thirty inches is the least clearance advised for one adult, and this amount is scarcely adequate unless careful attention is given to the hinging of cabinet, refrigerator, and range oven doors. A clearance of more than 5 feet requires unnecessary walking from one work center to another. This fact may be made clear by considering two kitchens, each with a floor area of 144 square feet. One room is 12 feet by 12 feet, the other 9 feet by 16 feet. Although equipment varies somewhat in width, the average width is about 2 feet, so that an allowance of 2 feet on each side of the kitchen should be adequate; the equipment on one side will lack in width what the equipment on the other side needs. In the 12-foot-wide room there will be a clearance, therefore, of 8 feet, in the 9-foot room a clearance of 5 feet. Three feet of space are worth considering in an attempt to reduce the fatigue and so increase the efficiency of the housewife.

Mary Koll Heiner has pointed out that "efficiency ceases when fatigue begins," with these resulting effects, "first, a decrease in the power to do work; second, a decrease in pleasure taken in work; and third, a decrease in enjoyment away from work."[2]

In an L-shaped kitchen the number of steps which must be taken may be reduced by grouping the work centers toward one end of the L and using the other end for a breakfast alcove, or, when laundry must be done in the kitchen, for the laundry equipment.

Appliances are most efficiently arranged in a small kitchen when the kitchen is square, for the worker may stand in the center and reach equipment on all sides, but when the small kitchen is rectangular in shape, only one side may be used for the placing of equipment, and a good many steps must be taken. The situation is similar to the circular work space advocated by Dr. Gilbreth.

Size.—The size of the kitchen will depend primarily upon the location and type of home, and the type of home will in turn depend upon the income of the family and whether or not outside service is employed, the number in the family and the age of the children, the standard of living, and the purposes for which the kitchen is used. Nevertheless it is probably true, as Carter concludes, that "kitchen sizes are largely 'accidental,'" and that "research work is needed to establish the most suitable size or group of sizes—based upon the equipment needed, and the operations or activities carried on in the kitchen."[3]

[2] Heiner, Mary K. This Business of Housekeeping. p. 6.
[3] Carter, Deane G. Studies in the Design of Kitchens and Kitchen Equipment. p. 11.

The kitchen in the small city apartment usually provides only for the preparation of breakfast and other occasional meals which are simple and easy to prepare. Formal meals are eaten outside the home. Suburban and town kitchens are larger, and village or farm kitchens several times the size. In these cases meals are rarely eaten away from the home and not infrequently guests are invited into the home, even when the homemaker has no outside help. Where maid service is employed and the maid alone works in the kitchen, the kitchen need be no larger than for the homemaker.

The number in the family and the age of the children have a definite influence on the size of kitchen required. If the children are small they may need to be in the kitchen for part of the time where the mother can keep an eye on them while she is doing her work. When there is excessive heat and steam this is far from an ideal arrangement, but may be necessary. A German architect seeks to obviate this difficulty by suggesting that the doors and walls of the kitchen should be of glass as far as possible.

More clearance space between pieces of equipment is required when the children are partly grown and one or two daughters assist the mother in the kitchen tasks; and where the kitchen is also the dining room and sometimes, for part of the year at least, even a general living room, as in many of the rural homes, it must be large in size.

Kitchens of the various types will be discussed somewhat more in detail in the following pages, with floor plans to illustrate the points covered.

Apartment kitchens.—The kitchen in the one- or two-room city apartment may be of the wall or of the alcove type, or in some cases it may be a square remodeled closet. Although kitchens of this class may have a right and wrong arrangement so far as maximum efficiency is concerned, there is little chance for step-saving, since at the most a minimum of steps is taken.

The wall type of kitchen is usually about 8 or 9 feet long and allows for from 24 to 26 inches of clearance space in front of the equipment. In order for this space to be sufficient, storage-cabinet and utensil-compartment doors must be narrow and hung to swing without blocking each other or interfering with the worker. As an alternative, sliding doors may be used. Mechanical refrigeration is used if possible, to eliminate the services of the ice man, for many of the wall kitchens do not border on a hall to permit outside icing. The refrigerator is built under the work table or even under the range to conserve space, modern methods of insulation making this possible. The range oven is frequently located above the burner plate, or a separate oven is used. People who live in such small apartments usually eat lunch and dinner outside the home and the oven is rarely used. Cabinets for china, utensils, and staple supplies are built above sink and work table, with drawers and a ventilated fruit or vegetable bin below. A closet 6 inches deep with a shelf for

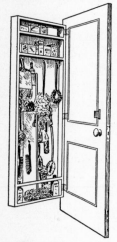

cleaning supplies and hooks for broom, mop, etc., may be fastened to the inside of one of the doors. (Fig. 6.) Oiled mops and dust cloths are often used, so the closet and the door against which it is placed should be of fireproof material. Since the wall type of kitchen opens off from the dining room or combination living-dining room with sliding or folding doors, some efficient means of ventilation must be provided. There are usually no windows, but connection with a ventilating shaft near the ceiling should be made.

In the kitchenette combined with dining alcove, space is conserved by building together range and refrigerator, sink and china cabinet,

Fig. 6.—Cleaning closet attached to kitchen door.

and work table, vegetable bin, and supply cupboard. Usually, however, the equipment occupies three walls instead of a single one, with a 30-inch clearance space as a minimum. Here again ventilation is essential. Windows are usually at the end of the dining alcove, but there should be at least a vented hood over the range in the kitchenette.

Kitchenettes 4 to 6 or 7 feet square may have equipment grouped on two or three sides in as efficient combinations as possible. Cupboard doors in the smaller kitchenettes will usually interfere with each other, no matter how carefully planned, and open shelves are necessary. Increased work space may be obtained by having a work table hinged to the door on the kitchenette side. This table may be let down into the dining room when the door is open, and used as needed. The person working in such a small square kitchen may stand in the center and without taking any steps reach equipment on the two or three walls, against which it has been placed.

Rural kitchens.—A direct contrast to the miniature kitchens which have just been discussed are the large kitchens in farm or rural town homes. In many states rural homes are still in the majority. Of the population of the United States given in the 1930 census, 43.8 per cent lived on farms or in towns of less than 2,500. Here, at least, the kitchen is still the most important room in the house. If the average homemaker spends from 45 to 50 per cent of her working hours in the kitchen, the mother on the farm must spend a much larger percentage of her time there. Around it centers the family life, not only because it is the scene of extensive food preparation upon which the health and, therefore, the happiness of the family depend, but because much of the social life is also carried on here. During the colder months of the year many of the meals may be eaten in the kitchen. Outer wraps used by the men may be hung in a corner and heavy boots left on the floor beneath. The kitchen may be used for laundry operations.

The ideal kitchen should provide first of all for the efficiency and comfort of the housewife. A coal or wood range may necessitate a larger kitchen than is common in urban homes, but not so large a one as the rural kitchen often is at present. Hoyt, in a study of families living on Iowa farms, found that the average size of 247 rural Iowa kitchens was 171 square feet, with an average total distance connecting work centers of 37 feet. A kitchen which serves as a passage-way to other parts of the house is a most difficult place in which to do efficient work, and yet a large number of doors opening into the kitchen makes passing back and forth across the kitchen almost inevitable.

A rearrangement of the work centers or a regrouping of equipment in the centers may often do away with objectionable features and result in worthwhile step-saving. Figs. 7 and 8 suggest changes which are possible. In this case the rearrangement of the equipment and the addition of window space have greatly increased the efficiency of the work area and made possible a breakfast corner in the kitchen.

When there is no bathroom or it is on another floor, it is essential, for sanitary reasons, to have a wash room, or at least a lavatory, apart from the sink.

Moderately sized kitchens.—Between these two extremes are the kitchens found in the one-family homes and in the apartments of four or more rooms in the larger towns and cities. These kitchens are square or oblong in shape, usually of moderate size, varying from about 75 square feet to 130 or 140 square feet in floor area. (Figs. 2, 3, 9.)

Number and position of openings.—Each kitchen has doors and windows, which not only affect the amount of natural light

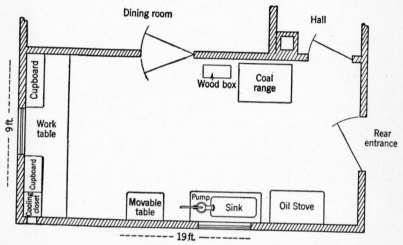

FIG. 7.—Many unnecessary steps were taken between the scattered equipment in this kitchen.

which is available and the ease of ventilating the room, but also noticeably influence the arrangement of the work centers. The kitchen should have, if possible, at least two outside walls. Windows may then be placed on two adjoining walls giving a well-lighted room and cross ventilation. Window area should equal about one-fourth or one-fifth of the floor area and should not be sacrificed to provide space for built-in cabinets. The windows should be high enough above the floor to allow the placing of equipment beneath them. Most sinks and ranges will fit beneath a window sill 50 inches from the floor, but even if the sill is 54 or 55 inches high all but the unusually short worker may still look out with ease. For the sake of the outside appearance of the house the tops of all windows are the same distance from the floor.

There is some question as to the advisability of having windows directly over the sink. More light is transmitted by high than by low windows for high windows transmit light which is largely reflected from the sky rather than from the ground, and sky light is usually more than twice as bright. High windows facing the worker may, therefore, cause glare, which is to be avoided at all times. An awning or a porch will reduce the intensity of the light, or the win-

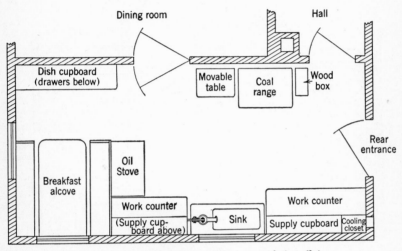

FIG. 8.—A rearrangement has greatly increased the efficiency.

dows may be built over the drainboards instead of over the sink. A window or windows in the wall to the left of the sink gives a very satisfactory light. (Fig. 9.) When windows are on only one side of the kitchen and an outside door is on the adjoining wall, light may be increased by having a window in the door.

When one rents or buys a house already built, there is little choice in the outlook from the kitchen windows, but when choice is possible, let the outlook be interesting and attractive and on to a suitable playground for the children. Windows should be curtained with sheer, easily washable materials such as scrim or a better grade of cheesecloth. The present tendency is to use colored materials to match the color scheme of the kitchen. Since kitchen curtains need somewhat frequent laundering fade-proof materials should be selected, and the curtains should be simple in design without ruffles.

Most kitchens have at least two doors, many of them three or four. Doors more than windows prevent the efficient grouping of equipment, making impossible a continuous work surface. The number of doors may be reduced to two by having one open into a back hall from which there is access both to the outside and to the cellar. (Fig. 3.) But sometimes a door into a play room off the kitchen saves the steps of the mother with small children, and a door into

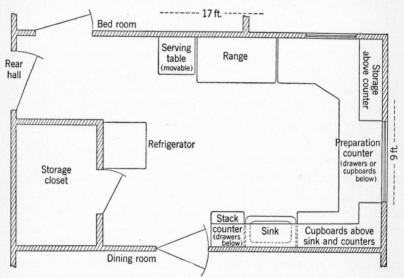

FIG. 9.—The doors are grouped to conserve wall space.

a hall connecting directly with the front door is more convenient than having to pass through several rooms to answer a door bell. When more than two doors seem necessary, group them toward one end of the room to save cutting into the wall space. (Fig. 9.)

The dining room door may be hinged so that it will swing in either direction, an arrangement which prevents a too direct view of the kitchen from the dining room. It is advisable not to have a door or window in the kitchen directly opposite the dining room door; when the window or door is open a draft will blow undesirable odors into the dining room. The doorway to the dining room must be wide enough to allow a tea-cart to pass.

Artificial light.—Artificial light is necessary morning and evening for several months of the year in all temperate climates, the amount depending upon the location of the home and the percentage of dark days common in that section of the country. The kitchen is the homemaker's workshop, and requires careful lighting to prevent shadows. A light for general illumination is almost essential. Shadows are eliminated if this light is near the center of the ceiling and has a surrounding white glass globe to diffuse the light evenly in all directions.

In addition to the central light, separate lower lights over sink, work table, and range increase efficiency by giving added light at spots where it is usually needed. The use of "Daylight" lamps in the fixtures makes it possible for the housewife to see meats and vegetables in natural colors, as the foods would look in outside daylight. When kerosene or gasoline is used for lighting, bracket lamps may be located at these work centers, the light being directed by a metal reflector placed behind or over the chimney. A gas or kerosene light cannot be placed close to the ceiling.

Ventilation.—Doors and windows are commonly used for ventilation. The newer gas and electric ranges have such well-insulated ovens that heat from baking is reduced to a minimum, but surface-burner cooking produces both heat and steam, which, however, may be prevented from spreading throughout the kitchen by building over the range a hood which connects with the flue. Windows which extend almost to the ceiling of the room may be opened at the top, permitting odors and steam to pass out through the opening. Newer homes sometimes have shuttered ventilators, provided with an electric fan to suck out the vitiated air. An opening near the floor allows fresh air to enter. These openings may be closed when the fan is not running, or should close automatically with the shutting off of the fan. Humidity is more enervating to the worker than heat, since humidity in the air hinders the evaporation of perspiration from the body. Even a very small and inexpensive electric fan, which keeps the air circulating in the kitchen, greatly reduces the fatigue of the worker. A hot, humid kitchen is not suitable for the eating of meals or as a play room for children.

Location.—Little choice is usually permitted the homemaker in the exposure of the kitchen, but when choice is possible, the exposure chosen will depend upon the general latitude of the home, the direction of the prevailing winds, and the time of day for the preparation of dinner. In climates where the warm months are four or five in number and the heat is often intense, the kitchen should have one exposure toward the north. North light, being reflected light, is especially desirable. When dinner is eaten at noon the northwest corner is probably preferable for the kitchen; when dinner is at night, the northeast corner is better, unless prevailing winds make another location more desirable.

Floor and wall finishes.—A floor material suitable for a kitchen should be resilient to the feet, impervious to moisture and fruit and grease stains, and have long wearing qualities. Wood floors, even of hard wood, require frequent renewal of paint or varnish to remain in condition, and are not resilient. Rubber or linoleum mats, placed at spots where the worker most frequently stands, overcome to some extent these objectionable features. Tile is easy to clean and offers lifetime wearing qualities, but has no resiliency, and is, therefore, hard to stand on for any length of time. Composition floors possess many of the desirable qualities, but as yet are fairly expensive and not in common use. Rubber is resilient, but requires special care in cleaning, and some varieties are spotted by grease. Of the various materials studied in the equipment research laboratory, linoleum proved most satisfactory. Inlaid linoleum has more lasting qualities than the printed variety, but either kind is easily cleaned, does not spot with any of the common household stains or greases, and is resilient. Printed linoleum will wear longer if it is varnished or lacquered occasionally and is waxed after being wiped. Linoleum should not be scrubbed frequently with a lot of soapy water for such treatment tends to make it brittle.

Wall finishes should also be impervious to moisture and common stains, a requirement which rules out wall paper unless it is varnished, or is of the waterproof variety. Oilcloth may be used and can be obtained in many appropriate designs and colors. Oilcloth should be put upon the walls with waterproof cement to prevent corners or edges from loosening when cleaned. Tile is attractive and satisfactory, but too expensive for many homes. Various types of wall board, painted or enameled, give a pleasing finish. Painted plaster is probably the most common finish used. Several coats of high grade paint should be applied to both walls and ceiling or the ceiling may be treated with cold water calcimine and recalcimined when necessary. The ceiling is hard to wash by ordinary methods.

The color used will depend to some extent upon the exposure of the room. A northeast room is more cheerful if warm tints are used, buffs, creams, and warm grays; in rooms of sunny exposure, pale greens, grays, or blues are satisfactory. Neutral colors are more pleasing as a background than bright unusual colors. Always use light tones of the color selected.

The color of the walls very directly influences the light available in the kitchen, for different colors have different reflection factors. Some colors reflect too much light for comfort, but may be used on the ceiling. A gloss finish tends to produce image reflections of the artificial lights and cause glare.

The reflection factors of a few common wall colors are given in the table:[4]

Color	Reflection Factor Per Cent	Color	Reflection Factor Per Cent
White gloss	84	Pink	72
Flat white	82	Ivory tan	67
White eggshell	81	Light green	63
Ivory white	79	Light gray	58
Silver gray	75	Buff	55
Cream	74	Light blue	54

The woodwork may be painted the same general color as the walls, but a tone or two darker, or in a harmonizing color. Colors in the floor covering and curtains may repeat the color note suggested by the walls.

Storage cabinets.—Sufficient storage space should be provided to prevent deterioration of supplies. Storage cabinets properly placed make it possible for the worker to have everything with which to work at the desired spot. Cabinets may be separate units or may be built into the kitchen, the built-in cupboards, if well planned, saving space and aiding in an efficient arrangement of the kitchen. The present tendency to conserve corner space by building cupboards and work surfaces in a circular form around a corner is very satisfactory. (Fig. 10.) When built in, cupboards should be built from the floor to the ceiling, this method of building eliminating the necessity of

[4] Dahl, J. O. Lighting Up the Dark Spots in the Hotel's Kitchen. p. 161.

keeping the top of the cabinet free from dust, or having to clean the floor beneath.

The top section of a cabinet built to the ceiling may be left without shelves, or the upper shelves may be used for the storage of utensils required only occasionally, as during the canning season, or

FIG. 10.—Cupboards built around a corner conserve space.

for roasting the Thanksgiving turkey. Sometimes the top shelves have separate doors; such an arrangement keeps the equipment stored on the upper shelves more free from dust. Whatever the type of cabinet, the shelves should be of such a width that dishes or utensils may be stored in single rows, easy of access. Shelves should be near enough together to prevent waste space. Shelves 8 inches apart provide storage space for the commonly used dishes and utensils, a wider space being left for larger kettles and saucepans. Spices, extracts, baking powder, etc., in small containers may occupy a very shallow shelf above the preparation table or be kept in a rack on the inside of the cabinet door, built so that the rack will not interfere with the use of the shelves or with the closing of the door. Another suggested arrangement is a series of step-like shelves of correct width and height to hold small cans.

All doors should be hinged in such a way that they will not interfere with one another, with other pieces of equipment, or with the worker. As a rule, single doors should open away from the direction from which they will be most frequently approached.

The lower part of the cabinet may be fitted with drawers: shallow ones to hold small appliances, partitioned ones for cutlery not easily hung from hooks, larger drawers for kitchen linens. Cupboards and storage bins are also built below cabinets. All hardware used in cabinet construction should be of the highest quality.

When cabinets are built above work surfaces, sufficient space must be left above the table to permit opening the cabinet doors without moving any equipment on the table, or sliding doors may be used. If cupboards or drawers are built below work surfaces, toe space should be left near the floor to allow the worker to stand with comfort. Work surfaces on the standard kitchen cabinets which may be purchased as complete units usually slide out, giving ample knee space for the worker wishing to use a stool.

A variety of materials are used for the covering of work surfaces; tile, zinc, aluminum, Monel metal, porcelain enamel, oilcloth, linoleum, either printed or inlaid, rubber tile, and composition materials. Select a kind which will not spot or stain with the usual household acids, alkalies, or greases, will stand up under the abrasives commonly used, will not scratch, will not be affected by heat, and will give reasonably long service.

Cabinets or closets for holding cleaning appliances such as brooms, mops, dust cloths, and the waxes and polishes, may be built in, or purchased as separate units. When space permits, put the closet in a back hallway, otherwise near the outside door, to allow emptying dust containers and shaking mops and dust cloths out-of-doors. The cleaning cabinet sometimes interferes with the routing of work in the kitchen, a difficulty which may be eliminated by the cleaning equipment "pocket" fastened to a door. (Fig. 6.)

Dish-washing utensils, soaps, and scouring powders are stored at the sink. A shelf below the sink for these articles may be concealed by a latticed door, which gives the needed ventilation. A built-in ironing board should be placed so that the shadow of the worker will not fall on the board.

Carter, of the University of Arkansas, has made an extensive study of built-in cabinets, and proposes that certain standard measurements for door and window widths, and door and window and ceiling heights, be adopted, to make possible the development of standard measurements for kitchen storage spaces. He suggests a work surface height of 32 inches with an added inch or two of base adjustment to meet individual needs; an open space between the work top and upper cabinet of 16 inches; and a 48-inch cabinet to extend to the ceiling, the cabinet to be made of two sections, one of 32 inches, and a second higher one of 16 inches. These measurements are all in multiples of 8 and fit in with the proposed 80-inch door and window height and 96-inch ceiling.

The proposed depths are 12 inches for top cases, and 24 inches for work surfaces and base sections. In the studies made, the width of the single unit approximated 20 inches, and units were used singly or in multiple.

Pantry.—The compact grouping of storage space in the kitchen saves steps, time, and energy, so that many of the more recently built homes do not have a pantry. In some cases, however, pantries are still a necessity. When the family is large or when a lot of entertaining is done, extra storage space will be needed. Expensive homes often have a "butler's" pantry between the kitchen and dining room, with cabinets for the more costly china and glassware, and a separate sink where these dishes may be washed. Below the cabinets there is usually drawer space for the fine linens. Pantries are common in farm homes so far away from town supplies that flour, sugar, and other staples must be kept in large amounts. Earlier homes were built with pantries, and many of these pantries are still in use, but in some instances the kitchen has been remodeled, storage space has been built in, and the pantry converted into a breakfast nook.

Sink.—Soapstone sinks are used in some parts of the country, but the enameled iron sink is the more common variety. It comes in numerous sizes and designs and at present is obtainable in an acid-resisting finish. Some sinks have two drainboards, some only one, and others none at all. When only one drainboard is desired, it should be at the left of the sink, unless the worker is left-handed. A wooden drainboard, either stationary or detachable, may be used with a sink having no drainboard of its own. Such a wooden drain-board may be made at home. It does not need to have grooves, simply a tightly cleated edge that will not leak. It should be finished to be impervious to water, and should be set on a slant to permit the rinse water to run back into the sink. In fact, some of the at-tached drainboards on the new sinks are not grooved. The flat sur-face gives added work space upon which bowls or pans may sit securely. The bottom of the sink slopes toward the middle or one end to permit rapid and complete draining. A back splash-board on the sink protects the wall, and an apron-type rim improves the ap-pearance and adds to the sanitary character of the sink. The drain-boards and back should be integral with the sink to increase the ease of cleaning.

A sink built into a work surface should have a flat rim or be rimless, but there is some question as to the desirability of having the sink built in. For most people, when the work surface is the correct height, the built-in sink is too low; and when the sink is correct, the work surface is too high. The height at which the sink is placed depends upon the height of the worker, and whether the dish-washing is to be done standing or sitting. When the sink is already installed and is too low, the dish pan may be raised on a wooden slat.

An enamel sink is cleaned most satisfactorily with hot soapy water. Abrasives injure the surface. Scarring and roughening of the enamel may be decreased by setting the dish pan on a rubber mat or thin slat of wood. Monel metal sinks are very attractive in ap-pearance and have insulated drainboards, this insulation greatly re-ducing the noise of handling dishes at the sink. Monel metal is not easily scratched and is not injured by abrasives; in fact, the appear-ance is apparently improved by scouring. The cost is somewhat high for the moderately priced home.

The sink should never be placed in the corner of the kitchen. Belonging to more than one work center, as it does, the sink should occupy a central position easy of access from all parts of the room. A mixing faucet to give water of the desired temperature is an advantage. This faucet is usually high enough to allow for the convenient and easy filling of kettles, and is on a swivel, so that it may be swung to one side out of the way. All faucets should be of a nontarnishing metal.

Working heights.—Heights of work surfaces should be adapted to the height of the worker. The use of small muscles requires finer adjustment and produces more tension than the use of the large muscles. Work at too high a surface lifts the shoulders, resulting in the use of the small muscles and so causing fatigue; work at too low a surface causes the worker to stoop. The shoulders should be kept level or allowed to drop slightly. The correct height is usually found by standing erect and at ease and allowing the hands to rest palms flat upon the surface. The correct height for the sink is found by doubling up the hands and letting the knuckles rest on the floor of the sink. Good Housekeeping Institute suggests 8 inches below the worker's elbow as the correct height for the work surface.

Carter concludes, from results obtained by Mason, that the work surface for all women of average height will be approximately 33 inches. Mason found that workers whose heights varied from 5 feet 2 inches to 5 feet 8 inches selected working heights between 32.33 inches and 33.80 inches. It is necessary to use some such average in building cabinets and table surfaces into homes which will be occupied by changing tenant families.

Work surfaces which are too low may be raised by casters or blocks beneath the legs, the worker may sit instead of stand, or the utensil may be placed on a rack or tray. Too high surfaces may be lowered by cutting off the legs, wherever possible, or the worker may use a platform upon which to stand.

Suitable heights for shelves may be found by measuring the height to which the housewife may reach with comfort; she should be able to reach to the middle of the shelf rather than merely to the front edge. Correct sitting heights keep the arm in relatively the same position as in standing at work. When a chair or stool does not do this, it should be raised on blocks or a small platform, or be lowered by cutting off the legs.

Clearance space.—The clearance space needed depends upon the circular size of the worker and upon the type of perpendicular surfaces opposing each other. When the oven door is hinged at the bottom to form a shelf, when cupboard doors swing outward, or there are drawers, and the opposite piece of equipment has a solid front, more clearance space is needed than when the opposite piece of equipment is a work surface with an open space beneath. The worker should be able to move and stoop with ease. And what is comfortable for one person may not be for another.

The selection of the refrigerator and range will be considered in the studies on refrigeration and fuels.

Planning desk.—For some homemakers a low rocker or other easy chair where she may relax for brief moments between tasks is a kitchen necessity. A nearby shelf may hold cook books and a file for menus, kitchen accounts, and memoranda. Almost any narrow box will do for the file. The homemaker herself will think of other useful additions. A few necessary tools may be kept in a bag below the shelf or in a drawer. Small repairs made in time obviate large ones.

Summary.—Certain general principles brought out in this study will apply to any kitchen. These principles may be summarized as follows:

1. Keep the kitchen free for activities centering around meal preparation.
2. Group large equipment in three work centers.
3. Arrange the equipment so that the worker moves from right to left (unless left-handed), or continuously in one direction. This arrangement saves steps.
4. Place the equipment as closely together as possible to give a continuous work surface.
5. Equip each work center with needed small utensils.
6. Have few doors, and group the doors near together to avoid cutting into the wall space. This arrangement prevents cross traffic.
7. Place the sink where it may be accessible from all parts of the room. Avoid corner sinks.

8. Provide adequate storage space. Build cabinets to ceiling. Allow sufficient clearance space over work tables, and toe space at the floor.
9. Have the work surfaces a comfortable height for the individual worker, so that large muscles may be used rather than small muscles.
10. Allow sufficient window space for adequate light and cross ventilation. Place some windows high enough to accommodate equipment beneath them.
11. Have one central, well-diffused artificial light to give general illumination, and secondary lights at work centers.
12. Finish walls, woodwork, and floors with easily washed, non-absorbent materials.

In other words, apply some of Miss Bane's ideals for the home to the kitchen. Make the kitchen "mechanically convenient, physically healthful, mentally stimulating, artistically satisfying, and economically sound."

References

1. Carter, Deane G. Studies in the Design of Kitchens and Kitchen Equipment. Agric. Expt. Sta. Bul. 276. University of Arkansas College of Agriculture, Fayetteville, Ark. 1932.
2. Dillon, Mary E. A Kitchen Made to Your Own Measure. Brooklyn Borough Gas Company, Brooklyn, N. Y. 1930.
3. Four Model Kitchens. New York Herald Tribune Institute, New York. 1930.
4. Gilbreth, Lillian. Living With Our Children. W. W. Norton & Co., Inc., New York. 1928.
5. Heiner, Mary Koll. This Business of Housekeeping. Hygeia 2:6-10. 1924.
6. Household Management and Kitchens. The President's Conference on Home Building and Home Ownership, Washington, D. C. 1932.
7. Hoyt, Elizabeth Ellis. Value of Farm Living on Iowa Farms. Agric. Expt. Sta. Bul. 281. Iowa State College, Ames, Iowa. 1931.
8. Kendall, David M. How to Plan a Practical Kitchenette. The American Architect 139:40-41. 1931.
9. Kitchen Practical. Brooklyn Borough Gas Company, Brooklyn, N. Y. 1930.
10. Kneeland, Hildegarde. Abolishing the Inefficient Kitchen. Jour. Home Ec. 21:475-481. 1929.
11. Lynn, Gertrude. The Step Saving Kitchen. Home Economics Bul. 47. Iowa State College Extension Service, Ames, Iowa. 1926.
12. McDonald, John R. H. Modern Housing. John Tiranti & Co., London. 1931.
13. Pennock, Grace. Efficient Kitchens. Delineator Institute, 161 Sixth Avenue, New York. 1932.
14. Sherman, Roger W. Small Kitchens for Apartments. The Architectural Forum 53:389-394. 1930.
15. Whitten, Robert H., and Adams, Thomas. Neighborhoods of Small Homes; Eco-

nomic Density of Low-cost Housing in America and England. Harvard University Press, Cambridge, Mass. 1931.

16. Whitton, Mary O. The New Servant. Electricity in the Home. Doubleday, Page & Co., Garden City, N. Y. 1927.

17. Wilson, Maud. Use of Time by Oregon Farm Homemakers. Agric. Expt. Sta. Bul. 256. Oregon State Agricultural College, Corvallis, Oregon. 1929.

ILLUSTRATIONS: Fig. 2, Best Electric Co.; 3, Vivian Brashear; 4, 5, Herald Tribune Institute; 6, The Servidor Company; 7, 8, 9, W. H. Peet; 10, Curtis Companies Service Bureau.

CHAPTER II

MATERIALS USED IN HOUSEHOLD EQUIPMENT

For intelligent buying of household equipment, it is important that the purchaser have some knowledge of the properties of the materials used in construction, since certain properties are essential for efficiency and durability. The characteristics which are desirable vary with the use to which the equipment is put.

The materials are grouped into (1) materials used largely in the framework or surface finish of appliances, (2) materials used primarily for insulation, and (3) materials for floor coverings. No hard and fast line separates the groups, nor is any group all-inclusive. The discussion will be somewhat general, other properties being considered in connection with the individual appliances.

FRAMEWORK AND SURFACE FINISHES

Aluminum.—Aluminum, a metal found in all clay, constitutes approximately 8 per cent of the earth's crust. Aluminum is derived commercially from the clay, bauxite, of which the largest mines are in Arkansas. In its natural state aluminum occurs as aluminum oxide which is separated from the other impurities in the clay by a highly technical and chemical process. The resulting product, a pure white powder, known as "alumina," is reduced to metallic aluminum by an electrolytic process, and the molten aluminum cast into pigs or ingots. These ingots are practically pure aluminum since they rarely contain over $1\frac{1}{2}$ to 2 per cent of impurities.

In the early years of the nineteenth century Sir Humphry Davy in England and Frederick Wöhler in Germany attempted the separation of aluminum from clay. Wöhler finally obtained a few small globules. A bar of aluminum, worth $90 a pound, was displayed at the World's Fair in Paris in 1855, and attracted much attention. But it was not until Charles Martin Hall, experimenting in his father's woodshed in Oberlin, Ohio, succeeded in 1886 in separating the metal by the aid of an electric current, that the price became low enough to be within the reach of manufacturers of kitchen utensils.

Pure aluminum exists in three distinct physical forms, cast, hard-worked, and annealed. In the cast form, pure aluminum is soft and ductile, and finds little practical use. Cast aluminum cooking utensils usually contain from 6 to 8 per cent of copper.

Pure cast aluminum, however, is the first stage in the production of aluminum sheets and wire. The pure aluminum pigs are melted and recast into rectangular slabs, the slabs are heated and while hot are rolled under enormous pressure into sheets from $\frac{1}{2}$ to $\frac{1}{4}$ inch in thickness, and the sheets are then cold-rolled into plates of any desired thickness. During the cold-rolling process the hardness and hence the tensile strength of the sheet metal increase and ductility decreases; as a result, sheet metal very high in tensile strength does not lend itself to construction processes. The manufacturer usually adjusts the tensile strength of the sheet by varying the thickness or by removing some of the hardness, due to cold-rolling, by annealing. Pure aluminum in sheet form is sufficiently pliable and ductile for the making of cooking utensils. Because of its ductility, it can be spun, drawn, and stamped. It can also be machined, riveted, and welded.

Aluminum is a bluish white metal which will take and hold a high polish. It can be finished in a satin, frosted, or chrome-plated finish, can be etched, engraved, and painted. Aluminum is light in weight, has high thermal and electrical conductivity, is low in emissivity and absorption powers, does not corrode readily, does not rust, and if cold-rolled is very hard and durable. Aluminum is affected by alkalies and by certain food acids, the blackening of aluminum cooking utensils often being due to alkalies in the food products.

Aluminum combines readily with most metals to form a large number of aluminum alloys of greater tensile strength than aluminum itself.

Cast iron.—Cast iron is produced from pig iron, which is made by fusing iron ore with coke, coal, or charcoal, and limestone in a blast furnace. The limestone acts as a flux and carries off foreign matter. The molten metal is drained from the furnace and cast into ingots, called pigs. Pig iron often contains from 5 to 6 per cent of carbon, and small amounts of silicon, manganese, phosphorus, and sulphur. If the carbon is present in uncombined form as flakes of graphite the iron is known as gray iron, but if combined chemically the iron is called white iron. Mottled irons are grades between these two extremes. Gray iron is tough and can be easily machined; white iron is hard and brittle and does not lend itself to machining. The mottled grades are used largely for castings, unless machining and unusual strength are essential; then gray iron is used.

Cast iron will rust, is relatively low in tensile strength, and is brittle. It should be used only in castings such as water pipes and radiators which do not require special strength. Cheap tools made of cast iron are not durable. Cast iron is a good conductor of heat and has high absorption and emission power.

Malleable cast iron.—When articles made of cast iron are given a long annealing at a high temperature, part of the carbon on the surface is oxidized, and the metal loses its brittle characteristics. Castings so treated are known as malleable cast iron.

"Armco."—Armco iron is a trade name given to commercially pure iron produced by the open-hearth process. The manufacturers guarantee a maximum of 0.16 per cent impurities. Armco iron is rust-resisting, hard, and of high tensile strength. It is comparatively high in electrical conductivity, has unusual welding properties, and enamels well, owing to its relative freedom from occluded gases.

Steel.—Ordinary steel is made by refining pig iron to remove a portion of the impurities, casting it into ingots, and rolling or forging it into the finished form. Steel is of various grades depending primarily upon the amount of carbon present. Hard steel contains 1 per cent or more of carbon whereas soft steel contains less than 0.1 per cent of carbon. Between these two is a wide range of products differing chiefly in carbon content.

Hard steel is hardened by heating and quenching in water. It is used for articles such as knives and razors where a keen cutting edge is desired. Soft steel may be welded and worked and formed cold. Stainless steels are alloys of steel and chromium or of steel, chromium, and nickel. They have high tensile strength and are resistant to corrosion after they have been hardened and polished.

Galvanized iron.—Galvanizing is the process of coating a base metal with zinc to protect against rusting. Iron and steel are commonly used as the base metal.

Zinc is not as pliable and ductile as iron and steel, and hence galvanized iron does not lend itself to most forming and drawing operations. Heavy coatings of zinc are likely to crack and peel off under severe strain. Galvanized iron is best adapted for flat wares or where the forming strains are slight and is used in buckets, wash boards, lids of fruit jars, and in articles which are in constant contact with moisture.

Tin.—Tin was early used as a protective covering for metals. It was mined in England in very early times and about 1670 was employed in the manufacture of utensils for the home. The extensive production in the United States dates from 1892.

Tinware, as used in the home, consists of sheet iron or more frequently sheet steel coated with a film of pure tin. Tinplate is graded according to the thickness and quality of the base plate of steel and of the tin coating. There are two grades of tinplate, charcoal and coke, depending on the fuel used in the manufacture of the steel. The cheaper grade is made with coke. "Block" tin is a term applied to the most heavily coated sheets, and refers to the quality of the tin.

The manufacture of tinplate is similar to the manufacture of enamelware. (See p. 30.) The steel sheets are annealed and pickled before the tinning process, and the tin coating must be evenly applied. Unlike the manufacture of enamelware, the tinning is done before the sheets are made into utensils, and not afterward. This is possible because the tin coating is pliable and shapes with the steel base.

The quality of the tin coating largely determines the life of tinware. Perfect sheets are made into better grade utensils. The presence of tiny pinholes in the tin exposes the steel base, which corrodes rapidly when reached by moisture. Tinware is readily affected by food acids and should not be used in cooking such foods as tomatoes and rhubarb. Tinware is light in weight, is a good conductor of heat, but is low in its absorption and emission power.

Porcelain enamel.—Porcelain enamel is a glass-like substance fused upon the surface of a metallic base. The metals used are principally sheet iron and steel and certain types of cast iron.

The process of enameling was discovered in China centuries ago. From there it was carried to Europe and later to America. At present, enameled appliances of one kind or another find extensive use in nearly every home: in cooking utensils, as a finish for ranges, refrigerators, washing machines, and table tops, and for wall tile.

The enamel coating is made by fusing the mineral ingredients together at high temperature until a clear liquid is formed. The molten glass is drawn off into cold water and owing to the sudden contraction breaks into fine particles known as "frit." The frit is pulverized, mixed with clay and water to form a thick cream, and stored in barrels to age.

The base metal to which the enamel coating is to be applied is cut, stamped, and drawn into the desired shape. Any wrinkles are removed by "spinning," handles and spouts are welded on, and the utensil annealed. The utensil is finally "pickled" in acid to remove all impurities from the surface, rinsed, and dried. It is then ready for the enamel.

The first coat is always applied in liquid form and is usually dark blue in color because it contains a certain percentage of cobalt oxide which has a strong affinity for iron. The base metal is dipped into the liquid enamel, dried, and placed in the enameling furnace. Temperatures in the furnace of 1,400° to 1,800°F. cause the glass to melt and fuse into the pores of the base metal. This first coat serves as a binding between the base metal and outer coats.

Enameled appliances may have one, two, or three coats, depending upon the product. If sheet metal is used as the base, the remaining coats are usually applied in liquid form, dried, and heated until they fuse, forming a smooth surface. If cast iron is used as the base the remaining coats are frequently applied as dry powder. The powder is sifted onto the surface of the piece when it is withdrawn from the furnace at a bright cherry-red heat. The piece is then replaced in the furnace and heated until the coat has fused.

An enamel product has practically all the properties of a glass product. It is non-soluble, will not scratch, peel, rust, or discolor, and is not affected by atmospheric conditions. Its thermal conductivity is determined to a large extent by the base metal. It has high absorption and emission power. If subject to sudden changes of temperatures or to undue strain, enamel will chip or crack. The coloring matter used in enamel is metal oxides which are fused into the enamel; hence they never fade or wear off. Porcelain enamel is easy to care for and is reasonably durable when properly handled.

Copper.—Copper was one of the earliest used metals. It is separated from its ores and cast into ingots, from which it is made into sheets, wire, and castings. Pure copper is one of the best known conductors of electricity and of heat. It is malleable and ductile and lends itself readily to various forms of manufacture. Copper tarnishes easily, however, and requires constant burnishing to be kept bright. When used in cooking utensils the inner surface is usually tinned to avoid corrosion.

Nickel and chromium.—Nickel is a white, malleable metal, which is highly resistant to the action of air and water and is not affected to any extent by food acids and alkalies. Its thermal conductivity is approximately one-sixth that of copper. Chromium is a grayish white, hard, brittle metal, also not affected by air, water, or food acids and alkalies. Large deposits of nickel are found in northern Canada, and chromium comes from South Africa.

Chromium and nickel, because of their high resistance to corrosion and their metallic luster, are extensively used in electroplating. The base metals are usually iron, steel, copper, zinc, or aluminum. The process takes place in a series of steps. The base metal is polished, copper-plated, and again polished, then coated with nickel and polished, and finally plated with chromium. The copper plating is apparently necessary, because of the better adhesion of the nickel and chromium to copper than to iron.

Appliances electroplated with chromium and nickel have a hard, highly polished finish which is attractive and durable. Nickel plating tarnishes slightly but is easily cleaned with whiting and alcohol; chromium plating does not oxidize and needs only to be wiped with a damp cloth.

An alloy of nickel and chromium is commonly used for the heating elements of electric appliances, because of its high resistance to the disintegrating effects of heat and oxygen. The metals are usually combined in the ratio of four parts of nickel to one of chromium.

Wire of this alloy is sold under various trade names as "Nichrome" and "Chromel."

"Monel."—Monel is a trade name for a nickel-copper alloy of high nickel content. Monel metal is of silver-like luster, has high tensile strength, is very resistant to denting, scratching, and staining, does not corrode, and is unaffected by food acids and alkalies. It takes and retains a good polish. Monel metal is a comparatively poor conductor of heat. It is used for sinks, table tops, laundry equipment, oven linings, various appliances, and fittings and trimmings.

Glass.—Glass in its various forms finds many practical uses in the home. For household appliances, with which the housewife is chiefly concerned, it must be heat-resisting.

Heat-resisting glass has been developed within the last fifteen years and has found wide application in the field of cooking utensils. Heat-resisting glass is hard and if handled with care is strong and durable. It is an average conductor of heat but has high absorbing and emission power. Its high absorption power makes it particularly adaptable for use in range ovens where the heat transfer is largely by radiation. The coefficient of expansion of glass is high in comparison with the various metals and as a result it cannot be subjected to sudden changes of temperature.

Earthenware.—Earthenware is a clay product. A variety of kinds of earthenware are manufactured under different trade names. These products vary chiefly in the quality of clay, the method of making, and the glaze which is used. Earthenware is opaque, comparatively coarse in texture, and porous when fractured. It is little affected by food acids and alkalies or by sudden changes in temperature.

INSULATION

"Bakelite."—Bakelite is a resin formed by the chemical reaction of phenol (commonly called carbolic acid) and formaldehyde, but with physical and chemical characteristics entirely different from those of the substances from which it is made. In its finished form Bakelite is heat-resisting and a good electric insulator. It is impervious to moisture, oils, and the common household solvents; is light in weight, mechanically strong, and chemically inert. Bakelite lends itself readily to machine operations and in the raw state can be easily molded into any shape. It is odorless and tasteless.

Bakelite is sold on the market in different forms. Bakelite molding materials, liquid products such as varnish, cement, lacquer, and enamel, and laminated sheets, tubes, and rods, find a varied use in the home.

Molding material is prepared by combining a cellulose compound such as wood-flour with the initial resin. These two substances are finely ground and mixed together and by the application of heat and high pressure give molded products subject to less shrinkage and of greater toughness than the pure resin. Finely divided asbestos is used in place of the wood-flour where greater resistance to heat is required; and powdered graphite is used in products such as bearings where low friction is desired.

Molded Bakelite is used for radio parts, electrical insulation, telephone parts, knife handles, pan handles, handles for electrical equipment, and many other articles. Bakelite molded parts reproduce the surface polish of the mold, which eliminates all finishing operations except the removal of a thin mold "fin." Molded Bakelite resists moisture, oil, and other household solvents, is impervious to most acids, but is susceptible to attack by caustic alkalies. Most products will withstand temperatures up to about 150°C. A somewhat higher heat-resisting product is obtained when asbestos is used as a filler.

Bakelite liquids are formed by dissolving the initial resin in a suitable solvent. These liquid products find many uses in the industries. Bakelite varnish is used in the electrical industry for the insulation of electrical coils and windings. It is also used as a coating to increase the durability of various materials. Liquid Bakelite is excellent for mending metal, porcelain, wood, rubber, fiber, and glass where a tenacious heat-resisting cement is required. In the use of all the liquid products baking is necessary, to obtain maximum resisting qualities.

Laminated Bakelite is made by subjecting layers of paper, linen, or canvas, impregnated with Bakelite varnish, to heat and pressure. This process gives a hard, dense board which will not separate, cannot be re-softened by heat, and possesses unusual strength. Rods and tubes are also made by rolling the impregnated sheets under heat and pressure. Laminated Bakelite is hard, generally smooth, and can be produced with a high luster. It is usually black or brown in color, but a variety of wood and marble effects can be secured for ornamental purposes. It is a good electrical insulator, is not attacked by most reagents—acids, solvents, and oils—but is affected by hot alkaline solutions. Laminated Bakelite is used extensively in the electrical industry, and for gears, cafeteria counters, table tops, push plates for dining room doors, etc.

Mica.—Mica is one of the most commonly occurring minerals. Chemically it is a silicate. Two varieties, white and amber mica, are used commercially.

In mining, the mica crystals usually break up into plates an inch or more in thickness. The plates are passed through a cleaning and trimming process and are then split by hand with a dull-edged, sharp-pointed knife. Owing to the almost perfect cleavage of the crystals, the split pieces are exceedingly thin, not exceeding 0.002 inch in thickness. These thin pieces are built into mica sheets by the use of shellac or similar binding materials. In the best grades of mica, which are free from impurities, the sheets are highly transparent. They are soft, flexible, and elastic, but strong. Mica is a fairly good conductor of heat and a poor conductor of electricity. These two properties make it particularly adaptable for use as an electrical insulator in electrical heating appliances.

Asbestos.—Asbestos is a term used to designate a group of minerals which have a fibrous crystalline structure. The principal asbestos of commerce is found in serpentine, which is mined chiefly in Canada and Rhodesia.

Asbestos occurs in slender, flexible fibers which are easily separated from the rock. After separation the fibers are graded according to length and fabricated into different types of material. The long fibers are spun into yarn and woven into cloth; the short ones are pressed into sheets. Asbestos is light in weight, has low thermal conductivity, and high heat-resisting qualities which make it a good insulating material. It is used principally in cords on heating appliances and as insulation for gas and electric range ovens. Asbestos is not moisture-proof unless specially treated.

Rock wool.—Rock wool is a mineral product made from calcium magnesium silicate. The stone is obtained from open quarries, and is heated to an intense heat until melted. While in the molten condition, the rock is blown into cooling chambers. The resulting product is a fine white fibrous material of low thermal conductivity. After the material has cooled, it is manufactured into a variety of products as felts, flexible blankets, pipe coverings, insulating bricks and blocks, acoustic plaster, and insulating cements.

As insulation for household equipment, rock wool is used in two forms, granulated rock wool and flexible blankets. The blankets are made by packing the wool into sheets between wire netting.

Rock wool will not burn, deteriorate, or attract vermin or mice. It is chemically stable and durable, but is not moisture-proof unless especially treated. Certain manufacturers treat rock wool in the molten state so that the fibers are annealed as they are blown. This annealing process tends to toughen the fibers and render them resistant to moisture.

Cork.—Cork is obtained from the bark of the cork oak tree. Spain, Portugal, Algeria, and Tunis supply the bulk of the cork at the present time. Cork possesses certain properties of great commercial value; ability to retard the flow of heat, freedom from capillaries, and resiliency.

Cork is used in several different forms: granulated cork, cork board, and cork tile or bricks. For insulation in household equipment, cork board manufactured from cork waste is the most efficient. The cork is ground and placed in iron molds where it is compressed to the desired thickness, and the mold is then baked for several hours. The heat during the baking process liquefies the natural gum of the cork and the gum binds the cork particles together. The gum also acts as a waterproofing agent.

When examined under the microscope, cork appears to be a mass of tiny sealed air cells. Baking increases the volume of confined air by driving off all the moisture and part of the volatile matter. The heat spreads the natural waterproof gum over the surface of each separate granule. As a result, cork board absorbs less moisture and is a better insulator than natural cork.

Cork board will char but will not burn. It is light in weight, odorless, odor-proof, practically moisture-proof, and resilient. In household equipment, cork board is used as an insulating material in refrigerators. It is also cut into blocks and used as floor tile.

FLOOR COVERINGS

Linoleum.—Linoleum is a product made from cork, oxidized linseed oil, and burlap. There are four kinds of linoleum; plain, jaspé, inlaid, and printed.

Plain linoleum is plain in color without design. The thicker gauges are known as battleship linoleum because they are used in the United States battleships. Jaspé linoleum is plain linoleum with a two-tone striated appearance instead of one solid color. In jaspé linoleum the graining goes through to the burlap. Inlaid linoleum is made in patterns with the colors also extending through to the burlap.

Printed linoleum, as the name implies, is plain linoleum with the designs printed in heavy and fairly durable oil paints. Printed linoleum is not as durable as the plain, jaspé or inlaid, by reason of the fact that the design does not extend through to the burlap and will wear off with constant use. The painted oil surface, however, is easy to clean. In some makes of linoleums the surface is coated with a special lacquer which is forced, under air pressure, into the surface of the linoleum. This gives a stain-, dirt-, and grease-resisting floor covering.

Linoleum is used largely for floor and table-top coverings. Good linoleum absorbs very little water, is resilient, not easily marred or cracked, and if properly laid and cared for is very durable. It may be purchased in a variety of attractive colors and designs.

"Linoflor."—Linoflor is a new floor covering similar to linoleum with a backing of asphalt-saturated felt instead of burlap. It is made in two varieties, plain and inlaid. Linoflor is moisture-resistant, has great durability, and is very resilient.

"Linotile."—Linotile is a tile flooring made from cork and linseed oil. The tiles are made in a variety of sizes and colors and give a floor of high resiliency. Linotile should be lacquered when laid and if given the proper care will not buckle, crack, or open up at the seams with changes in atmospheric conditions.

Cork tile.—Cork tile is manufactured from pure cork compressed in molds and baked. The heat in the baking process melts the gum or resin in the cork and cements the particles into a firm mass. The heat also produces several natural shades of brown depending upon the duration of the heating process. Cork tile gives a quiet as well as a very resilient floor covering.

Asphalt tile.—Asphalt tiles are manufactured from asphalt, asbestos, and mineral pigments, in both plain and marbleized colors. Asphalt tile will not absorb water and is particularly suitable for basement and laundry floors.

Rubber tile.—Rubber tile is manufactured from a good grade of rubber and comes in a variety of plain and marbleized colors. Rubber tile gives a floor covering of high resiliency, but some makes are not entirely resistant to dirt, grease, and stains.

Summary.—The efficiency and durability of household appliances depend in part upon the materials used in their construction. For convenience, materials are grouped into those used in the framework and surface finish of appliances, those used for insulating purposes, and those used for floor coverings. Methods of manufacture and outstanding properties which determine the choice are considered.

References

1. Bakelite Molded. Third edition. Bakelite Corp., New York. 1928.
2. Bakelite Laminated. Bakelite Corp., New York. 1928.
3. Development and Service of Armco Ingot Iron. Amer. Rolling Mill Co., Middletown, Ohio. 1928.
4. Encyclopædia Britannica. Fourteenth edition. Encyclopædia Britannica, Inc., New York. 1931.
5. Friendly Enemy, The. Hoskins Mfg. Co., Detroit, Mich. n.d.
6. From Clay to Cooking Utensil. Aluminum Goods Mfg. Co., Manitowoc, Wis. n.d.
7. How Enameled Ware Is Made. Geuder, Paeschke & Frey Co., Milwaukee, Wis. n.d.
8. Kenyon, Reid L. Armco Ingot Iron. Reprint from Transactions of Amer. Soc. for Steel Treating, Cleveland, Ohio. (With additional data by author.) 1929.
9. Materials for the Household. Bureau of Standards Circ. 70. Dept. of Commerce, Washington, D. C. 1917.
10. Miskella, Wm. J. Some Observations on Japanning and Enameling. Amer. Gas Jour. 133:46-48. 1930.
11. Nickel and Its Alloys. Bureau of Standards Circ. 100. Second edition. Dept. of Commerce, Washington, D. C. 1924.
12. Orton, Edward. Porcelain Enamel. Address in response to Westinghouse salute to enameling industry. Oct. 7, 1930. (Unpublished.)

13. Piersol, R. J. Historical Survey of Chromium Plating. Metal Cleaning and Finishing 3:29-34. 1931.
14. Rock Wool. Bul. 100. General Insulating and Mfg. Co., Alexandria, Ind. n.d.
15. Rowe, Bess M. The Romance of Oven Glass. Farmer's Wife. March, 1931.
16. Story of Floors, The. Armstrong Cork Co., Lancaster, Pa. 1929.
17. Sullivan, E. C. Glass Characteristics. Corning Glass Works, Corning, N. Y. 1929.
18. Von Elm, W. Tinware. A. Kreamer, Inc. 1930. (Unpublished.)
19. What You Should Know About Porcelain Enamel. Porcelain Enamel Institute, Inc., Chicago, Ill. n.d.
20. Woolley, Edward M. The Aluminum Age. Aluminum Cooking Utensil Co., New Kensington, Pa. 1925.

CHAPTER III

FUNDAMENTALS OF ELECTRICITY

From the earliest discovery of electricity to the present day, attempts have been made to learn the nature of the electric current. Although the years of research have resulted in only a succession of theories regarding the elemental constitution of electricity, definite laws with regard to its action have been established. Electricity can be generated, directed, controlled, measured, and put to work.

Electric current.—The flow of electricity in a definite direction through a substance is called an "electric current." Electric currents are measured in amperes.

Conductors and non-conductors.—Certain metals transmit electricity readily, and are known as good conductors. Other materials such as glass, rubber, and wood are non-conductors or insulators. It is not possible to draw a definite dividing line between conductors and non-conductors, but if materials are listed in the order of their ability to transmit an electric current, the materials at the top of the list are termed good conductors and the materials at the bottom of the list, insulators.

Aluminum and copper are the two best conductors in commercial use; glass and porcelain are two of the most commonly used insulators. Mica, because of its heat-resisting qualities, is also used for an insulator in types of equipment where high heat is developed. Pure rubber is a good insulator, but must be used where it is not subject to heat or weather conditions. On portable conductors, such as cords for small appliances and lamps, cotton, silk, asbestos, and rubber are the usual insulators. Water and the ground are good conductors, and care must be taken not to come in contact with currents of electricity when shoes are damp.

Generation of electric currents.—To speak of the generation of an electric current is erroneous. What is generated is the force which starts the current moving in a definite direction. In the early nineteenth century Michael Faraday found that when a conductor was moved across a magnetic field, cutting the lines of force, an induced electric current flowed through the conductor. The rotating coil of copper wire which forms the conductor is known as the "armature," and the magnetic field and the magnet, the "field" of the generator. The armature and field magnet together make a generator.

An electric generator within itself is a useless piece of machinery. It is only when some outside form of mechanical energy turns the armature that the generator produces the desired electrical pressure or voltage. This outside energy may be of different forms such as water power, steam, a gas engine, or even wind. A generator is, therefore, a device for converting mechanical energy into electrical energy. Electrical pressure is measured in volts.

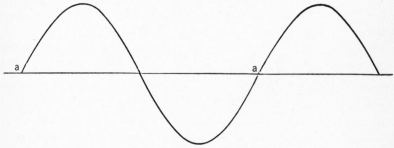

FIG. 11.—The cycle of an alternating current.

Alternating and direct currents.—As the armature revolves in the magnetic field the voltage rises from zero to a maximum value, falls again to zero, reverses in direction and continues to a negative maximum, and once more returns to zero. The direction of the current changes with the reverses in voltage and is known as an alternating current. The curve (Fig. 11) shows graphically the variations in voltage. The distance from *a* to *a* is called a cycle. The current will follow a similar cycle. The number of cycles through which alternating current passes per second is known as its frequency. The frequencies of electric current commonly used in the home are 25 and 60 cycles. The current may be transmitted as an alternating current, or, by means of a commutator, the current may be taken off from the armature always in the same direction, and will then be transmitted as a direct current. Direct current is used

in the industrial centers of large cities, as in the Loop district in
Chicago. Certain commercial processes, refining of metals, electroplating, and charging of storage batteries, require a direct current.

Transformer.—Because of the ease with which the voltage may
be increased and decreased, alternating current is used for long-
distance transmission. The higher the voltage, the smaller the current and the smaller the wire needed to carry the current. Voltage
is increased or decreased by means of a transformer. The transformer usually has an iron core, on which are wound two insulated
coils of wire. The coil through which the electric current first flows
is known as the primary coil, the other as the secondary coil. Current and voltage are induced in the secondary coil. The change in
voltage is in proportion to the ratio of the number of turns of wire
in the two coils. For example, if the low voltage coil, connected to
a 220 volt circuit, has 10 turns, the high voltage coil of 1,000 turns
will have a voltage of 22,000 volts. Transformers which increase
the voltage are known as "step up" transformers and those which
decrease the voltage as "step down" transformers. The coils are
frequently immersed in oil, which keeps them cool and also helps
to insulate them.

In large distribution systems the transformer is usually the prop-
erty of the electric company, who takes care of all repairs and depre-
ciation due to heating. It is the policy of certain companies serving
rural sections to make the customer buy his own transformer. Where
this is the policy, it is advisable for the customer to be certain that
the transformer purchased is of sufficient size to carry his anticipated
load without undue heating. For an electric range and motors not
larger than 3 horsepower, a 3 kilovolt-ampere transformer should
be used.

Circuit.—The voltage forces the current through the entire length
of the conductor and back to the generator. This path over which
the current travels is known as an electric circuit.

Sources of electricity.—Electricity as it is used in the home is
obtained from two sources—the central station, and the home plant.
Depending on the type of power used to drive the generator, central
stations are classified into water or hydro-electric plants and fuel
power plants.

Transmission and distribution.—The discovery of the alternating current and the transformer have made possible the transmission of high-voltage current to distant points with small line losses. The current is carried from the station over the "high line" to a substation, or distributing center. At the substation, the voltage is stepped down. There may be a single substation if the city is small, or several to service different districts of a larger city. Large territories are often served by several interconnected generating stations. Transmission lines are of copper or aluminum. The wires are fastened to the supports by insulators of porcelain and glass.

Customer's circuits.—From the distribution lines service circuits lead to the individual houses. These circuits are of the two- or three-wire type. If only lighting and small appliances are used, the two-wire, 110 volt circuit is most common, but if an electric range is used, a three-wire, 110-220 volt circuit is more desirable, as most of the new ranges are wired for a 110-220 volt circuit. In the installation of new wiring systems the three-wire, 110-220 volt circuit is recommended.

National Electric Code.—All electric wiring installations must conform to the National Electric Code. This code consists of regulations and standards set up by the Electrical Committee of the National Fire Protection Association, which have been approved by the American Standards Association and adopted by the National Board of Fire Underwriters.

Distribution main to house.—According to these regulations, the overhead conductor from the distribution main to the house shall have an approved rubber or other weatherproof covering. The wire is usually attached by means of an insulator to the side of the house near the eaves and is carried down the side of the house to the point at which it passes into the interior. A conduit pipe with a non-corrosive lining of zinc or enamel shall carry the wires on the side of the house, if there is any danger of injury to the wires; otherwise, they may be protected with a weatherproof covering. Sometimes the wires are not carried overhead, but down the pole and through the ground in a conduit, or are protected from moisture by a lead covering. The wires pass through the walls of the house inside of an insulating tube, at a point as near as possible to the location of the service switch. The service switch is used in case of emergency to disconnect the entire wiring system of the house from the outside distribution system.

Fuses.—From the service switch the wire conductor passes through a master fuse or circuit breaker to the meter. The fuse or circuit breaker is a safety device placed in an electric circuit to protect the lighting equipment and electrical appliances from damage caused by excessive current.

Fuses are of two kinds, plug and cartridge. The plug fuse is commonly used in the home, and the cartridge fuse in public buildings. Each type contains a link strip of metal alloy, which melts at a low temperature. In the plug fuse the alloy strip is enclosed in a porcelain or glass cup, which screws into a socket. The contact tip of the screw base is of copper or aluminum and is usually marked

Fig. 12.—A fuse "blows" when the link melts.

with the ampere capacity. Fuses are rated in amperes. A mica window over the metal strip makes it possible to see when a fuse has been blown. The cartridge fuse has the alloy ribbon enclosed in an asbestos tube. A blown plug fuse must be replaced with a new fuse, but only the melted ribbon need be replaced in the cartridge fuse. (Fig. 12.)

Circuit breaker.—A circuit breaker is a device designed to open automatically when the current in the circuit becomes excessive. The circuit breaker is reset manually when the cause of the tripping has been removed.

Meter.—In the use of the electric current, the housewife is chiefly concerned with the quantity of work electricity will do for her and the rate at which it will accomplish the work. The rate at which work is done is known as power, and the unit of electrical power is the watt. The watt is equal to a volt times an ampere. The watt is such a small unit that the kilowatt, 1,000 watts, is used commercially in measuring power. The homemaker is not so much interested in power alone as in the length of time through which the power is used. Multiplying power expressed in kilowatts by length of time in hours gives kilowatthours. The kilowatthour is, accordingly, the unit by which electrical energy is sold by the power company to the consumer. Rates per kilowatthour vary with the type of central station and the distance of the home from the generating plant. The electric meter records on a series of dials the number of kilowatthours of electricity consumed. (Fig. 13.) The dials are interconnected by a system of cog wheels, and every dial is, therefore, numbered in the reverse direction from the dial preceding or following it. In making a reading, the digit on each dial immedi-

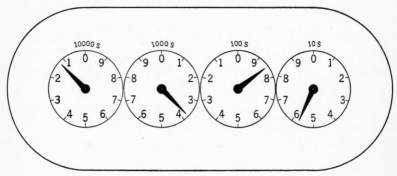

FIG. 13.—Dials of an electric meter.

ately preceding the pointer is read. Some authorities suggest reading the dials from right to left and setting down the numbers backwards. This method eliminates any question with regard to the position of a pointer.

Fuse panel and branch circuits.—From the meter the wires run to the panel containing the fuses which control the several branch house circuits. The branch circuits are of three types: lighting branch circuits, appliance branch circuits, and combination branch circuits. The lighting branch circuits supply current to lighting outlets only; the appliance branch circuits supply current to convenience outlets and perhaps also to a permanently attached appliance of medium wattage. Both lighting and convenience outlets are on the combination circuit. All outlets are wired in parallel. The range has a separate circuit.

Size of wire.—The size of wire used in the circuits is dependent upon the quantity of current the wire is required to carry. For convenience, the sizes of wire are designated by gauge number. The wire gauge most commonly used in the United States is the B. & S. gauge of the Brown and Sharp Manufacturing Company. Gauges are marked 0000, 000, 0, 1, 2, 3, etc. As the gauge numbers increase in numerical value, the size of the wire decreases. The gauges most frequently used in the home are Nos. 14, 12, and 10 for lighting and appliance circuits and No. 6 for power circuits. Nos. 16 and 18 are used in flexible cords for portable lamps, and No. 14 for small heat appliances. Larger appliances such as the ironing machine and glow heater should use No. 12 wire. Systems of house wiring and regulations with regard to the different branch circuits are discussed in the chapter on home lighting (p. 247).

Cost.—Electricity at the central station is a relatively cheap commodity, in many plants the cost being less than one cent per kilowatthour. But the initial cost of the chemical or mechanical energy which is converted into electrical energy is only a small fraction of the cost of the electricity delivered in the home. In the case of a coal-burning central station, Wyer estimates that 21 per cent of the consumer's charge is for generation and 79 per cent for transmission and distribution. In the home the cost of electricity depends upon the type of appliance used. Heating appliances, as the range, toaster, and electric iron, use much more power than do motor-driven appliances like the washing machine and vacuum cleaner. Because of its continuous use, the electric refrigerator, although a motor appliance, also uses considerable power.

Electric system compared to blood system.—In the flow of current through the circuits, force alone is expended. The same amount of current returns to as leaves the central station. The system may be compared to the blood system in the human body. The heart is the central station. The arteries are the transmission and distribution lines, the capillaries the home circuits. The blood flows through the arteries in a pulsating stream, but returns to the heart, through the veins, its force dissipated, to be again energized for another trip.

Home plants.—Home generating plants are classified into three types according to the form of energy used to run the generator;

gas engine plants, and wind or water power plants. The largest percentage are of the gas engine type for they are adaptable for use in all sections of the country. Gas engine plants are of two kinds, battery plants and non-battery plants.

The battery plant consists of a direct current generator, a gasoline engine, switch, instrument panel, and storage battery. The battery may be hand controlled or semi-automatic.

In the hand controlled plant the gasoline engine drives the generator to develop the voltage which is stored in the battery. The distribution system operates from the battery. When the voltage of the storage battery drops to a certain point, a switch known as the "low voltage release" disconnects the battery from the line, and before the plant can again be put into operation this switch must be closed by hand, the engine started, and the battery recharged. The frequency of recharging depends upon the size of the battery and the number of lights and appliances used in the system.

The more recently designed systems are semi-automatic. These plants operate from the storage battery until a definite quantity of current is used; then the generator automatically starts running and the current is taken directly from the generator.

The non-battery type replaces the large storage battery with a small battery which is used only for starting the motor. These plants are completely automatic in that the turning on or off of a light or of an appliance starts and stops the generator. The only energy that is stored is in the small battery which is used for starting purposes.

Capacity of battery plants.—Battery plants may be purchased in 32 volt, 16 cell plants or in 110 volt, 56 cell plants. The capacity rating of the battery plants varies from 600 to 15,000 watts. Non-battery plants are designed with both 32 and 110 volt generators.

Cost.—The initial cost of the different types of home plants varies according to the size of the generator and the number of cells in the battery. The cost of battery plants ranges from $500 to $1,250. Of this price $150 to $300 is for the storage battery. Extensive surveys of gas engine plants show the average life of this type of plant to be approximately 10 years. The average life of the storage battery is 6.3 years.

Use of equipment with house plants.—The equipment which may be used on a home plant depends upon the type and wattage.

Lighting equipment is purchasable for both 32 and 110 volt systems. Small heating appliances such as electric irons, toasters, waffle irons, percolators, heating pads, glow heaters, hot plates, and incubators, whose wattage runs below 650 watts, can be used successfully on the average plant. Care must be taken, however, not to overload the plant by operating several appliances or one appliance and several lights at the same time. One hundred and ten volt plants, of either the battery or non-battery type, usually have a greater wattage capacity, so that it is possible to operate more equipment at one time. Standard equipment is designed for a 110 volt system. Appliances for use on the 32 volt system must be of special construction and are often somewhat more expensive than the standard pieces.

Ironing machines and high wattage irons may be used successfully on plants of 1,500 to 15,000 watt capacity, and small electric motors can usually be operated on the home plant. Although 1 horsepower is equivalent to 746 watts, it has been found that a 1 horsepower motor uses approximately 1,000 watts from the plants, a $\frac{1}{2}$ horsepower motor, 500 watts, and a $\frac{1}{4}$ horsepower motor, 250 watts. This increase is due to losses in the line and in the motor. Electric motors do not operate efficiently if there is more than a 5 per cent drop in line voltage. On the 32 volt system the motor must be used within close range of the generating plant.

Motors used in connection with automatic equipment such as water systems and mechanical refrigerators often introduce a problem. Shallow well systems which do not use a motor larger than $\frac{1}{4}$ horsepower can usually be operated with safety from any system; but deep well systems, which require a larger motor, should not be used on small wattage battery plants, for they are likely to operate when the battery is already carrying a heavy load.

Logan, in his discussion of farm lighting systems, states, "Operating an electric household refrigerator from an individual farm electric plant has been a questionable procedure. During the summer months the refrigerator motor starts frequently and runs a considerable portion of the time, consuming from 50 to 75 kw. hr. per month. If this energy is taken directly from the battery it is quickly discharged and the frequent charging and discharging materially shortens the life of the battery. On the other hand, if the refrigerator motor starts the plant and takes its energy directly from the generator, other difficulties arise. To some the noise of the plant is objectionable, especially at night, and unless the charging rate of the battery is carefully regulated the batteries will be continually overcharged."[1]

Open circuit.—Although in the strictest sense of the term a circuit is a closed path, a specific section of the path is often spoken of as a circuit, and the whole path designated as a closed circuit. When there is a break in the closed circuit, it is said to be open.

Name plate.—Electrical appliances are constructed to operate under certain standard conditions. The conditions are specified on the name plate or rating plate, which may be separate or one and the same. The specifications include kind of current, a.c. or d.c., frequency of current, voltage, and either wattage or amperage.

In the selection of lighting equipment and heating appliances the kind of current is not of importance unless the appliance is equipped with an automatic control. Lighting and heating effects are produced by the resistance of the conductor to the passage of the current, and it is immaterial whether the current is always flowing in the same direction or alternately changing its direction. Automatic controls, however, are designed for a definite kind of current, as are electric motors, with the exception of the universal motor, which will operate on either direct or alternating current circuits. A motor is similar in structure to the generator. In the generator the armature is revolved in a magnetic field by means of mechanical energy and voltage is produced; in the motor the armature itself is connected to a source of electricity, and the attractions and repulsions, between the field of force set up by this current and the magnetic field between the poles of the surrounding field magnets, cause mechanical motion. The motion is transmitted to the mechanism of the appliance.

An appliance must be designed for the voltage on which it is to be used. Voltage forces a current through an appliance against resistance. The resistance depends upon the material of the conductor, the length of the conductor, and its cross sectional area. The resistance varies directly with the length and inversely with the cross sectional area. Electrical resistance is measured in ohms. In 1827,

[1] Logan, C. A. Farm Lighting System. p. 28.

a German scientist, Dr. G. S. Ohm, discovered that the current, the voltage, and the resistance bear a definite relationship to one another. This is expressed in Ohm's Law, $E = RI$.

This relationship finds many practical applications in the construction of electrical household equipment. If a definite number of amperes of current at 110 volts pressure is required to produce the heating effect necessary for toasting a slice of bread in a given time, the manufacturer determines the ohms of resistance which must be used in the heating coil to give this number of amperes.

After the toaster has been constructed the resistance becomes a constant quantity and the current is directly proportional to the voltage of the circuit. If the toaster is always used on a circuit of 110 volts the necessary heat is produced in the given length of time. When used on a circuit of less than 110 volts, not enough heat is developed to toast the bread in the required time, and if the pressure is more than 110 volts, sufficient heat may be produced in the given time to burn the bread.

If the difference in rated voltage is large, the effect is even more marked. When a lighting or heating appliance designed to use 110 volts is operated on a 32 volt system, not enough heat is generated to be of use, while the heat developed when a 32 volt appliance is used on a 110 volt circuit will burn out the appliance. An application of Ohm's Law will make this clear.

For example, in a toaster rated at 110 volts, 550 watts, the resistance of the heating coil is found to be 22 ohms. If the toaster is used on a 32 volt circuit,

$$I = \frac{32}{22} = 1.5A$$
$$W = (1.5)\ (32) = 48$$

If the power used is only 48 watts in place of 550, the heat produced will be negligible. A toaster rated at 32 volts, 550 watts, has a heating coil of which the resistance is approximately 1.86 ohms. If the toaster is connected to a 110 volt circuit,

$$I = \frac{110}{1.86} = 59.1\ A$$
$$W = (59.1)\ (110) = 6501$$

In this case the power used is 6,501 watts, or more than 10 times the wattage rating of the appliance. The element in the appliance will, therefore, be destroyed.

The wattage specified on the name plate gives an indication of the cost of using the appliance. Lamps and heating devices are rated in watts; motors are rated in watts or in horsepower. Lamps commonly used in the home are of 25, 40, 50, 60, 75, and 100 watts capacity. Small electrical appliances vary in wattage from 250 to 660 watts. Ironing machines may have a wattage as high as 1,500 watts. Electric ranges are rated from 6,600 to 8,800 watts. Household motors are 1/32, 1/16, 1/10, 1/6, ¼, and ½ horsepower, depending upon the type of appliance. One horsepower is equal to 746 watts.

Efficiency.—In any piece of electrical equipment the ratio of the output of heat, light, or mechanical energy to the input of electrical energy is known as the efficiency of the appliance.

Short circuit.—Occasionally the insulation on conductors becomes worn so that two wires accidentally come in contact with each other. The current then returns to the generator by a path of very low resistance. Since $E = RI$, when $E = 110$ volts, and R is negligible, I is temporarily very large, and will cause a fuse to blow. This circuit is known as a short circuit, and is often recognized by the momentary flash of light which occurs. Short circuits frequently occur in cords attached to small electrical appliances, especially the hand iron, which is moved so continuously backward and forward. Since water is a good conductor, a fabric covered cord may develop a short circuit if it becomes damp. It is not a safe practice to handle electrical appliances attached to live circuits when shoes are wet.

Summary.—The electric current is used in the home as a source of heat, light, and power. The current is obtained from a home plant, or is brought to the home from the central station over a system of transmission and distribution lines. An understanding of the generation, transmission, and use of electricity involves a practical knowledge of the following terms: generator, transformer, conductor, insulator, circuit, wire gauge, volt, ampere, ohm, watt, fuse, kilowatthour meter, open, closed, and short circuits, name plate, and Ohm's Law.

References

1. Abbott, Arthur. National Electric Code Handbook. McGraw-Hill Book Co., Inc., New York. 1932.
2. Application of Electricity to Domestic Use. Jour. Home Ec. 22:631-640. 1930.
3. Croft, Terrel. (1) Practical Electricity. 1929. (2) Central Stations. 1929. (3) Wiring for Light and Power. 1929. McGraw-Hill Book Co., Inc., New York.
4. Electric Light and Power Industry in the United States. Revised edition. National Electric Light Assoc., New York. 1928.
5. Electric Machinery Catechism. Bul. E100A. Fairbanks, Morse & Co., Chicago, Ill. n.d.
6. Farm Water Power. Farmers' Bul. No. 1658. U. S. Dept. of Agric., Washington, D. C. 1931.
7. Fuseology. A Primer on Fuses and their Use. Twelfth edition. Bussmann Mfg. Co., St. Louis, Mo. 1930.
8. Greenwood, Ernest. Aladdin, U. S. A. Harper & Brothers, New York. 1928.
9. Greenwood, Ernest. Amber to Amperes. Harper and Brothers, New York. 1931.
10. Hein, V. L. How to Read the Electric Meter. Eng. Ext. Dept., Iowa State College, Ames, Iowa. n.d.
11. Kurtz, Edwin. The Lineman's Handbook. McGraw-Hill Book Co., Inc., New York. 1928.
12. Kushlaw, Max. Hand Book of Industrial Electricity. McGraw-Hill Book Co., Inc., New York. 1931.
13. Logan, C. A. Farm Lighting Systems. Eng. Expt. Sta. Bul. 30. Kans. State Agric. College, Manhattan, Kansas. 1932.
14. National Electrical Code. Regulations of the National Board of Fire Underwriters for Electric Wiring and Appliances.
15. Paine, Frank D. Some Laboratory Installations now used for the Study of Electrical Household Equipment. National Electric Light Assoc., New York. n.d.
16. Paine, Frank D., and Zink, Frank J. Operating Costs of the Individual Farm Electric Plant. Electric Service for the Iowa Farm, Report No. 7. Eng. Expt. Sta., Iowa State College, Ames, Iowa. 1932.
17. Robinson, Myra Jane. Making Small Electrical Repairs. Home Economics Bul. No. 3. Hoover Co., North Canton, Ohio. n.d.
18. Wiring the Farm for Light, Heat and Power. C.R.E.A. Bul. Vol. 5, No. 1., Com. on Relation of Electricity to Agriculture, Chicago, Ill. 1929.
19. Wyer, Samuel S. Study of Electric Light and Power Service. Fuel-Power-Transportation Educational Foundation, Columbus, Ohio. 1929.

CHAPTER IV

FUELS

A fuel may be defined as a substance which burns to produce heat or light. Combustion is a chemical process, the union of oxygen with the substance, usually when in an incandescent or gaseous condition. Coal, wood, kerosene oil, gasoline, and gas, manufactured, natural, or bottled, are the common fuels used in the home. In the strict sense of the definition electricity is not a fuel, but for convenience it is classified with the others.

Fuels will be considered from the point of view of their use in the kitchen range. The range is used three times a day in more than 26,000,000 American homes. The choice of a fuel is, therefore, of no small importance. Choice may depend upon a number of factors—primarily upon availability, but also upon the cost, the storage and handling required, the cleanliness, and to some extent the efficiency of utilization. The fuels enumerated will be compared on these different points.

Coal.—Coal has been, and in the United States will probably continue to be, a main source of heat and power. Twenty times as much coal per capita is consumed at the present as was consumed in 1850. The United States has 52 per cent of the world's supply, widely distributed, with the anthracite largely in Pennsylvania and West Virginia, and bituminous beds in many of the states. Coal is, accordingly, available to all homes, except comparatively few located at a remote distance from railroads. It is delivered to the house by truck load or in bags, and requires both storage and handling. The removal of ashes tends to produce dust and dirt. With coal more time is spent in kindling the fire, replenishing the fuel, removing ashes, and cleaning the stove than with any other fuel. Coal is the cheapest of the fuels; at $15 a ton for anthracite, a million British thermal units[1] cost 63 cents. But the efficiency of the home range is low, if only its utilization for cooking processes is considered.

[1] See p. 83.

Kerosene and gasoline.—Kerosene and gasoline are different fractions obtained from distilling and refining the crude oil found in pools in several widely scattered areas in the United States. Gasoline distils off first at a comparatively low temperature; at a higher temperature the kerosene comes off; and at a still higher degree, heavy fuel and lubricating oils. The present demand for gasoline for automobiles has tended to decrease the production of kerosene, the heavier oils being cracked down to form additional supplies of gasoline. During the past seven years, cracked gasoline has increased from 26 to 42 per cent of the gasoline marketed.

For home use both kerosene and gasoline are delivered by can or tank. Storage and handling are necessary. Ranges are usually fitted with containers holding about one gallon. Time is required for filling the container and for the care and cleaning of the burners and range, if smoke and odors are to be prevented. At 17 cents per gallon for kerosene oil, a million British thermal units cost $1.21½. Tests give kerosene a thermal efficiency of 16 to 33.5 per cent, and gasoline from 20 per cent to as high as 41 per cent (approximately).

Gas.—Manufactured gas is obtainable in every state, but not in every locality; natural gas is at present either found in, or has been piped into sections of, 38 out of the 48 states; portable gas may be obtained almost anywhere. With the exception of portable gas, no storage or handling is necessary, the gas being piped to the consumer from gas holders. Cylinders of portable gas are usually stored outside the house in a cabinet, from which the gas is piped into the house. A minimum of handling is required. Gas is a comparatively clean fuel. Manufactured gas has a characteristic odor; natural gas is practically odorless.

The fuel costs are as follows:

If manufactured gas (average 540 B.t.u.) costs $1.00 per 1,000 cu. ft., 1 million B.t.u. cost $1.85.

If natural gas (1,050 B.t.u.) costs 60 cents per 1,000 cu. ft., 1 million B.t.u. cost 57 cents.

If bottled gas costs $10 per cylinder (equivalent to approximately 6,000 cu. ft. of 540 B.t.u. gas), 1 million B.t.u. cost $4.44.

Electricity.—Electricity is available in all states, but not in every locality. Storage batteries are commonly used in home plants, but the large majority of homes obtain current from a central station. Electricity is the cleanest "fuel," and tests seem to indicate that it has the highest thermal efficiency. It is also by far the most expensive. At 3 cents per kilowatthour a million B.t.u. cost $8.80.

Thermal and operating efficiencies.—The thermal efficiency of a fuel depends primarily upon how completely the carbon and hydrogen are oxidized. Maximum heat is obtained only when combustion is complete. The completeness of the process is influenced

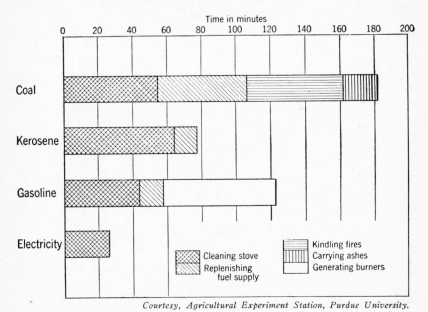

Courtesy, Agricultural Experiment Station, Purdue University.

Fig. 14.—Time spent per week in care and cleaning of cooking stoves.

by the type of appliance, and it is, therefore, "quite impossible to separate the fuel from the equipment in which it is burned."[2]

Thermal efficiency, however, should not be confused with operating efficiency, which takes into consideration the speed of performance. Operating efficiencies will be considered in connection with the study of the appliances using the different fuels.

Time for care.—In 1929-1930 the Home Economics Department of Purdue University made a survey of fuels used for cooking purposes in Indiana rural homes. The accompanying chart (Fig. 14),

[2] House Design, Construction and Equipment. p. 130.

taken from that report, shows the time spent per week in the care and cleaning of the stoves.

References

1. Apman, A. M. Domestic Gas Appliances. American Gas Journal, Inc. New York. 1931.
2. Egloff, Gustav, Morrell, J. C., and Leonhardy, E. C. Pressure Vessels for Oil Cracking. Indust. & Eng. Chem. 24:1264-1275. 1933 (Nov.)
3. House Design, Construction and Equipment. The President's Conference on Home Building and Home Ownership. Washington, D. C. 1932.
4. Rapp, Miriam. Fuels Used for Cooking Purposes in Indiana Rural Homes. Agric. Expt. Sta. Bul. 339. Purdue University, Lafayette, Ind. 1930.

CHAPTER V

THE ELECTRIC RANGE

The importance of selecting an electric range which is well constructed and which meets the needs of the individual home is recognized, but with electric ranges manufactured by thirty or more companies, and each company manufacturing from one to twenty-seven models, the problem of selection is at best a perplexing one. (Fig. 15.)

Types.—Electric ranges of three different types may be purchased. Small ranges, sometimes known as the bracket type because they are occasionally fastened to the wall, have the oven directly below the surface units. Ranges of the conventional type have an elevated oven at the right or left side, and the table-top type has the surface units and oven top on a level, with the oven at either the right or left. (Fig. 16.) The small ranges are compact in construction and adapted to kitchens in which only limited space is available. The conventional type requires more space but eliminates stooping. The table-top type may have a cover for the surface units, so that the entire top of the range may be used for a work surface when the units are not hot. A fourth, portable type, with one surface unit and a small oven below it, may be attached to a convenience outlet. (Fig. 17.) It should find extensive use in light housekeeping apartments or in an invalid's room.

Size.—Domestic electric ranges vary in size from the convenience outlet type to the four surface unit type with a large-sized oven. Most manufacturers have models with different sized ovens to meet the needs of various sized families. When a small amount of baking is done in the home, a small oven should be selected to save fuel. If large quantities of food are baked and oven dinners are popular, the large oven will prove the most economical.

Color.—Electric ranges may be purchased in white and a variety of colors, either plain or in combination. The colored range may fit in with a definite kitchen color scheme, but soft shades of ivory and gray are often more practicable in a piece of equipment which is to be used over a period of years. The important consideration is to select a color of which the housewife will not tire.

Construction.—For the sake of convenience in the study of the construction of an electric range, the range may be divided into five

Fig. 15.—The first successful electric range—built in 1910 by George A. Hughes.

different parts: the frame and exterior surfaces, the surface units, the oven, the switches, and the appliance outlets. Some special features are also found.

Frame and exterior surfaces.—The frame and legs of an electric range should be of a material which is strong and durable. Malleable cast iron, "Armco" iron, and steel are used in the construction. The legs should be of heavy channel iron, firmly attached to the frame by lock washers on the leg screws, which prevent loosen-

Fig. 16.—Modern table-top range, with oven in center.

ing and help maintain the frame's rigidity. Sheet steel is used almost universally for the side and top surfaces and is finished in vitreous enamel, which because of its durability, its attractiveness, and its ease of cleaning has largely taken the place on the better grade ranges of the once popular japan finish. Enamel trim is more practical than metal trim as it does not tarnish, and does not require mechanical fastenings. As far as possible, screw heads should be eliminated. Rounded corners are desirable.

The hinges and latches should be of a good grade of steel or malleable iron, nickel or chromium plated. Wood and composition materials are commonly used for the latch handle because of their low thermal conductivity.

FIG. 17.—This small electric range may be attached to a convenience outlet.

Surface units.—Surface units on the electric range may be divided into open types and enclosed types, several different forms of construction being found within each of these divisions. (Fig. 18.) Regardless of the construction, all units contain two coils in the heating element.

Open types.—The open labyrinth type of unit usually consists of a molded disc of unglazed pottery. In the upper surface of this disc are one or two labyrinth grooves into which the heating coils are laid. In most units this disc is set in a metal or vitreous enameled pan, which acts either as a reflector or as a support to the insulating block, frequently placed below the disc to retard the loss of heat downward. In some types of construction, the disc is used without the pan or the insulating material.

When the disc is molded with two parallel spiral grooves one coil is laid in each groove and is known as the "double spiral" type. Since the "medium" position of the switch permits the current to

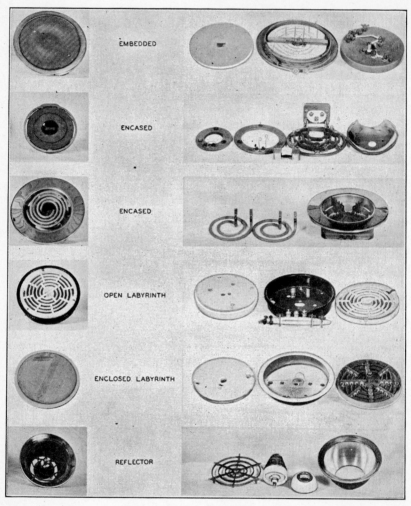

EMBEDDED

ENCASED

ENCASED

OPEN LABYRINTH

ENCLOSED LABYRINTH

REFLECTOR

FIG. 18.—Types of surface units.

flow through only one coil, the double spiral distributes this "medium" heat evenly over the entire surface of the unit. When only one spiral groove is provided, one coil is laid in the central portion of the groove and the other in the outer portion. In this type of wiring the inside coil is generally used for medium heat, and gives what is known as "hot spot" connection. Each type of connection has its advantage. When a large pan is used on medium heat the double spiral is more efficient; when a small pan is used, the hot spot connection is preferable.

Another open unit, the reflector type, consists of a truncated clay cone with spiral grooves in which the heating coil is laid. This cone is mounted in the center of a chromium-plated reflector which intercepts the radiant rays of heat and directs them upward toward the bottom of the vessel.

Closed types.—In the enclosed labyrinth type, the heating coils are mounted spirally in an insulated enclosed frame, the top of which is covered with a metal plate. A block of asbestos or infusorial earth is usually placed below the coils to prevent the downward loss of heat.

In the closed encased type, the heater coils are either encased in a metal tube or held between two thin metal discs. In the first type the element consists of a heating coil of nickel-chromium wire encased in a stainless steel tube. The wire is insulated from the tube with magnesium oxide powder which is firmly packed around the coil. The unit is made up of two of the tubes bent in spiral form, the tubes, supported on metal brackets, being attached to a reflecting base.

A second encased type has two stainless steel plates grooved to hold the heating element. When the plates are fitted together, the grooves form spiral tubes in which the Nichrome element is encased. The element is insulated from the steel plates by magnesium oxide. The plates are welded together and mounted in a skeleton pan with a chrome-plated rim, which protects the surface of the range from the heat of the unit. (Figs. 19 and 20.)

The other encased type consists of two metal ribbon elements wound on concentric mica discs. Each disc, insulated with mica or refractory cement, is held between two thin sheets of metal. The concentric discs are usually mounted in a cast iron ring with a metal reflector base.

The metal encased types are the so-called "high speed units," in which the thermal mass of the unit is low and the major portion of heat produced is directed immediately against the vessel above.

In another enclosed type, the heating coil is embedded in grooves on the lower side of a metal disc. The coil is insulated from the metal disc with a material of high thermal conductivity, and the

FIG. 19.—In this encased type the element is fitted into spiral grooves between two steel plates (outside view).

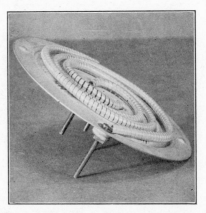

FIG. 20.—Inside view.

disc is backed with a refractory block. The metal disc and the refractory block are usually encased in a metal pan. The cast-in type, also an enclosed type, has the metal tube encasing the unit cast into the center of a metal disc.

Metals used for heating elements.—The wire used in electric range units is known as "nickel chrome" wire. It is sold under various trade names as "Nichrome," "Chromel A," and "Karma." Nickel-chromium wire maintains a uniform resistance with a minimum variation, and will withstand continuous high temperatures.

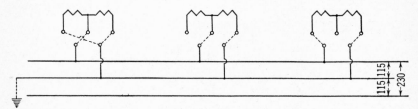

FIG. 21.—Two-wire switch connections.

Wiring of range units.—In most standard units the two coils in the heating element are of the same size wire and of the same length, i.e., they are of equal resistance. In the two-wire system the use of one coil alone gives medium heat, two coils in parallel, high heat, and two coils in series, low heat. (Fig. 21.) In the three-wire system high heat is obtained by connecting the two coils in series across the 220 voltage; medium heat, by using one 110 voltage coil;

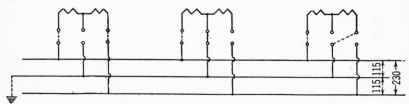

FIG. 22.—Three-wire load balancing switch connections.

and low heat, by connecting the two coils in series across the 110 voltage. (Fig. 22.) The wattage of the unit when on medium heat is one-half the rating on high, and the wattage on low heat is one-half the wattage on medium heat.

Wattage capacity of surface units.—The wattage capacity of surface units varies from 750 to 2,200 watts. High wattage is essential for bringing food quickly to the boiling point, but when a boiling temperature has been reached, the only heat necessary, in addition to the heat needed to maintain boiling, is that which must be supplied to equalize the losses from the sides and top of the pan. Tests conducted at the Electrical Testing Laboratories indicate that with the average sized vessel approximately 250 watts are required to maintain simmering. On a 1,000 watt unit low heat is, therefore, sufficient.

In units of lower wattage than 1,000 watts, medium heat has to be used to maintain boiling, and a portion of the heat produced is used in the vaporization of the water or, in other words, wasted. The low heat switch on units of wattage less than 1,000 watts is of little use. Units of higher wattage, as 1,500, 1,800, and 2,200 watts, will maintain fairly rapid boiling on low heat. These results would seem to indicate that at least one high wattage unit should be selected for speed and that the other units should be of such a capacity that the low heat position of the switch will maintain boiling in a pan of a size to fit the unit.

Comparative speed of different types of units.—In a study of the effect of the type of surface unit on boiling time, tests seem to indicate that transfer of heat from all electric units is largely by radiation. If this is true, the color and kind of pan used appreciably influence the speed of boiling (p. 75). The speed of heating is also affected by the thermal mass of the unit, the smaller the thermal mass of the unit, the less the amount of heat needed to bring the unit to operating temperature, and the more rapid the transfer of heat to the vessel.

The design of the unit should be such that a minimum amount of heat will be lost to the outside air, and that variations in heating with different pans will be slight. The metal encased and cast-in units seem to meet these requirements most satisfactorily, while certain units of the embedded type rank low.

Heating from a cold start with cast-in, embedded, and enclosed labyrinth units—all of high thermal mass—is comparatively slow, but the energy stored in the units will increase the speed of heating from a hot start. Units of this type are more efficient for long time cooking processes. In these cases where the thermal mass is high, sufficient heat is often stored in the unit that the current may be turned off and the last ten or fifteen minutes of the cooking period continued on the accumulated energy.

Comparative life of electric units.—The closed types of units are, as a rule, of longer life than the open types. Although nickel-chromium wire oxidizes rather slowly under normal conditions, the rate of oxidation increases when the wire is heated in contact with air and the wire will ultimately disintegrate. In the closed types the rate of oxidation is retarded and the life of the unit increased. The heating element in the open unit may come in contact with dirt, grease, and spilled foods, and certain foods burned on to the coils may cause short circuits.

The reflector type of open unit and the tube encased types of closed units have been on the market too short a time for their durability to be determined under the varied conditions of home use. Although laboratory tests are usually carefully controlled they often fail to duplicate home conditions sufficiently to be entirely satisfactory to the homemaker.

Ovens.—The size and right- or left-hand location of the oven are matters of personal choice, but the general construction, lining, insulation, units, and features of convenience have an important effect upon the efficiency of the oven, and will be considered in detail.

The construction of an electric oven is somewhat different from that of ovens used with fuels. Heat is supplied to the oven by an electric heating element. Air is not necessary to support combustion, or, after the preheat period, as a carrier of heat to or in the oven, since the heating elements are placed directly within the oven and the distribution of heat is largely by radiation. In consequence, the oven is practically air-tight and may be heavily insulated for the purpose of utilizing stored heat.

The frame of the oven consists of four parts; the outer walls, the inner walls or lining, the insulation, and the door. The outer walls have been considered in the section on exterior surfaces (p. 57).

Lining.—The inside walls or lining should be of a material which is rust-resisting and durable. Vitreous enamel on sheet steel, sheet aluminum, Monel metal, and chrome-plated steel are the materials most commonly used.

Monel metal is extremely durable, is not affected by food acids or alkalies, and does not rust or oxidize, but on account of its cost is not generally used in domestic ranges. It does, however, find wide application in commercial ovens. Chromium plating is comparatively new and is expensive so that at present it is not used extensively for oven linings. Sheet aluminum is light in weight and does not corrode. It is attractive in appearance when new but requires considerable care to be kept in good condition.

Vitreous enamel on steel is used in the largest percentage of domestic ovens. Both light and dark colors are used, but dark blue or blue speckled with white predominates. Dark blue enamel is the first coat applied to the steel and has a coefficient of expansion approximating that of the metal base. As a result dark enamel will not chip or crack during the heating and cooling periods as readily as will the outer lighter coats. Light colored enamels require constant care whereas dark surfaces do not show dirt readily.

Efficiency tests seem to indicate that the bright shiny metals are more efficient for oven linings than are the enamels. Housewives, however, are interested in ease of cleaning as well as in efficiency, and because of the care required by the metal linings, usually prefer the vitreous enamel.

Oven linings should be vapor-tight to prevent food vapors and moisture from penetrating the insulation. Moisture diffusing between the walls of the oven not only decreases the thermal insulating efficiency of the insulation but also has a tendency to cause the oven lining to rust, and if volatile food vapors penetrate the insulation they will produce undesirable odors which cannot be removed. Moisture-tight linings are secured by stamping the entire lining out of one piece of metal or by welding together the several pieces of metal used. Openings in the lining for the thermostat, open vent, and terminals for the units should be fitted with vapor-tight bushings to prevent leakage at these points. For the same reason the lips or flange of the lining at the door should extend beyond the door frame. In some ranges both sides of the oven lining are porcelain enameled to prevent rusting. To facilitate cleaning, oven linings are usually made with rounded corners, and the units, racks, and rack-supports are removable.

Insulation.—The insulating materials most commonly used in electric ranges are mineral wool, asbestos, and dead air spaces, or some combinations of the three.

Dead air is one of the best thermal insulations known but is not used extensively because of the difficulty of obtaining and maintaining dead air spaces over a period of time. Ovens in which dead air is used for insulation are usually constructed with double linings from ½ to ¾ inch apart. This space is frequently subdivided by a system of baffles which minimizes convection currents. The outer wall and the double linings should each be of a single piece of metal to decrease the possibility of air leakage.

Asbestos is ordinarily used in block air-cell form; the blocks are made from flat layers of corrugated asbestos cemented together to the desired thickness. The resulting material is a combination of asbestos and dead air. The cement or binder used determines to a large extent the quality of this type of insulation. Glue or organic materials which disintegrate under oven temperatures should not be used for binders. Air-cell asbestos can be cut into the exact size to fit between the oven walls, will not sag or pack, does not absorb odors, and has a small thermal capacity. This last factor is important when the range is to be used principally for short time baking processes.

Mineral wool is used in two forms, in bulk, and pressed into sheets between layers of wire netting. When used in bulk form and loosely packed, it settles and leaves air spaces. If firmly packed or held together with wire netting this difficulty is overcome, but if too tightly packed the thermal mass may be sufficiently high to increase operating costs.

Oven units.—The majority of electric ovens have two units, a top and a bottom unit, the bottom for baking and the top unit, as a rule, for broiling. Both units are used during the preheat period and some range directions recommend the use of the top unit for certain baking and roasting processes. A few range ovens have only one unit. Ranges of this type require a separate broiling oven. Oven units are of three types: the open coil, mounted by means of small insulating supports on a metal frame; the open labyrinth type, in which the heating coil is laid in grooves in a block of unglazed pottery; and the "Calrod" type. (Fig. 23.)

The total wattage capacity of the oven units ranges from 2,000 to 3,600 watts. In most ovens the top and bottom units are of equal wattage, but in a few the capacity of the lower unit is higher than that of the top unit. In ovens using only one unit, the wattage capacity is usually sufficient to give a preheating period comparable to that of ovens having two units.

Oven units should be removable for ease of cleaning and repair. The frame on which the heating coils are mounted should be suffi-

FIG. 23.—Open coil oven unit. (Removable side racks.)

ciently rigid to prevent warping. Interchangeable top and bottom units are convenient in case one unit fails to heat, but this interchange is possible only when the construction of the units is the same.

Baffle.—In an electric oven as in the surface units a large percentage of the heat transfer is by radiation. A piece of sheet metal known as a baffle is used to spread the radiant rays uniformly throughout the oven. In some ranges the baffle plate is fastened to the bottom unit; in others it is separate and removable. (Fig. 24.)

The design of the baffle is dependent upon the type and size of the oven and upon the kind of unit used. When the baffle is of the removable type the "top" and "front" are usually marked and care should be taken always to replace it properly, for in certain ovens the design of the baffle is such that if it is not properly placed in the oven it will prevent the even distribution of heat.

Fig. 24.—One type of oven baffle with air space between enameled metal sheets.

In some ranges the bottom unit is recessed in the bottom of the oven lining and a second floor is placed over the unit. This floor is flush with the open oven door and acts as a baffle for the lower unit. In this type of range both the added floor and unit should be removable for cleaning and repair. The top unit is never baffled unless the outer section of the top unit is connected with the bottom unit for baking. With this type of wiring a baffle must be provided for the outer portion of the unit.

Side racks and shelves.—Each side rack should be of a single piece of rust-resisting metal, and should be removable for cleaning. (Fig. 23.) The racks are usually held in place by lugs welded to the oven lining, or by thumb clips which should also be of rust-resisting material. The shelf racks, of non-rusting heavy gauge wire, should be of sufficient rigidity so as not to warp or sag.

Broiler pans.—Broiler pans are of two types, with and without a wire rack. When a wire rack is provided with the pan the food is placed on the rack and any extracted juices drip into the pan below. In the type without a rack, grooves, either around the sides or across the pan itself, catch the juices.

Door.—Since the door is one source of heat loss its construction must be given careful consideration. It should be well insulated and should fit tightly. The crack between the door and the door frame should be less than 1/16 inch.

Oven doors are hinged either at the bottom or at the side. The bottom-hinged type forms a shelf on which food may be placed, and consequently is considered more convenient than the side-hinged type. Oven doors should be provided with a counter-balancing mechanism to prevent the door from dropping suddenly or from snapping shut. The tension spring should be of such construction that the door will stay in any position to which it is opened.

Vent.—A vent in an electric range oven provides for the escape of steam. The vent is another source of heat loss and should be equipped with an adjustable damper. Vent dampers are thermally and manually operated, the manually operated damper being apparently the more popular, since it can be adjusted at will. For preheating and baking processes in which there is small vapor loss the vent is closed or only partially opened. For cooking processes such as broiling and searing, in which there is large vapor loss, the vent is opened wide. The vent should be so located on the oven that hot vapors will not flow directly against the kitchen wall, since such vapors produce discolorations which are difficult to remove.

Thermostats and heat indicators.—The majority of electric ranges are equipped with automatic oven temperature controls. (Fig. 25.) Temperature controls are of two types: those which maintain a uniform temperature at any degree for which they are set, and those which act as a temperature limiter and disconnect the heating unit from the circuit when the desired temperature is reached. With the latter type the thermostat must be reset when the temperature of the oven drops below the cooking temperature.

There are several designs of thermostatic controls, but each depends upon the expansion and contraction of a bimetal strip, coil, or rod to operate an electromagnetic or mercury switch, in turning the current on or off. The thermostatic temperature control is usually located on the side of the oven. On a few ranges, however, it is placed in the door or on the rear panel above the oven. Where the control is on the side of the oven next to the top units it must

FIG. 25.—A thermostat and time clock add to the convenient use of the oven.

be high enough not to interfere with pans on the surface units, and should be toward the front of the oven to eliminate a possibility of accident, if an adjustment is necessary when food is being cooked on the units next to the oven.

In addition to thermostatic controls many ranges are equipped with temperature indicators. The indicator is not connected to the current circuit and does not control the heat, but simply indicates the temperature within the oven. The indicator arrow is frequently placed on the same scale with the thermostat arrow. If the range is not equipped with a temperature control it should be equipped with a temperature indicator.

The calibration of the thermostat and indicator is important. Both the thermostat and indicator should be calibrated when the range is installed, and if subsequent adjustments are needed, the local company or range dealer shoulo be called.

The temperature control adds from $15 to $25 to the cost of the range, but experiments have shown that its use lowers the cost of operation approximately 25 per cent and also adds materially to the convenient use of the oven. The thermostatically controlled oven has helped to change the process of baking from guesswork to an accurate science. Automatically controlled heat eliminates failures in oven cookery due to improper temperatures, does away with the necessity of watching food while baking, and is indispensable in oven canning.

Time control.—One of the newer features on the electric range is the automatic time control. (Fig. 25.) This control consists of a clock-like device which is connected into the electric circuit of the oven by being plugged into an appliance outlet on the range or by means of a switch. Different ranges use slightly different types of construction in the control, but the principle of operation is the same. The clock is provided with two movable hands which are marked "on" and "off." In setting the time control, the clock is connected to the oven circuit and the hands moved to the hours at which it is desired to have the current turn on and off, the oven switch is turned on, and the clock automatically makes and breaks the connection at the hours designated.

In some of the newer de luxe range models an appliance outlet and one surface unit of the range can also be regulated by the time control. A time control is an added convenience in any home, but for the woman working out of the home it may cease to be a luxury and become a necessity. With a time control food may be prepared several hours ahead of time, placed in the oven, the time and temperature controls set, and no further attention given until the hour for serving the meal.

Switches.—Reciprocating switches for the surface units of electric ranges have four positions, "off," "high," "medium," and "low." Oven unit switches vary in design. In ovens having only one unit, the switch may be of the four-position type, as on surface units, or it may be a two-position switch which has only "off" and "on" positions. In most two-unit ovens, each unit is controlled by a four-position switch, but a few ovens use separate switches of the two-position type. Some of the newer ranges have a single switch controlling both top and bottom units. This is a four-position switch marked "off," "preheat," "bake," and "broil." In ranges of this type the preheat position turns both top and bottom units on high, the bake position turns only the bottom unit on high, and broil turns only the top unit on high. Since one oven switch reduces construction costs, it is gradually replacing the two separate switches.

The switches are usually placed at a convenient height where they may be easily reached. The different positions of the switch should be marked in large sized letters in a color contrasting with that of the range. An inclined switch panel aids materially in making the switches more accessible and the markings more legible. In most ranges the top surface extends over the switches to protect them from spilled liquids and foods, since food spilled on the switches is not only hard to remove but is likely to cause a short or ground.

Convenience outlets.—Every electric range has one or two convenience outlets, which not only increase the number of appliance outlets in the kitchen but make possible the use of small appliances at the lower power rate. It is an additional convenience to have the appliance outlet controlled by the time clock.

Convenience outlets are usually located on the switch panel or on the side of the range. When located on the side of the range they are more easily reached if near the front. Convenience outlets on electric ranges are separately fused with 15 ampere fuses. The fuse receptacle should be readily accessible.

Special features.—Pilot lights, separate broiler and pastry ovens, warming ovens, thrift cookers, utility drawers, drip trays, and separate fuses are special parts not common to all ranges.

The broiler and pastry ovens, warming ovens, and utility drawers are features usually found on the higher priced de luxe models, and are considered luxury items. If a housewife is limited in storage space, however, the utility drawers may not be a luxury and the extra cost may be justifiable. A pilot light indicates when the current is flowing in the oven units and is a convenience. Ranges should have drip trays below the units to protect the range wiring from spilled liquids or foods.

In the early models of ranges separate fusing of each unit was considered essential. Separate fusings add considerably to the cost of the range without giving enough advantage, apparently, to offset the additional cost; so very few of the present day ranges have either separately fused units or a master fuse.

The thrift cooker is a special feature found on only two or three ranges. It is an insulated well with a tightly fitting insulated lid and a heating element in the bottom of the well. The two coils in the unit are of different resistances, so that high, medium, and low positions for the switch do not have the same values as in the ordinary unit. High is usually about 600 watts, and is used for preheating; medium is approximately 120 watts and is used for simmering; low, about 100 watts, is used for steaming or long process cooking.

The installation of an electric range.—The cost of installing an electric range depends largely upon wiring conditions. The National Electric Code requires that where only one range is to be installed in a private residence the wires must be of sufficient size to carry the connected power load of the range. There are somewhat different regulations where the house contains two or more apartments in which electric ranges are used. In the last few years it has been a general practice to wire a house with sufficiently large entrance feeders to carry both the light and range loads. When the range is to be installed in a residence where ample wiring in the entrance feeders is already provided, the installation cost of the range is comparatively low, as only service wires from the meter to the range must be added, but if the range is installed in a house in which the entrance feeders are for the lighting load only, a new service circuit must be installed from the secondary main to the meter and this additional wiring considerably increases the costs.

The size of wires used in range installation depends upon the type of wiring and the capacity of the range. In wiring a service circuit from the meter, however, it is good practice to use wires of sufficient size to carry a large-sized domestic range, in case of future need. The prevailing practice in range wiring seems to be to use three No. 6 or No. 8 wires on a three-wire 110-220 volt circuit and two No. 4 wires on a two-wire 110-115 volt circuit.

An electric range should not be connected into a circuit in which the voltage is ever more than 10 per cent above the voltage stamped on the heating units. Increased voltage increases the temperature of the heating coils, and experiments have shown that as the temperature of the coil increases, oxidation takes place more rapidly, and the life of the unit is unduly shortened. When the line voltage is below the voltage stamped on the units, the cooking time will be increased, and the efficiency of both surface and oven units will be lowered, for if the preheating and cooking periods are longer, there is a tendency for greater heat leakage to the outside air.

As a protection against electrical shocks, many power companies recommend grounding the frame of the range by connecting the ground wire to a convenient water pipe or some other suitable ground. The ground wire may have to carry a large current, and wire smaller than No. 10 copper wire should not be used. Other power companies recommend the installation of the range without a ground connection in the belief that there is greater safety in an insulated frame. An insulated frame eliminates the possibility of the manufacturer relying upon the ground connection to cover up deficiencies which may occur in the electrical insulation.

The National Electric Code requires that each appliance rated for more than 1,650 watts shall be provided with some means of "cut-off" from the electric circuit. The connection may be made by a switch or a plug and receptacle. A switch is perhaps more convenient to operate, but adds considerably to the wiring costs. The plug and receptacle eliminate the necessity of calling a mechanic every time the range is disconnected or moved.

The operation of the electric range.—Controlled heat is expensive unless used economically. Since electric range units transmit heat largely by radiation the size, shape, material, and color of the pan affect both heat transfer losses and losses by radiation from the pan. Flat-bottomed straight-sided pans which fit the unit or are slightly larger than the unit should be used. The flat bottom entirely covering the heating surface minimizes heat transfer losses, and straight sides offer less surface for radiation losses. The material and color of the bottom of the pan should be such that it absorbs radiant rays readily while the material and color of the sides should minimize radiant losses.

Glass and enamel absorb radiation more readily than do the shiny metals, but the metals emit fewer radiant rays than glass and enamel. Black bottom pans absorb more heat than brightly polished bottoms. Owing to the high percentage of heat transferred by radiation in the open unit, enamel pans are more efficient on the open than on the closed type of unit, but metal pans are, as a rule, more efficient on the closed type of unit because a portion of the heat transfer in the closed unit is by conduction. Tests with different kinds of materials and different colors, on all kinds of units, seem to indicate that the most economical pan to use on the electric range is one having polished reflecting sides, and a dull black bottom. The Electrical Testing Laboratories also found that the rate of heat transfer from the unit to the food is accelerated when the vessel has a black bottom.

When water is used as a medium for heat transfer, use small quantities. The temperature of live steam is the same as that of boiling water; hence the rate of cooking is the same in both mediums. Usually ½ to 1 cup of water is sufficient for cooking most foods. The size of the unit and the pan used should be determined by the quantity of food cooked. The lid of the pan should fit tightly to retain the steam. This rule does not apply, however, to foods in which the color is affected by steaming or by cooking in a tightly covered pan.

Use of different heats.—High heat is used for speed in bringing foods to the boiling point; medium heat for frying, sautéing, and for completing a cooking process when low heat is not sufficient. Low heat is used for completing the cooking process after the food has reached the boiling point, for "waterless" cookery, and as a substitute for the double boiler method of cookery. Whenever possible use heat stored in a unit and turn off the current during the latter part of the cooking period. It is necessary for the housewife to do a certain amount of experimenting to determine the most efficient use of the units.

Selection of utensils.—In the electric oven, heat transfer is largely by radiation. Enclosed vessels, such as casseroles and deep pans where the walls of the vessel transfer the heat to the food, should be of a material which will absorb radiant heat readily. Similar materials should be used when a thick heavy crust is desired on the food.

When the material and color of baking sheets, muffin tins, pie pans, and cake pans are such that they absorb heat too readily, the food may burn on the bottom before cooking is complete (p. 145). Baking sheets should be slightly smaller than the rack and should be placed in the center of the rack to allow circulation of heat around the edges. The length of baking time also influences the choice of material and color of pan. For long, slow baking processes, a pan should be selected which does not absorb heat readily.

Recent experiments on cooking meat in the electric oven seem to favor the use of a shallow pan in place of the once popular roaster, but if a roaster is used it should be of a material which absorbs heat readily. Tests seem to indicate that meats cooked in an uncovered shallow pan and started in a cold oven are as juicy and well-flavored as meats seared and cooked in a preheated oven. As heat losses from the oven start almost immediately when the units are turned on, this method of placing food in a cold oven decreases the total time the oven is in use and as a result minimizes leakage losses. After the insulated oven is thoroughly heated it holds the heat for a comparatively long period of time. This heat may be utilized in baking foods which do not require an ascending or constant temperature, such as custards, dried fruits, and escalloped vegetables. After the food is removed from the oven the rest of the stored heat may be utilized in heating water.

Arrangement of pans.—Whenever possible the oven should be used to its fullest capacity. Baking pans should be so arranged that they do not touch the sides of the oven or each other. This arrangement allows circulation of air around each pan and prevents baffling of the heat. Layer cake pans are alternated on top and bottom racks (Fig. 38). When covered dishes are used in the oven, the cooking is done by steam and the circulation of heat is not so important.

Economy in use of electricity.—Certain foods require a high cooking temperature. For this type of food the oven is preheated by turning both top and bottom units on high. When the oven has reached the desired temperature the top unit is turned off and uniform temperature maintained by the bottom unit on high. In an oven using a one-switch control for both units, the switch is turned to "bake" at the end of the preheat period. For economical use of electricity the food should be ready to be put into the oven when the desired temperature is reached. Each food has a definite cooking time at a definite temperature; and with an oven heat control, opening the door during the cooking process is not necessary. Tests have shown that opening the door of an oven heated to 500° F. for one minute produces a drop in temperature of approximately 50°. With many foods the heat may be turned off completely for the latter portion of the baking period, thus utilizing the stored heat.

Broiling.—In the majority of electric ranges the broiler unit is the top unit of the oven. Broiling is cooking with radiant heat; the electric unit is, therefore, especially adapted to this type of cookery. The broiling unit is turned on "high" a few minutes before the food is placed in the oven to allow the heating coils to reach the maximum temperature. The broiler pan is usually set about 3 inches below the coils. During the broiling process the vent is opened and the door left ajar.

Although the above suggestions for successful and economical operation apply to all electric ranges, each range has its own individual characteristics and it is advisable for the housewife inexperienced in electric range cookery to follow the directions given for her particular range.

Cost of operating an electric range.—The cost of operating an electric range depends upon the local rates, the quantity of cooking done, and the careful preparation of food by economical methods of cookery. Surveys in various parts of the country have shown that the average amount of current used for a family of four is approximately 120 kw-hr. per month.

The care of the electric range.—Electric ranges finished in porcelain enamel require an occasional washing with warm soapy water followed by a wipe with a cloth dipped in clear water, and drying. If the range has a japan finish it should be washed with soap and water and dried thoroughly. The luster may be restored by rubbing with a soft cloth to which a few drops of machine oil have been applied. Nickel trim may be washed and polished with metal polish, but chrome-plated parts require only washing, drying, and rubbing with a soft cloth. A hot range should never be washed. The unequal expansion of the enamel and metal base tends to cause the enamel to crack or check.

When an acid, as vinegar or lemon juice, is accidentally spilled on the enamel surface, wipe it off immediately with a damp cloth. Acids allowed to remain on enamel frequently stain, or remove the gloss.

Open units, because of their construction, require more care than closed units. Foods spilled on closed units may be wiped off, or, if necessary, removed with any mild abrasive; food spilled on an open unit must be burned off. The best method for quickly removing spilled food from an open unit is to invert a tin pie plate, which has been sprinkled with water, over the unit and turn the switch to "high" for 10 or 15 minutes. The food will char and may be removed with a soft brush. A stiff brush or sharp instrument should never be used because of the danger of injury to the heating coils.

The oven linings, racks, and supports may be taken out and washed with soap and water. Spilled food should be removed as soon as the oven has cooled, using a mild abrasive if necessary. It is a good practice always to wipe out the oven with a damp cloth after baking or roasting, since, with successive use, greasy deposits are burned on to the lining and are removed with difficulty. The oven door should be left open after the oven has been used to permit the moist air to escape and so avoid condensation which may damage the lining.

Electricity as a source of heat.—Electricity is a clean and a safe source of heat. Heat is produced by the resistance of a wire to the passage of an electric current, and there is no flame. The current is under control, is easily regulated, is not subject to atmospheric conditions or drafts, and will not be extinguished by the boiling over of liquids. Heat is largely confined to a small area so that the housewife has comparatively cool working conditions. Since electric heat is not a product of combustion, gases cannot be formed as byproducts.

Summary.

1. An electric range should be of easily cleaned material, simple in design, and durable in construction.

2. Ranges are manufactured in a sufficient number of types, sizes, and colors to meet individual requirements.

3. Open and closed types of surface units are manufactured in several different forms. One enclosed type, the metal encased unit, has a "high speed," due to the low thermal mass of the unit.

4. The heating element of a unit has two coils, which may be used singly or connected, to give high, medium, and low heats.

5. Oven linings, preferably in one piece with rounded edges, should be of rust-resisting, vapor-tight material, and insulated to retain the heat. Most ovens have a top and bottom unit. A metal baffle plate over the lower unit spreads the radiant heat uniformly throughout the oven.

6. The heating of the oven is regulated by a thermostat, which turns the current off or on, owing to the expansion and contraction of a bimetal strip.

7. Most surface and oven units have four-way reciprocating switches.

8. Some ranges have a clock-like time control which automatically makes and breaks the connection at the hours designated.

9. De luxe models often have special parts, such as utility drawers, warming ovens, and thrift cookers.

10. In installing a range, use wires of sufficient size, and connect to a circuit of approximately the rated voltage. Provide an easy means of disconnecting the range from the circuit, in case of need.

11. The careful selection of the right kinds of utensils, and efficient methods of cookery will make for an economical operation of the range.

12. Enameled ranges may be washed when cold. Wiping a hot range may cause the enamel to check or crack. A stiff brush or sharp instrument will injure the coils of an open unit.

References

1. Aumann, Willy. Wärmeregler in Theorie und Praxis. Electrotechnische Zeitschrift 48:1145-1148. 1927.

2. Baragar, A. E., and Snyder, Edna B. A Study of Five Commercial Electric Stoves. Agric. Expt. Sta. Research Bul. 68. College of Agric., University of Nebraska, Lincoln, Neb. 1933.

3. Brigham, Harriet C. The Electric Range for the Home. Eng. Ext. Service Bul. 102. Iowa State College, Ames, Iowa. 1929.

4. Cobb, H. E. Bimetal, the Temperature Sentinel. Elec. Jour. 25:288-291. 1928.

5. Dowler, Zula M. A Study of the Operation Cost on an Electric Oven. Unpublished thesis. Iowa State College Library, Ames, Iowa. 1927.

6. Graves, Clara L. The Sensitivity of Thermostatic Controls on Ovens. Unpublished thesis. Iowa State College Library, Ames, Iowa. 1930.

7. Haler, Mathilde. The Effect of Electricity on the Life of Women in Norway. Jour. Home Ec. 21:248-252. 1929.

8. Harrel, C. J., and Lanning, J. H. Ovens. Cereal Chem. 6:286-300. 1929.

9. Hotpoint Calrod. Sect. No. 4. Appliance Specialists' Sales Manual. Edison G. E. Appliance Co., Inc., Chicago, Ill. n.d.

10. Littleton, J. T., and Phillips, C. J. Electric Range Oven Performance. Elec. World 100:527-529. 1932.

11. Loizeaux, A. S. Electric Cooking Aided by Black-Bottom Utensils. Elec. World 99 (Part 2): 997. 1932.

12. Martin, Grace B. Determination and Utilization of Retained Heat in Electric Range Ovens. Unpublished thesis. Iowa State College Library, Ames, Iowa. 1932.

13. Pauling, J. W. History of the Heat Regulator. Heating and Ventilating 26:138-139. 1929.

14. Phillips, C. J., and Nordberg, Mary L. Ovenware and Fuel Economy. Jour. Home Ec. 26:37-41. 1934.

15. Piper, C. W. Electric Ranges. Eng. Expt. Sta. Bul. 2. Purdue University. Lafayette, Ind. 1919.

16. Rapp, Miriam. Some Factors Affecting the Efficient Operation of Electric Ranges. Unpublished thesis. Iowa State College Library, Ames, Iowa. 1926.

17. Roberts, Evelyn H. Utensils for the Electric Range. Agric. Expt. Sta. Bul. 283. State College of Washington, Pullman, Wash. 1933.

18. Robey, O. E. Experience with Electric Stoves. Agric. Eng. Sta. Quart. Bul. 3. Vol. 10. pp. 110-112. Michigan State College, East Lansing, Mich. 1928.

19. Sater, V. Enid. The Thickness of Sheet Aluminum as a Factor in Influencing the Thermal Efficiency of a Utensil Used in Surface Cookery on an Electric Range. Unpublished thesis. Iowa State College Library, Ames, Iowa. 1932.

20. Strawn, Bernice M. Determination of Moisture Content of Gas and Electric Ovens under Baking Conditions and the Effect of Varied Moisture Content on a Baked Product. Unpublished thesis. Iowa State College Library, Ames, Iowa. 1931.

21. Swartz, Ve Nona. Baking Vegetables Electrically. Agric. Exp. Sta. Bul. 251. State College of Washington, Pullman, Wash. 1931.

22. Vaughan, V. G. The Bimetallic Disc Type Thermostat. Elec. Jour. 21:532-534. 1924.

23. Wilson, Carroll L. Control of Electro-Thermal Devices. Machinery 33:27-29. 1926.

ILLUSTRATIONS: Figs. 15, 23, Edison General Electric Appliance Co., Inc.; 16, 19, 20, Westinghouse Electric and Mfg. Co.; 17, Everhot-Swartzbaugh Mfg. Co.; 18, Electrical Testing Laboratories; 24, 25, Malleable Iron Range Co.

CHAPTER VI

GAS

Gas was first used almost exclusively for lighting, but within the last thirty or thirty-five years there has been a gradual change until at present 90 per cent or more of the gas load is utilized for heating purposes.

History of gas.—Many centuries before manufactured gas was produced, natural gas was known, although usually its true nature was not recognized. The oracle at Delphi in ancient Greece is believed to have been natural gas issuing from a crevice in the earth. The Chinese, who reached a high degree of culture and development while Europe was still largely inhabited by half-civilized tribes, found natural gas in scattered regions of their country, and piping it through bamboo tubes, utilized it for light. In 1667 Thomas Shirley reported to the Royal Philosophical Society of London the discovery of a spring, through which bubbled a gas which could be ignited.

But before this time, in 1609, Van Helmont of Brussels had found that in the burning of fuels an invisible substance was given off, which he called "a wild spirit." He named this spirit, gas. Van Helmont used wood to make the gas, but fifty years later Dr. John Clayton, a Yorkshire minister, heated coal in closed vessels and also obtained a combustible gas. He liked to amuse his acquaintances by collecting the gas in bladders, pricking the bladders, and lighting the gas as it escaped through the holes.

It was more than a hundred years later, 1792, that William Murdock, generally regarded as the father of the gas industry, produced gas by the distillation of coal in an iron retort and used it to light his home. Murdock was a construction engineer in the employ of James Watt, of steam engine fame, and after his experiments had proved sufficiently successful he lighted the Soho foundry where the steam engines were built. Later he established gas works to light a cotton mill in Manchester.

Meanwhile similar experiments were being carried on in other countries. Investigators in both Belgium and France had succeeded in distilling gas from coal, and in 1812 David Melville of Newport, Rhode Island, manufactured gas and lighted his home and the street in front of the house. But it was a German, Frederick Winsor, who first advocated and attempted the use of gas on a large scale. He went to England and there obtained the first patent for making gas. Winsor pointed out the advantages of gas for heating as well as for lighting and showed what valuable by-products might be saved in this way. He finally convinced the authorities of the feasibility of gas for street lighting, and in January, 1807, his company lighted Pall Mall in London. The company obtained a charter in 1812—the first gas company in existence—and in spite of prejudice and opposition the lighting of London streets spread rapidly. Baltimore was the first American city to have a gas lighting company. This was in 1816.

Other cities soon followed. Later gas was used in public buildings, and in the private homes of some of the wealthier citizens; only very gradually did it find extensive use in the average home. Today, as has been noted, it is most widely employed for heating purposes, not only in the home but also in industry. It has been estimated that industry alone has found more than 25,000 different uses for gas.

Physics.—Gas is composed of molecules continually in motion. Since a gas tends to expand and diffuse, the molecules completely fill the containing vessel, and their motion is limited only by the size of the inclosed space. They exert equal pressure in all directions. The tendency of a gas to diffuse is the fundamental essential for gas flow. Just as water flows from a higher to a lower level and heat flows from a hotter to a cooler body, so gas flows from a place of higher pressure to one of lower pressure.

Heating value.—When the principal use of gas was for lighting, the consumer was interested in its candle power. Today, with gas so largely a source of heat, he wishes to know the heating value. This value is expressed in British thermal units (B.t.u.). A British thermal unit is the amount of heat required to raise the temperature of one pound of water one degree Fahrenheit. A relatively recent trend in this country, following its adoption in England, is to charge for gas by the "therm," which is equivalent to 100,000 British thermal units.

Coal gas and carburetted water gas.—During the earlier years the gas industry relied almost entirely upon coal gas which was prepared from bituminous coal heated in closed vessels known as retorts. Coal gas manufacture continued as the standard production process in this country until 1873 when Thaddeus S. C. Lowe developed practical methods for utilizing the action of steam on incandescent carbon, the fundamental basis of carburetted water gas manufacture. The chief constituents of coal gas are hydrocarbons. Carburetted water gas consists of a mixture of carbon monoxide and hydrogen, which has been enriched with a spray of preheated gas oil.

The type of the processes used in the manufacture of gas, together with the manner of its distribution, necessitates employment of a storage holder. From the storage holder, gas is distributed in a system of underground mains in which the pressure is automatically controlled at all times. The mains are commonly of cast iron or steel, iron usually being preferred because it is less susceptible to stray electric currents. Gas passes from the distribution mains to smaller lateral pipes which run into the individual homes.

Natural gas.—Natural gas, frequently mixed with gasoline and oil, is found filling the interspaces of porous rocks, known as "sands," which are often more than half a mile below the surface of the earth. Above the sands is a thick stratum of impervious rock which has prevented the gas from working its way to the surface of the earth and escaping. Just how nature made this gas is unknown, but by some means or other large volumes of the gas have been forced into cavities between the grains of sand and are held there at various pressures known as "rock pressure." Rock pressure decreases as the gas is withdrawn through a well, since the gas remaining expands and fills the crevices at a lower pressure. The rock pressure causes the gas to flow mechanically from the well to the consumer.

When the well has been drilled down into the cap rock above the gas sand, a casing is set in the hole to prevent water from seeping in at the sides. Through the center of the casing, drilling continues, and other casings may be set before the desired depth is reached. Finally a pipe is dropped inside the casing and fastened in such a way that the gas must come up through this "tubing" and not escape around the sides.

The gas expands as it comes out of the well, and it may be necessary to recompress it in order that sufficient pressure may be secured to overcome friction of the pipe. Any gasoline or oil vapors mixed with the gas are also removed, and the gas is cooled. If the gas has to be transmitted a long distance there may be other compressing stations along the line.

Butane-air and undiluted liquefied petroleum gases.—In about 100 towns in the United States the gas supply is furnished by gas made from liquefied petroleum products consisting of propane and butane. Usually the gases are distributed as air-butane mixtures from a central mixing plant through an all-welded steel distribution system. The mixture contains 550 B.t.u. per cu. ft., giving a gas similar to manufactured gas in its heating value, although similar to natural gas in its flame characteristics.

Other communities distribute an undiluted vapor of a very high heating value, between 2,500 and 3,000 B.t.u. per cu. ft., but such a system will be found only in warm territories such as California. The undiluted gases burn with characteristics similar to the bottled gases described later; in fact, they are identical with the bottled gases except that they are vaporized in a central system rather than from individual house installations.

Bottled gas.—Bottled gas, also called portable gas and cylinder gas, is in use in more than 125,000 installations in locations not adjacent to gas distribution systems. Both the air-pentane[1] system and bottled gas form very satisfactory sources of gas supply for homes not able to secure gas from the utility sources. In recent years bottled gas has become more popular than the air-pentane system, probably because of the lower first cost.

The fuel in the bottles is compressed liquid propane.[2] This material, now principally derived from wet natural gas sources, is

[1] High grade or aviation gasolines, or pure pentane, mixed with air in a special carburetor buried under the ground near the building in which the gas is to be used.

[2] Commercial propane is probably 93 propane and 7 per cent of other gases in the same chemical family. Certain brands of propane consisting of more nearly equal proportions of propane and butane are available for use with special vaporizing burner equipment. In this system the burners are so arranged that one lighter burner heats the pipe containing the incoming liquid and gasifies it before it is ignited.

liquefied and shipped to distributing points in special, insulated tank cars. From the distributing points it is delivered to the home in cylinders containing 47 or 95 pounds of the liquid. These cylinders are placed in a cabinet outside the home and are connected, through a pressure-regulating valve, to the house gas-piping system. Some distributors fill the cylinders at the customer's premises from a tank truck; others replace used cylinders with fresh ones from the central distributing point.

Propane changes to a gas under all temperature conditions likely to be encountered in the United States, and consequently a uniform gas at a uniform pressure is obtained as long as there is any liquid at all in the cylinder. A 95-pound cylinder contains approximately 2,057,000 B.t.u.

Chemical composition of gases.—The exact chemical composition of various commercial gases is relatively constant in any one locality, but varies from town to town, depending on the source of the raw materials from which the gas is made or of the wells from which natural gas is drawn. Consequently the compositions which are given here represent typical cases, and it should be borne in mind that any one gas may be quite different. (Table I.)

TABLE 1*

PROPERTIES OF TYPICAL COMMERCIAL GASES

GAS	Constituents of Gas—Percentage by Volume								Specific gravity (air = 1.0)	B.t.u. per cu. ft. Gross
	Carbon Dioxide	Oxygen	Nitrogen	Carbon Monoxide	Hydrogen	Methane	Ethane	Illuminants		
Natural gas (Birmingham).	...	...	5.0	...	...	90.0	5.0	...	0.60	1002
Natural gas (Los Angeles).	6.5	...	...	...	...	77.5	16.0	...	0.70	1073
Coke oven gas............	2.2	0.8	8.1	6.3	46.5	32.1	...	4.0	0.44	574
Coal gas (horizontal retorts)	2.4	0.75	11.35	7.35	47.95	27.15	...	3.05	0.47	542
Carburetted water gas	4.3	0.7	6.5	32.0	34.0	15.5	...	7.0	0.67	534
Commercial butane........	(Butane 93.0, propane 7.0)								1.95	3225
Commercial propane.......	(Propane 93.0, other hydrocarbons 7.0)								1.52	2572

* Table condensed from "Combustion," published by the American Gas Association.

Other commercial gases are made today by various combinations of the gases described in the table, and by reforming of natural gas through a process analogous to the water gas process. Communities will also be found in which gases are derived from oil, and from time to time in various parts of the world gases have been produced from almost any material which will burn. Coffee has been used in Brazil; corn stalks have been tried experimentally. All of these interesting facts illustrate how adaptable gas and gas making really is.

Specific gravity.—From the table it will be noted that the specific gravity of all of the fuel gases except the liquefied petroleum

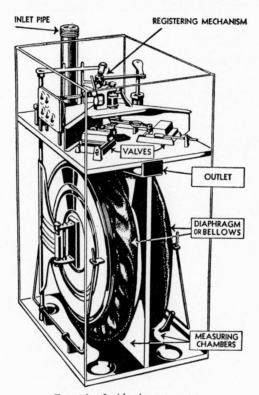

INLET PIPE

REGISTERING MECHANISM

VALVES

OUTLET

DIAPHRAGM OR BELLOWS

MEASURING CHAMBERS

FIG. 26.—Inside the gas meter.

group is lighter than air. Air weighs 0.0765 lb. per cu. ft. at 60°F.; the fuel gases weigh from 0.029 lb. per cu. ft. for coke oven gas up to about 0.054 lb. per cu. ft. for natural gas. Liquefied petroleum gases are anywhere from one and one-half to two times as heavy as air.

Heating value.—The heating value of typical gases has also been given in the table, but will vary in individual towns from 450 B.t.u. per cu. ft. to 650 B.t.u. per cu. ft. for straight manufactured gas, with the majority of plants operating at 500-550 B.t.u. per cu. ft.

Heating value of manufactured gas is subject in many places to strict state regulation, and companies are permitted only a very small variation from the standards which have been prescribed by the regulatory authority.

Differences in natural gas are also encountered, and the typical value of 1,000 or 1,050 B.t.u. per cu. ft. may be exceeded by as much as 500 B.t.u. when high percentages of ethane are present. The B.t.u. values of the liquefied petroleum gases have already been given.

The meter.—Gas piped into the home from a distributing center is measured by a meter. The meter has a top partition in which there

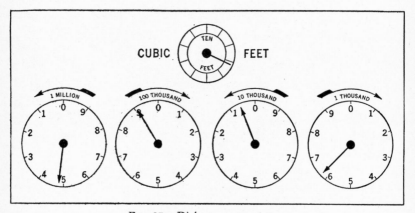

FIG. 27.—Dials on a gas meter.

are two slide valves to turn the gas into the lower chambers. The lower part has a partition through the center, and each half contains a flexible leather diaphragm, oil-treated to keep it pliable. (Fig. 26.)

The gas comes through the inlet pipe into the top chamber and is directed through the valves into the lower chambers, which fill and empty alternately, causing the gas to flow from the meter in a steady stream. The meter operates only when a consumer turns an appliance cock, lowering the pressure and causing the gas to flow.

A crank connected to the valves is geared to dials which record in cubic feet the amount of gas passing through. The dials are interconnected, and one complete revolution on a given dial is indicated on the dial of next higher value by the distance between two units; e.g., when the hand on the 1,000 dial has made one complete revolution, the hand on the 10,000 dial will have moved from 0 to 1. Owing to the interlocking of the gears, every alternate dial records in the reverse direction. Always read the last number which the pointer has passed. Set down the figures reading from left to right, and add two ciphers. The dials in Fig. 27 indicate a reading of 490,600 cu. ft.

It is not customary to turn the dials back to zero each month, but the meter reading for any given month is subtracted from the reading for the previous month. This method counteracts any error which may occur in any reading.

Summary.

1. Gas is commonly obtainable in three forms, manufactured, natural, and portable (bottled gas, so called).
2. Manufactured gas is made in all the states, natural gas is now (1934) piped into 38 of the 48 states, portable gas is distributed in all states. None but portable gas is available in all localities.
3. Gas-flow from source to appliance depends upon the tendency of a gas to diffuse from a place of higher pressure to one of lower pressure.
4. Gas is rated by B.t.u. heat capacity.
5. Manufactured gas has an average heating value of 550 B.t.u. per cu. ft. Portable gas (propane) has a heating value of approximately 2,500 B.t.u. per cu. ft. Natural gas has an average heating value of 1,050 B.t.u. per cu. ft.
6. Gas is measured by a meter which operates when an appliance cock is turned.

References

*1. Abbot, A. H. Underground Pipe Protection. Eighth Gas Meter Short Course. Eng. Ext. Service Bul. 100. Iowa State College, Ames, Iowa. 1928.
*2. Barr, C. C. Most Economical Percentage of Blow-run to be Used. Ibid.
3. Cortelyou, Geo. B. The Gas Industry. Amer. Gas Assoc. Monthly 15:41-48. 1933.
*4. Dushane, C. Benson. History and Development of the Gas Meter. Ninth Gas Meter Short Course. Eng. Ext. Service Bul. 104. Iowa State College, Ames, Iowa. 1930.
5. Encyclopædia Britannica. Fourteenth edition. Vol. 10. pp. 41-52. Encyclopædia Britannica, Inc., New York. 1931.
6. Facts about the Gas Meter. Amer. Gas Assoc., Inc., 1933.
7. Leckie, R. B. (1) The Thermal Basis of Charge for Gas. Gas-Age Record

62:263-266. 1928. (2) Use of Bottled Gas in America. Gas World. 307-309. March, 1930.

8. Lorain Regulator and How it Operates. American Stove Co., Chicago, Ill. n.d.

9. Morgan, Jerome J. Manufactured Gas, a textbook of American practice. (2 vol.) Jerome J. Morgan, New York. 1926.

10. Norman, Oscar E. Romance of the Gas Industry. A. C. McClurg & Co., Chicago, Ill. 1922.

*11. Ruhling, John A. Protection of Underground Gas Lines. Tenth Gas Meter Short Course. Eng. Ext. Service. Bul. 106. Iowa State College, Ames, Iowa. 1930.

*12. Setrum, O. W. Utilization of Liquefied Petroleum Gases in the Various Phases of the Gas Industry. Ninth Gas Meter Short Course. Eng. Ext. Service. Bul. 104. Iowa State College, Ames, Iowa. 1930.

13. Smith, O. K. Problems Encountered in Changing from Manufactured to Natural Gas Distribution. Address, Gas Meter Short Course, Iowa State College, Ames, Iowa. 1931. (Unpublished)

14. Story of Natural and Manufactured Gas. Amer. Gas Assoc., Inc., New York. 1930.

15. Therm Basis for Gas (editorial). Gas-Age Record. 65:925. 1930.

16. Wilcolator Instruction Manual. Wilcolator Co., Newark, N. J. n.d.

*17. Wuestenfeld, W. J. Use of Commercial Butane as an Enricher for Gas. Eighth Gas Meter Short Course. Eng. Ext. Service. Bul. 100. Iowa State College, Ames, Iowa. 1928.

18. Wyer, Samuel S. (1) Study of Ohio's Natural Gas Situation. East Ohio Gas Co., Cleveland, Ohio. 1930. (2) Study of Natural Gas Situation. Fuel-Power-Transportation Educational Foundation, Columbus, Ohio. 1931.

* Out of print.

ILLUSTRATION: Fig. 26, American Gas Association, Inc.

CHAPTER VII

THE GAS RANGE

The gas range is the gas appliance most commonly found in the home. More than half of the families in the United States, 16,000,000 out of 29,000,000, cook with gas. Gas is also extensively used for house heating, space heating, laundry equipment, hot water heating, and refrigeration. Space heaters and central heating appli-

Fig. 28.—Grate top gas range.

ances are considered briefly in the chapter on house heating; gas refrigerators are discussed in the chapter on refrigeration, and hot water heaters in the chapter on plumbing.

Types of ranges.—The materials which are used in range construction, and the general structural features which are desirable have been specified in the chapter on electric ranges (p. 57). Approximately three-fourths of range cookery is done on top of the stove. The top of a gas range may be of two types, the open or grate top (Fig. 28), and the closed or "smooth" top. In the grate top, the grates support the cooking utensils, and are so designed that the flame does not impinge upon the grate but the principal part of the flame is employed in heating the utensil. The closed top resembles somewhat the top of a coal range, with removable lids. It has different zones of heat which permit of varying speeds of cooking. Directly over the lighted burner is an area of maximum heat, around this area a circle of medium heat, and still farther away a surface of low heat. These zones of heat are possible because the flame heats the top of the range first and then the utensil. Beneath the top burners

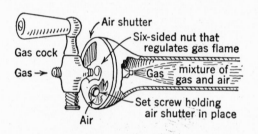

Air Mixer

Fig. 29.—Gas and primary air mix in the burner throat.

is a removable tray to catch whatever falls through the grates. This tray usually has a raised edge and an easily cleanable, rust-resisting finish.

Burners.—The burners on most gas ranges are similar, with the bell end, mixing throat, and burner head cast in one piece. The bell end has an opening for the inserting of the gas orifice and carries an air shutter attached to it. (Fig. 29.) The burner head is most frequently an eight-pointed star or a pine tree in shape, but some of the recent range models have various shaped burners. The most radical departure from the conventional type is one with the openings on the side, and a vertical throat. (Fig. 31.)

The openings in a gas burner are known as ports. In the star and pine shaped burners the ports on the upper surfaces are drilled vertically; the ports on the inner surface at an angle of 45°, to direct the flame toward the center. The burner with the ports on the outside is made in two pieces screwed together. The central cone is easily removed for cleaning. Burners on the closed top range generally have fewer ports than those on the open top, and often the ports are raised.

Size of burners.—Most ranges have burners of three sizes: the giant, the regular or standard, and the simmerer, but some ranges are fitted with "two-way" burners, in which the simmerer is a part of the large burner. When the gas cock is partly closed, the gas is shut off from the large burner, and only the simmering burner heats. (Fig. 30.) Another burner, on a recent model, has a "two position" gas valve, which provides full or simmering heat as required, but in this burner both full and simmering flames cover the entire burner, assuring evenness of heat. The most efficient method of operation

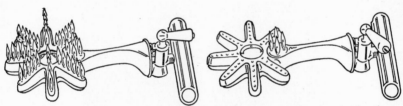

Fig. 30.—Two-way burner. The full burner may be turned off and only the simmer burn.

is to have the gas turned on full. The simmering burner is, therefore, to be preferred to a larger burner turned down—the simmerer is burning at full speed, and only the size is reduced. The new type burner with the ports on the side, to which reference has been made, is a three-in-one type, and may be used as giant, regular, or simmerer, as desired. (Fig. 31.)

Heat capacity of burners.—The giant burner is built to have a heating capacity of not less than 12,000 B.t.u. per hour; the regular burners, not less than 9,000 B.t.u. per hour; and the simmering burner, not less than 1,800 B.t.u. per hour. This is equivalent to approximately 22 cu. ft., 16 cu. ft., and 4 cu. ft. of manufactured gas per hour, respectively. Since natural gas has a higher B.t.u. content, the burners consume less gas to give the same amount of heat. The giant burner consumes an average of about 11 cu. ft. per hour, the regular burner an average of 8.3 cu. ft. per hour.

Courtesy, American Stove Company.

FIG. 31.—Vertical-throat burner at different heats.

Path of gas flow.—The pipe on the front of the range, through which gas flows to the different burners, is called the manifold. On the manifold are the gas cocks, operated by hand, which direct the gas into the burners. The gas passes through the orifice and into the mixing throat. Orifices are usually adjusted by turning the hexagonal nut on the spud, to the left to decrease the flow of gas, to the right to increase it. The gas is forced through the orifice with a velocity of 100 to 160 ft. per second, and the suction developed by this rapid flow of gas draws in air from the room through the partially open shutter. This air, known as primary air, mixes with gas in the throat before the mixture is ignited. The mixture of gas and air will not burn, however, without the presence of secondary air which surrounds the burner, and supplies the additional oxygen required. When the ratio of gas to air is properly adjusted, the gas flame consists of two cones, an inner green one and an outer very pale

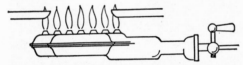

Fig. 32. —Correct flame adjustment.

bluish lavender cone. (Fig. 32.) With natural and portable gas of higher B.t.u. content the orifice is made smaller than with manufactured gas.

Lighting the burner.—In lighting a burner turn the gas on full, and apply the lighted match a little above the burner ports. A flame should ignite within three seconds.

Combustion of gas.—According to usually accepted theories, combustion of gas takes place in two steps. The first step consists of the partial combustion of the hydrocarbons in the gas, principally to carbon monoxide and hydrogen. This results in an inner cone of light blue or green. The second step consists of the complete combustion of the carbon monoxide and hydrogen to carbon dioxide and water vapor, which produces the almost colorless outer cone. The two cones must be allowed to develop completely before the flame impinges on any surface which might tend to cool the gas.

"There is also a peculiar relation between the total amount of air needed for combustion of a gas and the heating value of the gas.

It is found that for rough estimates, the amount of air needed for a given amount of gas is equal to the B.T.U. value minus 50 and the result divided by 100. To express it in a formula—

$$\text{"Parts Air} = \frac{\text{B.T.U. of gas} - 50}{100}$$

"For a 540 B.T.U. gas, the air needed is found to be

$$\frac{\text{"}540 - 50}{100} \text{ or } 4.9 \text{ air to 1 gas.}$$

"or for a 1,050 B.T.U. gas—

$$\frac{\text{"}1,050 - 50}{100} = 10 \text{ air to 1 gas."}[1]$$

Flue on closed top range.—A closed top range is carefully designed to obtain the requisite amount of secondary air, by placing the burners at a greater distance from the top of the stove, and by having the vents above the burners connected to a flue. The products of combustion are easily and quickly removed through the flue and do not interfere with the further burning of the gas. A closed top should never be placed on an open top range. Secondary air will be partly shut off, and incomplete combustion and the escape of toxic gases result.

Flame.—The flame which burns at each burner port is of the Bunsen type. The correct flame, which is obtained with the right mixture of gas and air, has been described. (Fig. 32.) The burners on a range designed for portable gas are usually placed nearer to the grate than on the range using manufactured or natural gas. The tip of the flame should just touch the bottom of the utensil placed over it. Reddish flashes in the flame are due to minute dust particles. This condition will not blacken the cooking utensils, and does not indicate incorrect adjustment.

Correct and incorrect flames.—A very high flame, rising above the grate, indicates too much gas; a very short flame, too little gas. The flow of gas through the orifice is changed by turning the six-

[1] Apmann, A. M. Domestic Gas Appliances, pp. 23-24. © Courtesy, American Gas Journal.

sided nut on the spud to the left or right, as the case may be. (Figs. 33 and 34.)

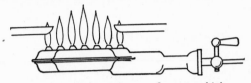

FIG. 33.—Too much gas—flame too high.

A sputtering, singing flame or one that tends to float off from the ports or flash back to the orifice has too great a mixture of air. This flame, called a "hard" flame, has a sharp inner cone and is often lighted with difficulty. (Fig. 35.)

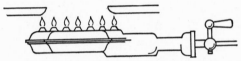

FIG. 34.—Too little gas—flame too short.

When the flame burns with a yellow tip not enough air is mixed with the gas. This is known as a "soft" flame. (Fig. 36.) The amount of air may be regulated by loosening the screw on the air

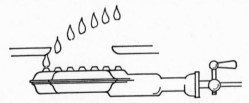

FIG. 35.—"Hard" flame—tends to float off from burner.

shutter, adjusting the shutter to admit the correct amount of air, and then tightening the screw again.

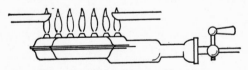

FIG. 36.—"Soft" flame—yellow tips.

If the flame is at too great a distance from the cooking vessel, or if an excessive draft tends to blow the flame to one side, gas is used inefficiently and wastefully. Gas is also wasted if the burner is at so great a distance from the grate that a long flame is used for heating. In this case a large proportion of the heat from the flame passes off at the side.

Cookers, conventional, and table-top ranges.—Gas ranges are divided into three classes, according to the location of the oven or ovens. Small ranges with the oven and broiler directly below the surface burners are generally known as cookers; with the oven elevated, as conventional type or cabinet ranges; and with the oven below and at the right or left of the surface burners, as the table-top type. On any of these types there may be a single baking oven, a combination baking and broiling oven, or separate broiling and baking ovens. When the ovens are separate, the broiling oven is usually below the baking oven, and the same burner is used to heat both ovens. The height of the oven and cooking surface is important and should be such as to eliminate unnecessary stooping which tends to cause fatigue.

Range ovens.—With regard to the method of heating, ovens are classified into four types:

1. Direct action, where the burner is in the oven proper and not below an oven bottom or baffle.
2. Semi-direct; the burner is under a bottom or baffle plate, but there are no flues directing circulation.
3. Circulating, where the flue gases are directed by a system of flues.
4. Fresh air, in which no products of combustion enter the oven, but only fresh air which has been previously heated by circulating in a separate flue over the burner.

Whatever the method used, the products of combustion and the steam and other volatile by-products of the baking process pass out at a flue on the upper back side of the oven.

Oven burner.—The oven burner generally has a double row of ports on either side, at an angle of about 30° from the vertical, so spaced that when the burner is lighted at one point the flame runs along from port to port. In some burners the ports are on the top side, in others on the lower side of the burner. The oven burner has a mixing throat similar to those of the top surface burners. When turned on full the oven burner has a heat capacity of not less than

10,000 B.t.u. an hour per cubic foot of oven space up to 2.4 cu. ft. It should heat the oven to 500°F. within 20 minutes.

Insulated ovens.—The present tendency is to insulate the oven with a packing of mineral wool or asbestos, which should be sufficiently thick to prevent the heated air from leaking through to the outside. An insulated oven requires a longer preheating period than the uninsulated oven, since the insulation itself must absorb part of the heat; but after the oven is heated less gas is required to keep the oven at a desired temperature. An uninsulated oven takes about 12,500 B.t.u. per hour to maintain a 500°F. temperature, which is approximately 60 per cent of the full capacity of the burner. In the insulated oven only 8,800 B.t.u. per hour are needed to maintain the temperature at 500°F. This amount is only about 38 per cent of the rated capacity of the burner turned on full, and is tangible proof of the value of insulation. The longer the insulated oven is used at one time, the greater the saving in gas.

In some ovens the insulation is of sufficient thickness to permit the gas to be turned off when the cooking process is two-thirds to three-fourths completed. The cooking is finished on retained heat.

Efficient use of oven.—In all baking the use of gas is most efficient, and the results most satisfactory, if the baking pans or sheets do not interfere with the circulation of air in the oven. Free circulation is most easily obtained by placing the pans in alternate positions on the racks, and by leaving a space between the pans or baking sheet and the sides of the oven. (Figs. 37 and 38.) Using the oven to capacity also results in an efficient use of gas. Dorothy Shank's tests carried on in the research laboratory of the American Stove Company showed that 71 per cent more B.t.u. was used when four layers of cake were baked in the oven at one time than when a single layer was baked alone, but when the four layers were baked separately one after the other, the numbr of B.t.u. increased 400 per cent.

Miss Shank also proved that when meat, vegetables, and potatoes were cooked in the oven at the same time only 10 per cent more B.t.u. was needed than when the meat was cooked by itself. Meat, vegetables, potatoes, muffins, and a dessert consumed only 15 per cent more B.t.u. than meat alone. The arrangement of pans in the oven when the whole meal is prepared is less important than when cooking baked products, since the food for the meal is not cooked by dry heat, but by steam.

FIG. 37.—Incorrect arrangement of baking pans.

Experiments conducted in the household equipment department at Iowa State College indicate that the oven need not be preheated. Even such foods as cake and baking powder biscuits were placed in a cold oven at the time the gas was lighted and baked satisfactorily.

FIG. 38.—Correct arrangement of baking pans to obtain free circulation of heat.

Oven heat regulator.—The heat regulator is a great aid in the efficient use of the oven. (Fig. 39.) By its use a constant temperature may be maintained and more uniformly baked products obtained. The regulator prevents the oven from being heated to too high a temperature. Excessive high heat tends to warp the oven. The housewife is not interested in an extremely high temperature, but in the quantity of heat available; in other words, in the B.t.u. content. Cooking temperatures are never above 500°F., and even that temperature is rarely used.

The regulator has two principal parts, the wheel device outside the oven, and a metal cylinder, sensitive to variations in temperature,

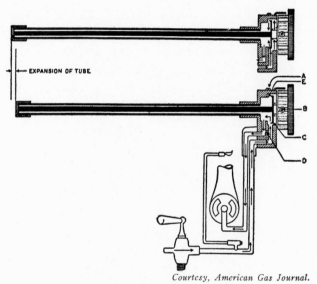

Courtesy, American Gas Journal.

FIG. 39.—Oven regulator in operation.

on the inside. A pointer on the wheel is turned to any desired temperature indicated on the adjoining dial.

The cylinder is made of metal, usually copper. Within the cylinder is a rod of material having a different expansion coefficient from that of copper. Porcelain or carbon is frequently used. At the end away from the dial the cylinder and rod are rigidly joined. As the copper expands it draws the non-expanding porcelain rod with it, and a spring, back of the valve which controls the flow of gas to the burner, is released, partially closes the valve, and reduces the entering volume of gas. A study of Fig. 39 will make this clear.

Gas enters through the cock and passes up the inlet pipe, under the control valve at *C*, and down to the oven burner. When the copper cylinder expands and draws the inner rod with it, the pressure of the rod against the spring (*B*) is released. The spring then presses against the valve (*C*) with sufficient force to close the gas passage-way to such an extent that only enough gas may flow through to maintain the required temperature.

The setting of the dial regulates the initial size of the opening at *C*. At low temperatures the opening is very small, so that only a slight expansion will reduce the flow of gas; at higher temperatures the opening is correspondingly larger.

To prevent the flame from being extinguished when the valve is nearly closed, a by-pass valve at *D* always permits enough gas to flow to maintain a temperature of 250°F. Note that the gas for the pilot light (p. 102) comes directly from the main supply pipe, and is not affected by the condition of the regulator. The oven heat control works most effectively if the gas is turned on full at the beginning of the heating operation.

Other features.—Other less essential but very convenient features are found on many of the newest gas range models. The time clock is one of these features. The clock mechanism is connected with the oven regulator, and, by means of a second pilot light which heats an expansion element, the oven burner is ignited at the time for which the clock is set, and is turned off again at the other hour indicated on the clock. This addition may be very useful to women in business.

Top lighters and oven pilots.—Many gas ranges have top lighters and oven pilots. The top lighter is a tiny jet of gas burning constantly in the center between the top burners. By pressing the pilot button on the manifold the flame shoots out toward the burners and ignites the gas when it is turned on.

At present the top lighter is often in the form of an automatic igniter which almost instantly ignites the gas when the gas is turned on to any burner. Tubes run from the small central flame to each burner. When a burner is turned on, the air-gas mixture from the burner flows into the tube, and ignites at the central flame; then because the tube contains too large a proportion of air, the flame flashes back to the burner and ignites it also.

The oven pilot light is a safety device, to which sufficient gas flows to keep it burning continuously, whenever the oven burner is lighted. If the oven burner flame should accidentally go out, the pilot will relight the escaping gas and prevent an explosion.

Some ranges have self-latching gas cocks, which lock automatically when closed. One range with a burner cover has a valve guard which prevents the turning on of the gas when the cover is closed. It is also impossible to close the cover when any burner is lighted. These safety features are valuable where there are young children.

Table tops, utensil drawers.—Among other accessories are table tops on cabinet or table-top ranges, a folding top over surface burners, utensil drawers below the manifold, and oven racks which may be pulled out without tipping. A new broiler pan of cast aluminum may be preheated so that both sides of the food are seared at the same time. In some ranges the broiler pan is raised or lowered to position by turning the handle on the front panel of the broiler oven.

Care of range.—At present most gas ranges are finished in enamel. This is easily cleaned by wiping with a cloth dipped in soapy water. Do not wipe the range when it is warm. Enamel is a glass-like coating fused on to an iron or steel base and if washed when hot, will cool more rapidly than the steel base, and the unequal contraction may cause the enamel to crack. Cleaning powders tend to scratch both enamel and the metal chromium, sometimes used for trimmings and oven linings. The racks, rack glides, and oven bottom may be taken out and washed. Obstinate spots can usually be removed with baking soda or kerosene.

Cast iron burners and sheet iron ovens are kept free from rust by wiping them once every week or two with a cloth moistened with machine oil or liquid wax. Rusting in ovens may be prevented by leaving the oven door open for a few minutes when the gas is first lighted, to permit any moisture to escape, and again at the end of the baking period until the oven has cooled. Moisture from the combustion process tends to condense in the oven when the oven is cool, and before proper circulation has been established.

Greater efficiency is obtained if the burners are cleaned regularly. They should be removed from the range, all dust and food particles brushed from the top and throat with a stiff brush, and the air shutter cleaned. Sometimes it becomes necessary to clean the burners by boiling them in a solution of washing soda (1 tablespoon of soda in 3 quarts water). Aluminum burners must not be treated in this way since alkalies tend to darken aluminum, but they may be washed in warm soapy water and rinsed in clear hot water. Before replacing, dry the burners upside down in a warm oven. The pilot light valve may be cleaned with a piece of wire.

If the broiler pan is not to be used when the oven is heated it should be removed to keep the enamel from cracking. The pan will be easier to clean and there will be less smoke from the broiling, if, before use, a small amount of water is placed in the bottom of the pan. Before washing the broiler pan, spatters of fat may be wiped out with paper; fat which has burned on may be scoured with steel wool of a fine grade.

Flue.—It is generally desirable to have a gas range connected to a flue. In this way, odors, grease from cooking, and excess moisture are carried away, along with the products of combustion, and the result is a more comfortable kitchen. A flue is not absolutely essential, however, and ranges approved by the American Gas Association's Laboratory, if otherwise properly installed, are safe without a flue connection.

A.G.A. Approval Seal.—Most manufacturers submit their appliances to the American Gas Association Laboratory for testing. Judgment for or against is impartially determined. Requirements for gas ranges have been worked out by committees on which are representatives from the U. S. Bureau of Standards, U. S. Bureau of Mines, U. S. Public Health Service, U. S. Bureau of Home Economics, American Home Economics Association, U. S. Department of Agriculture, Canadian and American gas associations, and others. The committees have set up minimum requirements for safety, efficient performance, and durability. These requirements include gauge of metal used for the different parts; regulations as to flues, burners, cocks, ovens, etc.; essential conditions of gas consumption; protection against leakage, production of carbon monoxide, and fire hazard; and satisfactory testing of distribution of oven heat and thermal efficiency of top burner. If a range meets these requirements the manufacturer is required to mark it with the Laboratory Approval Seal—a blue star, surrounded by a double circle, in which appears the following statement, "Complies with National Safety Standards, Approved, American Gas Association."

In the purchase of any piece of equipment, the initial, repair or upkeep, and operation costs must be considered. Most gas appliances are of simple construction, and repair costs are, consequently, very slight. Operation costs depend upon local gas rates, but may be greatly reduced by the efficient use of the appliance.

Suggestions for the economical use of gas for cooking.

1. Have flames properly adjusted.
2. Keep all parts clean.
3. Use an oven regulator.
4. When possible use the smaller size burners instead of the large one.
5. Turn the flame down, or preferably use the simmer burner, after the water begins to boil. Slow boiling water is as hot as rapidly boiling water.
6. Do not light gas before needed. Gas is as hot the instant it is ignited as 10 minutes later.
7. Turn out gas and relight again if there are to be some minutes when it is not in use. Matches are cheaper than gas.
8. Use double or triple saucepans over one burner.
9. Boil only amount of water needed.
10. Use covered utensils whenever possible.
11. Use oven to capacity.
12. Turn gas off 10 or 15 minutes before end of baking period, and finish cooking on retained heat.

Summary.

1. Ranges may be classified as cooker, cabinet, and table-top types; or as open and closed top ranges.
2. The gas to be burned passes through the manifold, cock, and orifice into the throat of the burner. In the throat the gas mixes with primary air drawn in through the shutter, and flows from the burner ports, where it is ignited. The additional oxygen required for combustion is supplied by the secondary air.
3. Surface burners are of three sizes: giant, of 13,000 B.t.u. heating capacity per hour; regular, of 9,000 B.t.u. heating capacity; and simmer, of 1,800 B.t.u. heating capacity. The oven burner usually has a heating capacity of about 10,000 B.t.u. per cu. ft. of oven space.
4. The properly adjusted flame extends very slightly above the grate, has

a distinct inner bluish green cone, and an outer almost colorless cone, and burns without sputtering or hissing.

5. A closed top should not be placed on an open top range. Closed top ranges have special burner and flue construction to allow for proper circulation.

6. For all except short baking processes, insulated ovens are more efficient than non-insulated ovens, and when flue connected prevent excessive temperatures in the kitchen.

7. Thermostatic control of the oven saves gas and time, and gives more uniformly baked products. The regulator is generally made of two materials which expand at different rates when heated. By this means a spring is released and the gas pass-valve decreased in diameter.

8. To render efficient service gas ranges should be kept clean and adjusted.

9. The American Gas Association Laboratory has set up minimum safety, durability, and efficiency requirements for all gas appliances. Appliances conforming to these minimum requirements are stamped with the American Gas Association's Seal of Approval.

References

1. Apmann, A. M. Domestic Gas Appliances. American Gas Journal, Inc., New York. 1931.
2. A. G. A. Approval Requirements for Gas Ranges. American Gas Assoc. Testing Laboratory, Cleveland, Ohio. 1930.
3. Conner, R. M. The Laboratory Seal of Approval—Its Design and Use. Amer. Gas Assoc. Testing Laboratory, Cleveland, Ohio.
4. Gas Ranges. Ladies' Home Jour. Leaflet. No. 201. Curtis Publishing Co., Philadelphia, Pa. 1930.
5. Hulser, Marie. Modern Gas Range and Its Care. Practical Home Ec. 8:273. 1930.
6. Lutherer, Otto, and Kroeker, J. D. Flow of Gas through Orifices in Domestic Appliances. Bul. No. 1. Amer. Gas Assoc. Testing Laboratory, Cleveland, Ohio. 1928.
7. Mullaney, B. J. Economic Aspects of Laboratory Seal Defined. Amer. Gas Assoc. Testing Laboratory, Cleveland, Ohio.
8. Shank, Dorothy. The Oven Load. Bul. No. 34. Research Dept., American Stove Co., Cleveland, Ohio. 1929.
9. Strawn, Bernice M. Determination of the Moisture Content of Gas and Electric Ovens under Baking Conditions and the Effect of Varied Moisture Content on a Baked Product. Unpublished thesis. Iowa State College Library, Ames, Iowa. 1931.
10. Trip through the A. G. A. Testing Laboratory. Amer. Gas Assoc. Testing Laboratory, Cleveland, Ohio. 1930.
11. What's Within the Gas Range. Amer. Gas Assoc., Inc., New York.
12. Wright, F. R. Gas Changes and Appliance Adjustments. Amer. Gas Assoc. Monthly 14:146-152. 1932.

ILLUSTRATIONS: Figs. 28, 29, 30, 32-38, American Gas Association, Inc.

CHAPTER VIII

COAL, GASOLINE, AND KEROSENE RANGES

Coal range.—When a coal range is used over a period of time two defects tend to develop in the construction. (1) The joints tend to warp and open up, causing air-leaks which interfere with the flue draft. (2) The walls of the oven and inside flues begin to rust. If the cause of the development of these defects is known, they may be avoided in the purchase of a range.

All coal ranges must be connected to a chimney, through which the smoke and unburned fuel gases are expelled. The air in the chimney is warmer than the outside air and consequently produces a draft. For this draft to be as effective as possible there must be a continuous air-tight passageway from the opening below the fire-box, through the grates and flues, to the top of the chimney. There should be no leaks around any of the openings into the chimney or between the bricks of the chimney, and all stove-pipe joints must be tight.

Coal ranges are made of cast iron, steel, and malleable cast iron (see chapter on materials). When made of cast iron, or cast iron and steel, the parts are usually bolted together. These joints cannot be made entirely tight, and are filled with stove putty. With continuous heating the putty cracks and falls out, leaving openings through which air-leaks may occur. Ranges made of malleable cast iron and steel may have the joints riveted so that they will remain tight permanently. Top castings around the surface lids are more easily cracked when of cast iron than when of malleable cast iron. Such breaks will also permit leakage of air.

All coal contains an appreciable amount of moisture, varying from a small percentage in anthracite to as high as 24 per cent in sub-bituminous coal. This moisture passes off in the form of steam, and tends to condense in the flues as the range cools, causing the inside walls of the range to rust. Various finishes have been used in an attempt to protect the flues from rusting. Vitreous enamel, fused on to the flue castings, has proved to be one of the most effective linings. (Fig. 40.)

As a further surety of efficiency in operation and of economy in the use of fuel the covers and doors should fit tightly, the fire-box should be of moderate size, and the oven and top surfaces should heat evenly and quickly. The stove pipe should have few bends and joints so as not to interfere with the draft, which is regulated by the

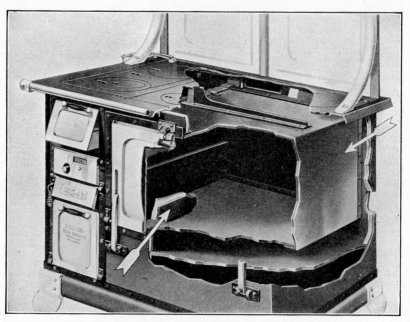

FIG. 40.—Rust-resisting flue linings of vitreous enamel.

damper at the bottom of the stove pipe. Allow sufficient space above the fuel in the fire-box for proper oxidation of the gas from the coal. Complete combustion increases the available heat.

Coal burns slowly because it is not possible to produce an intimate mixing of oxygen and coal. Kindling is necessary in starting the combustion. Products of combustion are carbon monoxide, carbon dioxide, nitrogen, excess oxygen, and free carbon. Anthracite has a low moisture content, is low in ash and volatile constituents, and high in percentage of fixed carbon. It is preferable to bituminous coal for the kitchen range. Ash from coal melts at a high temperature and forms clinker which may fuse with the fire-box lining and tend to destroy it. On the other hand a layer of ashes over the iron grates protects the grates from overheating, which in time will burn them out.

For keeping the coal range free from rust, and pleasing in appearance, a rub with a cloth dipped in light machine oil is recommended rather than blacking.

The heat radiated from the range makes the use of coal in summer very undesirable.

Gasoline range.—Gasoline ranges are of two common types. In one the fuel flows to the burners from an elevated fuel holder; in the second type it is forced into the burners by air pressure which has been generated in the fuel tank. The latter type is usually considered more safe from fire hazard, since in this type it is not possible to refill the tank when the burners are lighted.

The burners on a gasoline range may be flat with many narrow slotted openings, or deep with a circular groove into which the gasoline flows. The groove has an outer surrounding surface, 5 or 6 inches high, and encircles an inner perforated cylinder through which air circulates. The gasoline in the groove is ignited by a long lighter, and a collar over the top of the burner directs the flame under the utensil. As the burner becomes warm the gasoline is vaporized and burns as a gas.

In gasoline ranges with the flat slotted burners the liquid gasoline is converted into a gas before the burners are lighted. The air pressure in the fuel tank forces the gasoline through a vaporizing tube, which in some ranges is first heated by gasoline burned in a preheater-cup beneath the tube, and later by the lighted "master" burner. The vaporized gas, still under pressure, passes through a small orifice at the end of the vaporizing tube (also called generator tube) into the mixing chamber where it is mixed with sufficient air for efficient combustion. This mixture passes up through the burner slots and is lighted. The burner nearest the tank, called the master burner, is lighted first, and allowed to remain lighted, so that the heat from it may continue the vaporization of the liquid gasoline in the generator tube. In a new model the preheater is not used, but the generator primes itself in the master burner. The greater the air pressure in the tank, the hotter the flame, the size of which is further regulated by the generator valve. Because of the air pressure, the gas tends to burn with a slight noise in this type of gasoline range.

Most gasoline ranges have stationary ovens, below which are burners similar to the top burners of the range. A few use portable ovens.

Gasoline vaporizes readily, and care must be exercised in its use. It burns with a very hot clean blue flame and is an excellent substitute for gas. A study of fuels used in Indiana rural homes indicated an average consumption of 2.45 gallons per week in the 10.5 per cent of homes where gasoline was used.

Where the gasoline is of high grade, the range requires a comparatively small amount of time for care and cleaning. Dirty gasoline necessitates cleaning the fuel tank. Occasionally the gas tip of the generator tube becomes clogged with carbon. Often this carbon may be removed simply by opening wide the generator valve and then closing it, and repeating the operation several times. If this method is not effective the generator may be removed from the range, the valve stem disconnected from the generator, and the gas tip removed. The generator tube may now be cleaned with a piece of wire and rinsed in gasoline, the carbon scraped from the valve stem, and the gas tip replaced. The generator is again assembled and connected to the range.

Kerosene ranges.—Kerosene is widely used in homes where gas and electricity are not available, especially as a summer fuel; over 70 per cent of the rural homes included in the Indiana survey reported the use of kerosene for cooking in the summer months. Although, with the exception of coal, the amount of kerosene consumed, expressed in British thermal units, was higher than the amount of other fuels consumed, the actual cost was the lowest. Kerosene has about 19,800 B.t.u. per pound.

Kerosene was not obtained from oil wells until after such sources were accidentally discovered in 1859. Previous to that time, however, oil had been made from coal or shale, and had occasionally been obtained from natural oil springs. The first kerosene stoves were little more than kerosene lamps—and smoky, bad-smelling lamps at that.

Modern kerosene stoves commonly have from two to four burners for surface cookery. The stove may or may not have the cabinet back. One- or two-burner portable ovens may be used over the burners, or there may be a stationary oven with two additional burners for furnishing heat. These oven burners may be used for surface cookery by removing the baffle and using a rack for a grate. A few models have back of the burners a draft space which retains excess heat, and may be used for slow cooking or for keeping food warm.

To burn, kerosene must be changed to a vapor. This change is made possible by the burner. Burners are classified as short-drum, long-drum, asbestos-ring, and wickless. As a rule long-drum burners are provided with a wick, the short-drum burners have either a wick or an asbestos ring, and the wickless type has a burner similar to the burner on the gravity gasoline range. In this case the burner must be primed first with some easily ignited fuel such as gasoline or alcohol to heat the burner, before the kerosene will vaporize sufficiently to burn.

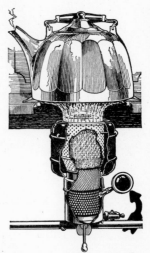

Courtesy, American Stove Company.

Fig. 41.—Short-drum burner.

Heat is carried from the burner in a kerosene range to the utensil largely by convection currents. A certain amount of heat is lost in the process. The short drum or chimney reduces the amount of exposed surface, but the long chimney protects the flame and so prevents excessive loss of heat. Enclosing the back and sides of the stove increases burner efficiency by cutting off drafts.

Short-drum burner.—The lower section of the short-drum burner (Fig. 41) has a wick-tube of brass, in which the wick-carrier with the wick is raised or lowered by a brass ratchet wheel at the end of an adjusting rod. The other end of the adjusting rod carries a hand-wheel for turning the wick. The inner wall of the wick-tube is corrugated to allow the wick to be adjusted with a minimum amount of friction. The wick-chamber surrounds a central shaft at the top of which there is a perforated automatic wick-stop, held in place by a lock-nut. The wick-stop permits the wick to be turned to the correct position for lighting and burning, and also provides for the circulation of air. A removable head on the wick-chamber increases the ease with which wicks may be replaced.

The upper part of the burner consists of an inner and an outer perforated combustion tube surrounded by a chimney of porcelain enamel, to which the tubes are securely fastened. The inner combustion tube tends to burn out owing to the high temperature pro-

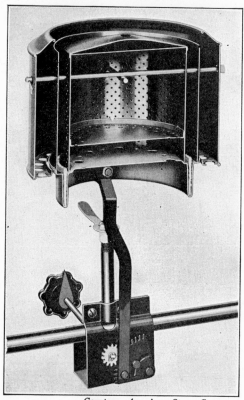

Courtesy, American Stove Company.

Fig. 42.—Asbestos-ring type of burner.

duced, but at least one manufacturer is now making this tube of a heat-resisting metal which carries a ten-year guarantee. The combustion tubes are tapered at the bottom to prevent food that has boiled over from reaching the wick. This upper section rests on the top of the central shaft.

When not lighted the chimney section is raised from the wick-chamber by a handle at the base of the wick-tube. The chimney should always be raised when the flame is extinguished at the end of a cooking operation; otherwise the oil tends to seep out of the wick-tube and spread over the outside of the wick-chamber. When this occurs, the burner will smoke when relighted, until this oil has burned off.

Kerosene burns in the short-drum burner with a clear blue flame. The oil is vaporized by the heat in the wick and rises into the flame. The flame will increase in size for the first five or ten minutes and must be lowered until properly regulated. All flames will grow until a maximum heat is reached.

The asbestos-ring type has an inner and an outer combustion tube, fastened to the chimney, as in the short-drum type, but a ring of asbestos, supported in a metal frame, is used instead of a wick. This asbestos ring rests in a shallow trough which is connected to the feed pipe, and the height of the flame depends upon the amount of oil allowed to flow into the trough. (Fig. 42.)

Long-drum burner.—The long-drum burner differs somewhat in construction from the short-drum. (Fig. 43.) The lower section has a double-walled wick-tube with a surrounding removable collar at the top. The inner tube is slightly shorter than the outer tube, and this difference in height gives a chisel-shaped edge to the wick. The wick-tube is fastened and connected to the feed pipe. There is also a hand-wheel by which the ratchet wheel is turned, in moving the wick-carrier up and down.

In place of the wick-stop the long-drum burner has a flame-spreader which is held in place by a central shaft which locks between two brass cams. The flame-spreader rests upon a circular perforated plate, known as the spanner. The spreader itself is perforated on the top and bottom and around the sides, the holes varying from large pin-pricks to holes a quarter of an inch in diameter. The flanged edge of the spreader is so shaped that it directs the air currents and gives a proper angle to the flame, preventing it from cupping over the top of the spreader. The spreader is not a wick-stop, and care must be taken not to turn the wick so high that it rests against the spreader. Some stoves have a spreader-lift to increase the distance above the wick when lighting the burner.

The chimney is of porcelain enamel, with a mica window through which the flame may be seen. Around the bottom of the drum are holes to admit the secondary air, which absorbs the heat from the flame and decreases heat loss. The diameter and height of the chim-

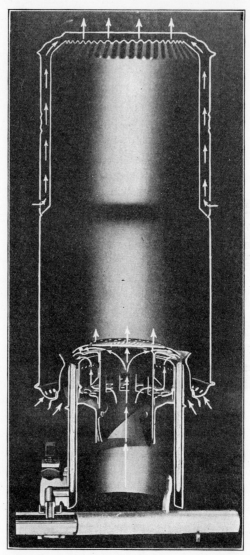

Fig. 43.—Long-drum burner with double wall.

ney apparently affect the velocity of the air so that the draft is greater in the long-drum burner than in the short-drum.

Some stoves have double-walled drums, the inner wall extending from the top about half-way down the drum. Where this inner wall fastens to the outer wall there is a row of holes on the outside. As the air surrounding the lower part of the drum is heated it rises and is drawn through the holes, and supplies extra heat to the utensil.

Two kinds of flames may be obtained with the long-drum burner: the blue flame, similar to the one with the short-drum burner; and a blue flame with white tips, an inch to an inch and a half high, above the blue body. (Fig. 44.) There should be a distinct blue

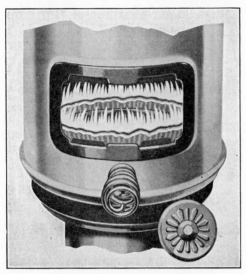

Fig. 44.—Hot white-tipped flame. Note the distinct line of separation between the blue body and white tips.

line of separation between the body of the flame and the tips. This white-tipped flame is hotter than the blue flame alone and reaches its maximum heat when the wick is turned just below the point at which the tips tend to converge. These tips contain some unburned carbon which was not completely oxidized in the body of the flame. As this incandescent carbon rises in the chimney and comes into contact with the hot air, oxidation is completed, and the intense heat is brought close below the utensil. The wick should not be turned to this highest flame until the burner is warmed; otherwise a break in the flame may occur. Such a break or gap in the flame causes oil seepage onto the wick-tubes and a disagreeable odor. An automatic wick-stop controls the height of the wick for the white-tipped flame. A flame should generate in 50 seconds and reach maximum heat in about 3 minutes, unless the stove is abnormally cold. In the long-drum burner the vapor is lifted from the wick by the currents of air instead of being driven off by heat, and this accounts for the more rapid generation of the flame. Experiments carried on in the laboratory indicate that long-drum burners heat more rapidly, i.e., have higher operating efficiency, whereas the short-drum burners heat more slowly, but have slightly greater thermal efficiency. Similar results were obtained by Snyder at the University of Nebraska. Snyder also found a very direct relationship between the thermal efficiency of any oil range and the distance between chimney top and grate. Up to a certain point the thermal efficiency increases and the heating time decreases as the distance between grate and chimney top is decreased. Where the distance is too short, however, the draft is not sufficient for complete oxidation and soot is deposited and odors occur.

The giant burner, found on some stoves in addition to the standard burners, is one to two inches larger in size and usually heats the utensil more rapidly than the standard burner, but is less efficient. Individual differences between stoves of the same type burner may be as great as between stoves of entirely different types.

Flames are extinguished in oil ranges by turning the wick down into the wick-tube, or by shutting off the supply of fuel. Oil remaining in the troughs of asbestos-ring and wickless burners will continue to burn until wholly consumed.

Oil burners are also designed for installation in the coal or wood range in place of the fire-box. Such a conversion of the coal range eliminates the dust and dirt caused by the use of wood or coal fuel, but keeps the advantages of the larger range.

"Any kerosene burner, to give satisfactory service, should meet the following requirements: (a) it should be quick to develop a steady flow of heat; (b) it should perform the operations of heating rapidly; (c) it should not be extravagant in the use of fuels; (d) its provision for draft should be such that the fuel is completely oxidized to prevent objectionable odor and the formation of soot; (e) the burner should be simple to operate and easy to clean."[1]

[1] Snyder, Edna B. A Study of Kerosene Cook Stoves. p. 5.

Level stove necessary.—The kerosene stove should stand level, otherwise the burner farthest from the oil reservoir will be flooded or will tend to burn dry and consume the wick unnecessarily, depending upon the direction of tip. If the reservoir becomes empty when the stove is in operation, all the burners will burn dry. A detachable reservoir is preferable, and when it is of glass, the amount of fuel is easily noted.

Care of range.—The fuel pipes should be drained and cleaned once in three months, or oftener if the kerosene contains water. When water gets into the wicks they will burn with a sputtery flame, or the flame will have gaps. The end of the fuel line away from the reservoir has a removable cap. After the reservoir has been tipped back this cap is taken off, and the opposite end of the stove lifted so that the oil may drain out. A stiff wire is run through the pipe to clean it, and it is rinsed out with fresh oil.

Wicks are an important part of the oil stove. They are made of closely woven high grade cotton, so constructed that the oil is broken up into tiny particles and drawn up through the capillaries of the wick to the top, where the oil may be ignited with a match. Wicks should be kept in condition by frequent cleaning, usually as often as once a day, though some authorities suggest once for every 12 hours of burning. To clean the wick, the chimney and the outside collar are removed; also the flame-spreader or wick-stop. The wick is turned level with the top of the wick-tube, and wiped with a piece of cloth from the center outward, until the charred edge is removed. Any loose threads may be removed with scissors, but scissors are not used for other trimming. Very uneven wicks may be burned off by lighting the burners with the reservoir removed. The charred edge is then wiped, and smoothed with the finger-tips. If the wick has a beveled edge, this should be carefully maintained.

Some makes of ranges are provided with a wick cleaner—a metal ring which fits down over the wick, and is turned to the right and then to the left to remove all the char from the edge.

When the wick has burned down to the carrier, it must be replaced. Long-drum stoves will use one set of wicks for about a year; short-drum stoves require more frequent replacement of wicks, sometimes as many as four sets a year; lighting rings do not burn out, but will need to be replaced unless cleaned regularly. Always buy wicks made especially by the manufacturer for the stove in use. Wicks are burned off at the factory to prepare them for lighting and should not be confused with old wicks. Before lighting, new wicks should be turned down into the wick-tube for 5 minutes to become saturated with oil.

Burners should be removed and the perforations brushed free from dust, which will impede air circulation. Occasionally they may be boiled in a soda solution, and carefully dried. Oil spreads in a thin film so that any seepage over the edge of the wick-tube must be wiped off to prevent smoke and unpleasant odors. Some grades of kerosene contain heavy oil which may drop out of the flame and condense on the wick-tube.

Oil stoves have only a few parts to get out of order, and parts needing to be replaced can usually be purchased at the local hardware store. It is well to select a range of which the parts are easily available.

Ovens.—Portable ovens are often built with heat-resisting glass windows in the door, so that the progress of the baking may be easily watched. Some ovens have heat indicators, and others have insulated walls and patented accessories for distributing the heat evenly throughout the oven space. Frequently, after manufacture, the ovens are oiled to prevent rusting. When the oven is first heated this oil burns off and may cause some smoke.

Safety of kerosene.—Kerosene is not volatile at ordinary temperatures and for this reason is considered a comparatively safe fuel. Gasoline is much more volatile and if mixed with oil in the reservoir of an oil stove will cause an explosion. The chemical formula for kerosene is given as $C_{13}H_{28}$. A temperature of approximately 700° F. is required to separate the carbon and hydrogen atoms. Every gallon of kerosene burned uses between 9,500 and 10,000 gallons of air for complete oxidation.

Summary.

1. Coal ranges should be constructed with warp-proof joints and rust-resisting flues.
2. There should be a continuous air-tight passageway from the opening below the fire-box to the top of the chimney.

3. Gasoline ranges are of the gravity or air-pressure type. The air-pressure type is considered safer.

4. Gasoline burns with a hot blue flame, and is an excellent substitute for gas.

5. Burners on kerosene ranges are of short-drum, long-drum, asbestos-ring, or wickless types.

6. The long-drum has the higher operating efficiency, the short-drum the higher thermal efficiency.

7. Differences between burners of the same type may be as great as between burners of different types.

8. Kerosene should oxidize completely to obviate soot.

9. Wicks should be trimmed regularly, and the range cleaned and wiped free from all oil seepage to prevent objectionable smoke and odors.

References

1. Oil Stoves and the Combustion of Kerosene. Perfection Stove Co., Cleveland, Ohio. n.d.

2. Rapp, Miriam. Fuels used for Cooking Purposes in Indiana Rural Homes. Agric. Expt. Sta. Bul. 339. Purdue Univ., Lafayette, Ind. 1930.

3. Safe Use and Storage of Gasoline and Kerosene on the Farm. U. S. D. A. Farmers' Bul. 1678. Washington, D. C. 1932.

4. Selection, Care and Operation of a Liquid Fuel Stove. Perfection Stove Co., Cleveland, Ohio. n.d.

5. Snyder, Edna B. A Study of Kerosene Cook Stoves. Agric. Expt. Sta. Research Bul. 48. College of Agriculture, Univ. of Nebraska, Lincoln, Neb. 1930.

6. Snyder, Edna B. Factors affecting the Performance of Kerosene Cook Stoves. Agric. Expt. Sta. Research Bul. 64. College of Agriculture, Univ. of Nebraska, Lincoln, Neb. 1932.

7. Wyer, Samuel S. Fundamentals of our Coal Problem. Fuel-Power-Transportation Educational Foundation, Columbus, Ohio. 1929.

ILLUSTRATIONS: Figs. 40, Malleable Iron Range Co.; 43, 44, Perfection Stove Co.

CHAPTER IX

SMALL EQUIPMENT, ELECTRICAL

It is not possible to discuss at length each of the many kinds of small equipment which may find a use in the home. But an attempt will be made to indicate in a general way what the housewife should know before purchasing one of these appliances, and such points in selection as construction, ease of operation, and ease of cleaning, which influence the efficiency of any piece of equipment. Materials used in household appliances have been considered in Chapter II. In this and the following chapter mention will be made of the common materials used for the appliance under consideration, but no details of the manufacture will be given.

Classification.—Small appliances may be classified into those electrically driven and heated, and those manipulated by hand. The electrical appliances include electric cookers and grills of several varieties, percolators, toasters, waffle irons, egg cookers, and a dozen or more different mixers. They will be considered in the order named.

Electric cookers.—The electric cooker has many of the characteristics and cooking advantages of a small electric range and a fireless cooker combined. In the cooker the housewife may boil, stew, bake, roast, and fry, may use continuous heat or stored heat. The cooker has a circular well with walls thickly insulated with rock wool or other thermal insulating material. The outside is of enameled iron or steel, the well-lining usually of aluminum. Certain designs have two wells, and one model has the well in a horizontal position.

The cooker may have only one electric unit, beneath the bottom of the well, or may have a unit below the well and a second one in the cover. On some models the cover unit may be turned either side up, may be used for surface cookery, or, reversed, may help in heating the well. The bottom unit may be controlled by a thermostat, which shuts the heat off automatically when a temperature high enough to cook the food on retained heat is reached. Cookers should be on casters or have a bail handle that they may be easily moved.

Electric cookers are supplied with various aluminum containers which permit several kinds of food to be prepared at one time. Manufacturers' directions include time charts for preheating, cooking with the current on, and cooking after the current has been shut off. Directions should be carefully followed until the person using the cooker has become familiar with its possibilities. Electric ele-

FIG. 45.—This table stove not only has a variety of utensils, but the unit is wired for three different heats.

ments must not be put into water, but after being disconnected the cooker should be wiped out with a cloth dipped in hot soapy water and then in clear warm water, and should be carefully dried. A certain amount of care should be exercised in using near the sink an electric appliance which is connected to a circuit. If the appliance has any defective wiring, and accidentally comes in contact with water pipe or faucet, serious injury may result. When the cooker is not in use, the cover should be left off, to keep the well fresh and sweet.

Table stoves.—Grills are small electric stoves square or round in shape for table cookery. Within limitations many cooking processes may be performed on them from poaching eggs and making toast for breakfast to broiling steak and baking chocolate cake for dinner. Grills have one or two coiled-wire heating units fastened into a frame which has supports for the racks and utensils below and above the units and, sometimes, between the units. The wattage varies from 660 to 1,500 watts. (Fig. 45.)

Grills or table stoves, as they are often called, are not insulated and may be expensive to operate on a lighting circuit if the rate is relatively high. The use of a grill for breakfasts, light luncheons, and for occasional suppers where only a small amount of cooking is to be done, permits the hostess to sit with her family and guests and adds a note of informal friendliness to the meal. The grill is especially useful for housekeeping in a one- or two-room apartment. Square utensils should have rounded corners for ease of cleaning.

Hot plates.—Disc stoves and hot plates may be used for cooking wherever one would use a surface electric unit. There is also an electric fry-pan of 660 watt capacity used on a wall outlet for table cookery. The fry-pan is of steel and is well-insulated with rock wool, so that food will stay hot for some time after the current is turned off. When the pan has been washed it must be thoroughly dried to prevent rusting.

Percolators.—Coffee may be made by several different methods, but the electric appliance most commonly used for the purpose is the percolator.

Better grades of percolators are made in one piece without seams. They are usually of copper, plated on the outside with nickel or chromium, and sometimes with silver; on the inside with tin. Some of the newer models are of Pyrex or vitrified china. The pot types are made in three, six, and eight cup sizes, the urns in six or nine cup. The standard cup used in measuring has a capacity of six ounces.

The heating unit of the percolator may be an insulated unit beneath the pot, or a "calrod" unit, which is an immersion type, projecting into the bowl of the percolator and heating the contents by direct contact.

The perforated coffee basket is fastened to a stem which rests on the floor of the percolator bowl, or on the top of the immersion unit when that is used. The lower end of the stem may have a valve or be valveless. In either case the water is forced or pumped up through the stem, sprays over the coffee in the basket, filters down through it, extracting the essence from the coffee, and drops back into the bowl. In the valveless type this action does not take place until the water is approximately at the boiling point; in the valve type percolation starts almost immediately, but must continue longer. Some coffee baskets have a cover with very tiny raised openings through which the water must drip before reaching the coffee.

Cold or hot water may be used at the start. The manufacturer's directions should be followed. In general, when starting with cold water, a percolation period of $2\frac{1}{2}$ to 3 minutes a cup is necessary to produce a moderately strong coffee, if a rounded tablespoon of mediumly ground coffee is used to each cup of water. Increasing the coffee and the time will make a stronger coffee, but too long a period tends to give a bitter flavor. When hot water is used the period may be shortened. Coffee not served immediately must be tightly covered to keep the aroma from escaping.

The temperature is most frequently regulated by plugging in or pulling out the plug but some percolators have a thermostatic control which holds the temperature comparatively constant, or a time control which automatically stops the action when percolation is complete. All percolators should have a protective device, either a fuse or an automatic cut-out, to shut off the current if the water boils away. Extra fuses should be kept on hand so that a burned-out fuse may be replaced without the necessity of sending the percolator to the power company or a repair shop. The automatic cut-out may be reset without the bother of replacing a fuse. A percolator is usually rated at about 400 watts.

The percolator should be well balanced with a sufficiently broad base to eliminate any tendency toward tipping. Handles and base must be insulated to prevent damage to the table or difficulty in handling. The spout or faucet should not drip, and an attached lid is usually considered a convenience. The terminals to which the plug is connected should be protected with a surrounding shield of metal.

To make good coffee, not only must the coffee be fresh, but the percolator must be spotlessly clean. The valve and stem should be cleaned with a stiff brush. The electric unit should not be put into water, but the percolator bowl may be washed out with warm soapy water and then rinsed with clear hot water. There is an oil in coffee which tends to deposit on the inside parts. This deposit may be prevented by percolating hot water in the pot about once a week and allowing the dry pot to stand open to the air. Avoid percolators with unnecessary seams and crevices where dirt may collect. A smooth, durable finish is easily kept clean.

Drip coffee pots.—Most drip coffee is not made electrically, but some drip pots are provided with a stand containing a heating unit upon which the pot may be placed to keep it hot. The unit is so regulated that the coffee cannot boil.

FIG. 46.—Vacuum-type coffee pot made of glass.

One variety of drip coffee is made in a vacuum-type pot formed of two glass containers, the upper constructed with a siphon tube which extends nearly to the bottom of the lower bowl. (Fig. 46.) Coffee is measured into the upper bowl and is prevented from falling into the lower bowl by a porous cloth pad or by a glass rod. The water is in the lower bowl, which stands on an electric unit. When the water has been heated sufficiently, the pressure of the air and steam on the surface of the liquid forces the water through the siphon tube into the upper bowl leaving a partial vacuum in the lower container. If the pot is removed from the heating element, the difference in pressure causes the water to drip back through the coffee into the lower bowl. The top bowl is then lifted off, and the coffee is poured from the lower container. The cloth pad must be carefully washed after use.

Toasters.—Toasters are made to toast one, two, or four slices of bread at one time. The toaster may be automatic, semi-automatic, or operated by hand; it may toast one side of the slice of bread at a time or both sides at once. The size and type selected will depend upon the quantity and quality of toast desired and the amount of money which is available for the purchase.

Two-slice toasters are the most common variety. These toasters usually have the reversible or turn-over sides with the heating element in the center. The slices are placed in approximately vertical racks on either side of the element, and when one side of the bread

FIG. 47.—Oven-type toaster for two slices of bread.

is toasted the slices are reversed by hand, by flipping, or by turning one rack at which the other rack turns automatically. This type of toaster tends to give fairly dry toast, since the side of the slice away from the element is drying out while the other side is toasting, the dryness depending upon the speed with which the toasting is accomplished.

Oven-type toasters, holding one or two slices, toast the bread on both sides at the same time by units on either side of the rack. (Fig. 47.) There are three units in the two-slice oven model, the center unit toasting the inner side of each slice. Bread toasted on both sides at once tends to be more moist in the center than when the slice is reversed.

A third type of two-slice toaster has a horizontal double rack above the unit. A baffle plate below the element throws the heat upward, and when one side is toasted the rack is reversed. (Fig. 48.)

Units are of two kinds; helically wound coils, and flat metal ribbon on mica sheets. Both coils and ribbon are wound more closely

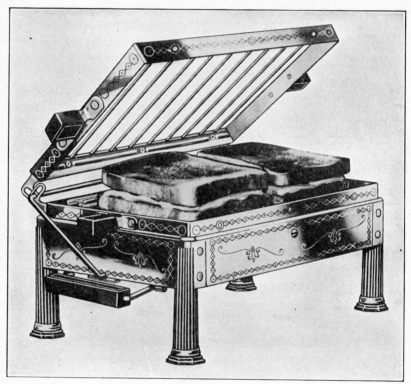

FIG. 48.—Toaster with horizontal rack. This type may also be used for toasted sandwiches.

together toward the bottom of the unit, since the vertical racks slant outward slightly at the bottom to give the toaster balance, and the lower half of the slice of bread is, therefore, farther away from the element. Occasionally coil elements sag with long use, and give too hot a temperature at the bottom.

The present tendency is to buy baker's bread rather than to make bread at home. Sliced store bread has an average maximum size of about 4¼ by 4½ by ½ inches, and toasters are built to hold slices of approximately this size. Slices of home-made bread are usually larger in size, and when they are to be constantly used for toast, a toaster must be selected which will hold them.

Most toasters have a wattage between 500 and 660 watts. After a preheat period of one minute, an oven-type toaster of 660 watts should toast bread to medium brownness in 1½ minutes; a reversible type in 3 minutes.

A toaster is usually plated with nickel or chromium. All handles should be well insulated to prevent burning the fingers in turning the toast, and the bottom of the toaster should be insulated to prevent damage to the table.

Some toasters have a semi-automatic device by means of which a lever may be set to indicate the depth of browning desired. The lever is controlled by clockwork and when the toast is done, it is lifted out automatically. In some toasters the current shuts off at the same time; in others the current may shut off and the bread remain in position. An automatic control of this kind prevents burned toast, but in selecting a toaster with a control, it is well to inquire if the control has been given a life-test at some recognized testing laboratory. There should be a manually operated release in case the automatic device fails to work.

The chief cleaning which toasters require is the removal of crumbs. When crumbs are allowed to collect, they may cause a short circut if they get onto the element. In many toasters crumbs are removed with difficulty, but a few toasters have a removable or hinged bottom tray which greatly diminishes the work of cleaning.

Sandwich toasters are of the double rack type, or have two solid metal surfaces, joined by flexible hinges which expand sufficiently to permit sandwiches to be placed between the surfaces. The outer side of each slice of bread is toasted.

Waffle irons.—Waffle irons, like toasters, are usually made of steel or copper, plated with chromium or nickel. The baking grids are commonly of aluminum. The terminal studs, which should be protected by a guard, are on the lower half of the iron and connecting wires to the upper unit pass through the hinge. The wires must be carefully insulated from the metal of the waffle iron, and must be protected from injury in the opening and closing of the iron. It is desirable that these wires shall not be covered with ordinary asbestos which absorbs moisture and may thus partly lose its insulating properties. At least one waffle iron eliminates the connecting wires through the hinge by having a separate plug for each half of the iron.

There should be sufficient freedom of action in the hinge to allow the waffles to rise, otherwise they will be soggy. The tray of the iron should be broad enough to catch any drippings of batter. All edges should be smooth, the bottom of the iron insulated to protect the table, and the handles made of heat-resistant material.

Depending upon the shape of the waffle iron, waffles may be rectangular, round, or square. The height and distance apart of the

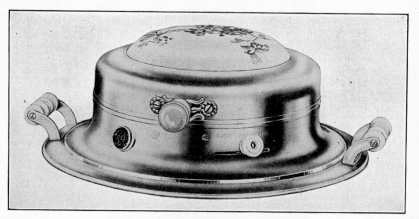

FIG. 49.—Waffle iron with heat indicator.

knobs on the grids apparently have a definite influence on the crispness of the waffle. Tests run in the household equipment laboratories at Iowa State College seem to indicate that the higher the knobs and the nearer together they are, the crisper the waffle. A soft and more moist waffle is made in irons with knobs farther apart.

The heating elements may be helical coils, insulated with porcelain posts or hollow tiles, flat ribbons on mica sheets, or "calrod" type units. Most waffle elements have a wattage of 660 watts.

Many of the newer irons have heat indicators or automatic controls. (Fig. 49.) The heat indicator is usually a bimetal pointer which shows when preheating is finished, but at least one model has a thermometer indicator in the center of the cover. The automatic controls hold the heat at a constant temperature for baking. If no indicator or control is present the correct temperature may be estimated by inserting a piece of paper between the grids until it becomes the desired shade of brown. The average of a number of tests run on irons of different makes gave 3 minutes as the time for baking the first waffle, after the preheat period. In general, second, third, and following waffles took slightly longer on account of the cooling of the iron.

Fig. 50.—Chocolate waffles served with whipped cream make a novel addition to afternoon tea or a buffet supper. Note the attractive, easily cleaned china base to the iron.

A tablespoon of batter to each section is the rule. The waffle should bake until steam ceases to issue from the opening between the grids. Grids should heat evenly, and each grid should heat equally well. Unfortunately, tests show that many irons on the market have an upper or lower grid which heats to a higher temperature than the other.

Electric waffle irons need not be greased, but must be seasoned before being used for the first time. This is done by preheating the waffle iron, brushing the grids with an unsalted fat, and cooking a first waffle until it becomes very brown. The fat seals the microscopic pores in the aluminum. After the iron has been seasoned, if the recipes contain melted fat (from 4 to 6 tablespoons), the waffles should not stick.

Do not wash the waffle grids. Brush out the crumbs and wipe the iron with a slightly damp cloth. The brown film which gradually forms on the grids does no harm to the waffles and prevents sticking. A steel wire brush will remove any excess amount of film. Wipe off the nickel or chromium with a damp cloth and polish with a dry one. Discolorations on the nickel may be removed with a mixture of alcohol and whiting.

Many different kinds of waffles may be made in addition to the usual plain ones: gingerbread, chocolate brownies, biscuit dough, corn bread, and cake all may be cooked in the waffle iron, also French toast and omelets. (Fig. 50.) Electric griddles are also on the market.

It is a convenience if the terminals on percolators, waffle irons, and toasters are of the same size and type so that connecting cords may be used interchangeably.

Egg cooker.—The electric egg cooker has helped to take the guesswork out of cooking eggs in the shell. A lower compartment, wired with an electric unit, contains a rack for four eggs. After the eggs are in place, water is added—one, two, or three teaspoonfuls, dependent upon the degree of hardness desired in the cooked product, the spherical cover is put on, and the electrical connection made. As the water boils, steam issues from a small opening in the top of the cover, and when the steam ceases the eggs are done. Some egg cookers have an automatic attachment which shuts off the current when all the water has evaporated. These cookers operate upon the conduction principle, with electrodes frequently exposed. It is essential, therefore, to avoid touching the electrodes with the fingers or with metal utensils. The egg cooker should never be used near the sink or near other grounded metal.

Mixing machines.—The small appliances considered so far have used electricity as a source of heat. Mixing machines are motor-driven and use electricity for power.

There is a large variety of mixing machines and beaters; large ones with many attachments for all kinds of operations, small ones with one, two, or perhaps three attachments; mixers permanently fastened to a stand, mixers which may be removed from the stand and used at any place within reach of an outlet, or which may be reversed in position for different operations; beaters so well balanced that they stand upright without support, others which must be held even though the motor whirls the blades. (Fig. 51.)

A manufacturer of one of the larger mixing machines has noted that "of the strictly mechanical operations carried on in the typical home kitchen approximately sixty per cent are performed in a bowl

FIG. 51.—A beater with a revolving disc on which the bowls turn automatically. The juice extractor is a removable attachment.

or receptacle of some kind, and are described as mixing, beating, whipping, stirring, folding in, creaming, kneading, etc."[1] The beater or whip is, therefore, the most important attachment of the mixing machine.

Most of the beaters are of the wheel or circular type. Two wheel-type beaters, each consisting of two circular steel blades, are fastened to the shafts below the motor case, and turn in unison. One large mixing machine has a whisk beater made of many fine wires. The mixer may have a double motion; the beater may revolve on its own axis, and at the same time rotate around the bowl, or the

[1] A Benevolent Robot, p. 4, KitchenAid Manufacturing Company.

beater may revolve, and the bowl itself turn automatically, by being placed on a rotating disc on the base of the mixer. In either case, the entire contents of the bowl are brought into intimate contact with the blades and are thoroughly whipped or blended. The blades must not touch the bottom of the bowl but should just clear it.

The beaters may be rotated at different speeds. Some machines allow for three distinct variations of speed; low, medium, and

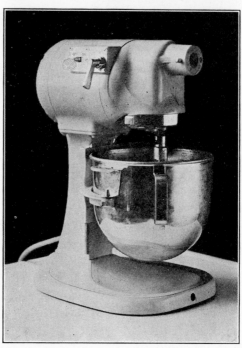

Fig. 52.—A large mixing machine with many attachments for a variety of operations.

high; other machines give a number of different speeds between low and high. In the smaller mixers the speed is usually controlled by a rheostat which varies, according to very definite proportions, the amount of current flowing to the motor, and, therefore, the speed of the motor. A large mixing machine has a constant-speed motor, and regulates the different speeds by gears. The speed control may be on the base of the mixer or in the housing with the motor. A lever turns the current on and off. (Fig. 52.)

Bowls which come with mixers are commonly made of aluminum, enamelware, or glass. Often two sizes are supplied. They are held in place by a supporting arm, by an adjustable clamp on the base of the mixer, or by the raised edge of the base. They should be easily removable for cleaning. Bowls which do not scratch or chip are to be preferred.

The beater blades may be removed for washing, or may be rotated in a bowl of warm soapy water, and then in rinse water. The motor should not be put into water. Follow the manufacturer's directions for oiling the motor. The right kind of oil, the right amount, and the frequency of oiling are important. Over oiling may be as injurious as too little oil. The motor housing and supporting pedestal and base are of enameled iron or steel, which may be wiped clean with a damp cloth.

In purchasing, choose a mixing machine with as quiet a motor as possible, and a machine which is easy to operate and easy to clean, with the minimum of handling. Select a mixer of a size in accordance with the need, and of a cost which is warranted by the family income.

Small mixers may give good service in beating eggs and cream and in making mayonnaise, but some small motors tend to become over-heated when used to any great extent for mixing batters, owing to the energy required to overcome the friction. Difficulties and apparent failures may often be surmounted, however, by modifying the recipe or the method of manipulation. There is opportunity for much valuable experimentation along this line. Many of the inexpensive mixers on the market are quite incapable of doing anything more than stirring solutions. They are good for drink mixers and possibly for beating eggs, but have very little other value.

A large mixing machine must be used very frequently or for a large amount of food to justify the money invested. It is not possible, however, to measure in dollars and cents the increased pleasure and satisfaction taken in work done without the excessive expenditure of energy which many hand operations require.

The fruit extractor is very often a second attachment on small mixing machines. Large machines have several kinds of mixing attachments, best suited to the type of operation, and in addition a vegetable slicer and shredder, food chopper, oil dropper, and even an ice-cream freezer.

Other small electrical appliances.—Other small electrical appliances include bottle warmers, immersion heaters, fans, corn poppers, etc. Information on any of these, and other appliances not discussed in the chapter, may be obtained from the manufacturers, from local merchants handling the appliance, or the testing institutes of certain magazines.

All reliable appliances have a name-plate, which indicates whether the appliance is to be used on alternating or direct current, the voltage for which it has been wired, and the wattage which will be used. To avoid possible injury to the appliance and to obtain most efficient results in its use, the requirements on the name-plate should be complied with.

Consultation with the local power company will often be helpful to anyone considering the purchase of equipment involving the expenditure of a considerable amount of money. Usually local power companies handle makes of appliances which they themselves have tested or in regard to which they have definite information from other reliable sources. When these companies do not handle appliances, they should be able to give the purchaser unbiased advice and suggestions.

Summary.

1. In selecting small electrical equipment, consideration must be given to durability of construction, ease of operation, kind of product obtained, and ease of cleaning.
2. On these four points, electric cookers and table stoves, percolators, toasters, waffle irons, egg cookers, and mixing machines have been discussed.

References

1. Benevolent Robot, A. KitchenAid Mfg. Co., Troy, Ohio. 1931.
2. Cassels, Lillian. Cooking with Small Electrical Appliances. More Power to the Home Series. National Electric Light Assoc., New York. n.d.
3. Goeppinger, Katherine. Coffee for Connoisseurs. Ladies' Home Journal. Jan. 1932.
4. Krüger, Gabriele M. (1) Über die Wirtschaftlichkeit einiger hauswirtschaftlicher Maschinen. Hauswirtschaftliche Jahrbücher 3:18. 1930. (2) The Comparative Efficiency of Electric and Hand Operated Utensils. Unpublished thesis. Iowa State College Library, Ames, Iowa. 1931.
5. Souder, Attie. Unpublished data.
6. Tests of Small Domestic Appliances. Electrical Testing Laboratories, New York. n.d.

ILLUSTRATIONS: Figs. 45, 47, 49, Landers, Frary & Clark; 46, Silex Co.; 50, Westinghouse Electric & Mfg. Co.; 48, 51, Chicago Flexible Shaft Co.; 52, KitchenAid Mfg. Co.

CHAPTER X

SMALL EQUIPMENT, NON-ELECTRICAL

Non-electrical small equipment includes everything from a cookie cutter to a roasting pan, and from a paring knife to a pressure cooker. For convenience and simplification the small equipment may be grouped into (1) equipment used in surface cookery, (2) equipment used in oven cookery, and (3) accessory equipment used in the preparation of food.

The first group includes kettles, saucepans, fry-pans, dutch ovens, waterless cookers, steamers, and pressure cookers; the second group, roasting pans, cake pans, muffin pans, biscuit and cookie baking sheets, and baking dishes and casseroles; the third group, measuring cups and spoons, sifters and strainers, egg beaters, mixing bowls, can openers, knives, forks, spoons, and spatulas, knife sharpeners, graters and slicers, molds, and fruit juice extractors. Can sealers may also be considered in group three. Other small pieces of equipment might have been included, but those selected are in most common use.

Any appliance may be judged on construction, efficiency, and care required. It must be well made and of a material fitted to the purpose for which it is to be used. It should be durable, simple in design, of suitable size and shape. To be efficient the appliance must be sufficiently easy to operate that it will accomplish the task for which it was made, in a reasonable length of time, and without undue expenditure of effort. The work required to keep the appliance clean must also be considered.

Materials used in surface cookery equipment.—Equipment used in surface cookery is usually made of iron, stainless steel, aluminum, enamelware, or of an alloy. Aluminum and iron are good conductors of heat; consequently the heat spreads evenly over the entire surface of the utensil. In contrast enamelware absorbs heat readily but is a rather poor conductor so that hot spots may develop. Thin utensils of iron and aluminum have a tendency, therefore, to

135

heat slightly more slowly than when of enamelware, but to heat more evenly and retain the heat better; with thicker vessels this difference tends to disappear. Food cooked with a very small amount of liquid is more apt to scorch in enamelware. On the other hand, aluminum discolors with alkalies, whereas enamelware does not. White sauces, custards, and lemon pie fillings are cooked by preference in enamel saucepans, but the stirring should be done with a wooden spoon to avoid marking the enamel. Enamelware may crack and chip if carelessly handled, but the better grades will give long

FIG. 53.—Enamelware saucepans with straight sides and black bottoms are efficient utensils.

and satisfactory service if used with care. Experiments at the Johns Hopkins and some other universities entirely discredit the theory that cancer or other diseases may be contracted by the use of aluminum cooking utensils.

Saucepans and kettles.—Black bottom pans have been found to be slightly more efficient than light-colored ones, but, except on units transmitting heat by radiation, the difference in efficiency is not sufficient to necessitate the buying of a black bottomed pan if the light one is preferred. At the present time, both aluminum and enamelware pans with black bottoms may be purchased, but it is well to select those on which the black finish is guaranteed to be comparatively permanent. (Fig. 53.)

Aluminum saucepans come in various thicknesses, but the very thin pans are usually to be avoided for thin pans tend to become dented, and dented pans waste fuel. Select enamel pots and kettles which have a smooth, even coating of the enamel. Utensils with fine cracks, thin places in the enamel, and other blemishes on the surface will not give satisfactory service.

The material of the pan has less to do with its efficiency than is generally supposed. The resistance of the material is very small compared to the resistance of the water film inside the pan, often not more than $\frac{1}{2}$ of 1 per cent. The gas film on the outside of the pan has a resistance many times that of the water film, so that the conductivity of the pan material itself is not a significant factor in determining the heating efficiency. Non-corrosive materials have less film and are, therefore, preferable. Stirring tends to reduce the

Fig. 54.—The handle on this aluminum saucepan is of good shape and length.

liquid film and boiling has a similar effect, an argument in favor of using high heat for rapid boiling.

The size of the pan should be proportional to the amount of food to be cooked. A large amount of food cooks more rapidly if it forms a thin layer in a large kettle or pan than when it is a deep layer in a small pan. Pans with seamless straight sides and flat bottoms which fit the burners are recommended. A well-rounded surface between the sides and bottom increases the ease of cleaning.

The edge of the pan may be turned or rolled, or it may be rimless. If turned or rolled, the finish must be smooth with few crevices where dirt may collect. A lip on either side of the pan is a convenience. When covers are used either the pan or the cover must have a beveled edge, that the cover may fit tightly; poorly fitting covers decrease the efficiency by lengthening the time for the cooking process, owing to the escape of steam.

If the kettle or pan has a handle it should be of heat-resistant material, and of a shape and length which is comfortable for the hand. (Fig. 54.) Too long a handle may overbalance the pan or may get in the way. In either case there is a tendency for the pan to upset. Too short a handle increases the probability of the hand coming in contact with the pan. Handles are joined to saucepans at different angles—some at almost a right angle, others at various acute angles. In selecting a pan, different handles may be tested, and the one chosen which the purchaser finds most convenient for lifting. Be sure that the handle is fastened securely so that it will not wear loose. The handle should be welded to the pan with a smooth joint, to prevent dirt from collecting. If the handle is of wood, a metal shank must connect the handle and the pan to eliminate the

FIG. 55.—Duplicate and triplicate pans save fuel.

possibility of the wooden handle being over the burner. Handles on fry-pans are usually in one piece with the pan. A ring or a hole in the end of the handle allows the pan to be hung up.

Duplicate or triplicate pans used over a single burner permit several foods to be cooked at one time with a saving of fuel. (Fig. 55.)

Dutch oven.—The iron kettle known as the dutch oven dates from colonial days; only recently has it been made of cast aluminum. (Fig. 56.) The dutch oven was brought to America by the Pilgrims. As is well known, the Pilgrims spent some years in Holland before coming to America. The *Mayflower* was a tiny vessel and baggage was limited. The dutch oven could be used for such a variety of cookery that it took the place of several other pots and pans and was, therefore, a favorite utensil of the early settlers.

The dutch oven comes in several different sizes, and has a rounded cover which adds greatly to its capacity. The cover fits closely to keep in the steam. The oven may be used with or without a rack.

Like the range oven, the dutch oven may be used for cooking most of a meal at one time. Meat may be seared, placed on the rack, and several vegetables placed around it; a separate vessel of fruit may be included. A small amount of water is added to the bottom of the oven and after steam has formed the heat is turned very low and the cooking continued for a long enough time to give tender products. Occasionally, more water must be added, but usually this is not necessary if the heat is kept low, and the cover is not lifted and the steam lost.

Waterless cooker.—The "waterless" cooker, so called, is a product of the aluminum age, but waterless cooking itself is not new. Waterless is somewhat of a misnomer, since two or three tablespoons of water are often added, or at least the vegetables are moist from having been washed. Even when no water is supplied from either of these sources, most products to be

Fig. 56.—Aluminum dutch oven.

cooked contain a high percentage of moisture, part of which is extracted in the cooking process and is the source of the steam.

Cooking in a small amount of water tends to preserve the vitamin and mineral content of the product. Green vegetables, however, should not be cooked in a covered container, or for a long time. The vegetable acids formed in the cooking process will destroy the bright green color, giving the vegetable an olive green or brownish hue, which is most unattractive. Strong flavored vegetables, such as onions, turnips, and cauliflower, are best cooked uncovered in a fairly large amount of water.

Waterless cooking may be done in any container which has a tight-fitting cover to hold in the steam, but the heat must be kept very low. Because of the even spread and good retention of heat by iron and aluminum, utensils of these materials are usually preferred.

The waterless cooker which is sold by that name is of heavy sheet or cast aluminum, and may have a clamped-on cover and be provided with a steel plate with a raised edge into which the cooker fits. The plate spreads the heat evenly and prevents scorching. Some types, however, do not have the plate, but are made of extra heavy aluminum. After the cooking process has been started and steam has been generated, the cooker, with or without the steel plate, is placed over a very low flame. (Fig. 57.)

Steamer.—Steamers have two compartments, a lower one to hold the water, and an upper section with a perforated bottom through which the steam rises. The food is placed in the upper compartment.

The vegetables whose color or flavor is impaired by being cooked in a waterless cooker should not be cooked in a steamer, since, of

necessity, the steamer is always covered. Steam cooking aids in retaining the valuable mineral and vitamin constituents of the foods, and in preserving the shape of the product.

Pressure cooker. — Several makes of pressure cookers are on the market, but all of them operate on the same general principle. The boiling point of a liquid varies directly with the pressure applied to the surface. When water is heated in an open kettle, the temperature of the water gradually rises to the boiling point, but gets no

FIG. 57.—Waterless cooker with the steel-plate base. Conserves minerals and vitamins.

hotter, for at that point heat is used up in the change to steam (heat of vaporization). The steam pressure cooker is a heavy aluminum pot or kettle with a closely fitting cover, tightly fastened by clamps. The steam is confined within the cooker and creates pressure, and the pressure increases the temperature at which the water will boil, and, therefore, the temperature of the steam itself.

The ancestor of the pressure cooker was first used in Spain. It was a heavy iron bean-pot which made use of steam pressure to increase the temperature and shorten the cooking process.

Modern pressure cookers are made of heavy pressed or cast aluminum molded in one piece, without seams or joints. (Fig. 58.) The rims of the pot and cover are accurately planed to form a tight union through which steam cannot escape. The rims should be kept clean and should not be scratched.

The devices for registering and regulating the pressure are on the lid. They are the pressure gauge, a safety valve, and the petcock. The pressure gauge is an open-faced dial, registering pressure from zero to 20 or 30 pounds, and sometimes also indicating the temperatures which correspond to the different pressures. A pointer on the dial shows the pressure within the cooker.

The safety valve and petcock are sometimes separate and sometimes combined. In most separate safety valves a steel ball fits

FIG. 58.—Pressure cookers.

loosely into a socket, and a nickeled brass rod, wound with a coil spring, rests on the ball and is held in place by the outer housing of the safety valve, through which it passes. Excess pressure raises the ball by contracting the spring, and permits some of the steam to escape. It is most important to keep the ball and ball-seat clean, and they should be wiped dry after use to prevent them from becoming sticky or rusty. It is well always to test the safety valve before starting to use the pressure cooker.

The double-duty type of valve often has a beveled steel point which fits into the steam exhaust port. When functioning as a petcock, it may be raised from the port; when it becomes a safety valve it rests in the port. The combination of petcock and safety valve makes for simplicity of operation.

The separate petcock is a nickel-plated brass rod which screws into a collar in which there are one or two vents. When the rod is unscrewed, air or steam may escape; when it is screwed down the vents are closed. Nickel-plated brass is used for all of these parts because it will not rust. Rusting might easily weaken some part, and so impair the action of the cooker.

The cover is fastened to the cooker by some sort of a clamping device. One method is by separate clamps, four to seven in number, at regular intervals around the cooker. Part of the clamp may be on the body of the cooker, the other part on the cover, or the whole clamp may be on the cover. When the clamps are entirely on the cover they do not become hot before the cover is put on, and the kettle part of the cooker is more easily cleaned. When there is an arrow or other mark on the cooker kettle and another one on the cover, to indicate where the two should come together, be sure that one is directly above the other before starting to fasten the clamps. If the clamps are tightened in pairs on opposite sides of the cooker, the pressure will be kept the same all the way around. Bolts and nuts used in the clamps are usually of brass.

Some pressure cookers have a single clamping band, either across the top or around the cover, which is tightened with a single thumb screw. This increases the ease of handling the cooker, but requires extra storage space.

The pressure cooker may be used for all sorts of steam cooking, to cook an entire meal in fact. It is especially useful in shortening long processes, as in cooking dried beans and tough cuts of meat, and in canning. The increased temperature greatly reduces the time needed. Meat may be seared directly on the bottom of the cooker, then placed on a trivet or in a pan. Several kinds of foods may be cooked in separate containers at one time. Time is saved by cooking together foods which require the same processing period and will be done at the same time; otherwise, it is necessary to cool the cooker, exhaust the steam, open the cooker, and start over again.

When the cooker is ready for use, add water below the trivet, put the cooker over a source of heat, set in the pans of food, adjust and clamp on the cover. When the safety valve and petcock are separate, screw the safety valve down tightly but leave the petcock open. If the two are combined, adjust the valve to permit the steam to escape. Allow the steam to issue from the vents from 3 to 5 min-

utes for ordinary cooking and from 7 to 10 minutes when canning
is to be done. A series of tests were made in the foods and nutrition department at Iowa State College to determine how nearly the
internal temperature of the pressure cooker checked with that indicated on the gauge, when the petcock (1) was closed at the appearance of steam, (2) was left open for 3 minutes after steam began
to escape, and (3) was left open from 7 to 10 minutes after steam
appeared. When the petcock was closed 5 and 7 minutes after steam
began to escape there was a difference of 4° F. between the actual
and indicated internal temperatures; when it was closed 3 minutes
after steam appeared, there was a difference of 8° F., but when the
petcock was closed as soon as steam appeared the difference was
39° F. If the pressure cooker is to give the desired high temperatures, it is essential that the petcock be left open sufficiently long.

When the necessary pressure is indicated on the dial, the pressure
may be held constant by regulating the heat. A fluctuating pressure
should be avoided since it tends to draw the juices from the products. Pressure cookers may be used over any source of heat: gas,
kerosene, electricity, gasoline, wood, or coal.

When the processing period is over it is usually preferable to turn
off the heat and allow the pointer on the dial to come back to zero
before opening the cooker; the cooling may be hastened by wrapping cold wet cloths around the cooker. This rule must always be
followed in glass canning and in cooking tender fruits or vegetables,
for if the pressure is reduced immediately by opening the petcock,
liquid will be withdrawn from the jars, or the form of the fruits
and vegetables will be injured. With tough cuts of meat, it makes
less difference, and when canning in tin the pressure should be
quickly reduced and the tins put into cold water.

In either case, before opening the cooker, open the petcock gradually, until the steam has escaped and normal pressure has been
restored inside the cooker. Then the lid may be unclamped and
lifted off.

The kettle part of the pressure cooker is washed in the same way
as any cooking utensil. The lid with the pressure gauge should not
be put into water, but should be wiped out. The lid should be left
off the cooker when it is not in use, to permit it to air.

The manufacturer of any pressure cooker will send complete

directions for its use. Cookers come in various sizes, depending upon where they are made. One firm manufactures cookers in 7, 11, and 18 quart sizes; another firm in 10, 12, 18, and 25 quart sizes.

Equipment for oven cookery.—"Materials of which baking dishes and pans are made react differently in the oven. The conductivity of all materials is not the same. Some utensils are lighter in weight than others and so heat through more quickly; these are most desirable for short time baking processes. The heavier weight utensils will require a longer time for heating, but will retain the heat longer than the utensils which are made of a lighter weight material. For this reason they make better utensils for long time baking processes."[1]

Roasting pans.—Covered roasting pans, oval or round in shape, with vented covers, are of enamelware, steel, and aluminum. The covered roaster is usually self-basting. Roasters with a smooth surface, rounded corners, and as few grooves as possible are easiest to clean. Steel wool is helpful in removing burned-on fat.

Uncovered roasting pans may be of aluminum or enamel and frequently are of iron. Iron pans usually have sharp-angled corners and joinings between sides and bottom which are difficult to clean, but an iron pan heats evenly and retains heat well.

Whether an uncovered or covered roaster is preferable is a question. Some experimental work on the two types has already been done, but as Lowe[2] states, "To prove which pan is preferable from the standpoint of the losses incurred will require more definite experiments under controlled conditions. That is, similar roasts, one from the right side and one from the left side of the same animal, will need to be compared under the same cooking conditions, except for the difference in pans. A few experiments of this type in the laboratory (Foods and Nutrition, Iowa State College) seem to favor the open pan for most meats with the possible exception of veal, as the open pans give smaller losses and thus a juicier meat. The open pans for poultry give a very hard, dry skin."

When uncovered pans are used, the meat is seared for a short time at a high temperature and the roasting then continued at a com-

---

[1] Shank, Dorothy E. How Well Do You Know Your Equipment?
[2] Lowe, Belle. Experimental Cookery. p. 196.

paratively low heat. The use of a meat thermometer helps in obtaining a roast of the desired doneness.

Meat should be placed on a trivet in the roasting pan. The trivet keeps the meat out of the extracted fat and juices and prevents sticking. Some roasters have perforated trays to hold the meat.

Cake and muffin pans.—Cake pans may be oblong, square, or round; deep, or shallow. They are of aluminum, oven glass, tin, russian iron, and enamelware. Rounded corners and edges make for ease of cleaning.

A food product is apparently affected by the kind of pan in which it is baked. Loaf cakes were baked in the laboratory in aluminum, tin, Pyrex, and enamelware pans of the same shape and size, and in the same position in the oven and at the same temperature. The cake in the enamelware pan baked most rapidly and had a thick, dark crust on the sides and bottom. The crust was inclined to be hard. The cake in the enamel pan also rose less evenly and tended to be high in the middle. Cakes baked in the Pyrex, tin, and aluminum pans were of a better shape and had a desirable, tender, light-brown crust. For equal results, the cake in the Pyrex pan must usually be baked slightly longer than that in aluminum and tin. Cakes baked in a shorter period in tin pans than in aluminum. These same results were obtained in repeated experiments and in both gas and electric ovens, indicating that the baking period must be shortened when enamelware is used, and must be lengthened when aluminum and Pyrex are used.

Somewhat similar results were obtained by Monroe in experiments with muffin pans at Kansas State Agricultural College. Monroe used muffin pans of tinned steel, polished and unpolished stainless steel, polished and unpolished aluminum, white enamel, blue enamel, and white enamel inside and blue enamel on the outside. All the muffins were cooked in the same positions in the oven. "According to the judges, the aluminum pans gave a crust which was too pale for muffins and the enamel, a crust too dark. For the baking time used, the crust obtained in the tinned steel and stainless steel was of desirable brownness."[3]

Muffin pans at best are hard to clean. Pans with few joints and

[3] Monroe, M. M. A Study of the Effect upon Muffins of Pans Made of Different Materials. p. 7.

creases should be selected. Individual muffin pans of Pyrex have certain advantages in this line.

Baking sheets.—Cookies, cream puffs, and baking powder biscuits rise and brown more evenly when cooked on baking sheets than when cooked in pans. Sides on pans act as a baffle to the heat, and the bottom of the cookie or biscuit becomes too brown before the top is the desired color. This is especially true if the sides are deep.

Hart reports a carefully controlled test in which ice-box cookies of uniform thickness were baked for 8 minutes in a 375°F. oven on baking sheets of enamel, sheet iron, tin, aluminum, and glass. She found that the most nearly standard cookies were baked on the aluminum sheet, with those on sheet iron and tin ranking second.

FIG. 59.—Casseroles and ramekins.

The cookies on the enamel sheet were burned and those on the glass not browned at all, again indicating the necessity of varying the baking period with the material of the pan.

Baking dishes.—Any of the materials used for other types of pans may also be used for baking dishes, but covered casseroles and many uncovered bakers are frequently of heat-proof glass, earthenware, or china. They come in graduated sizes, the smaller individual ones being known as ramekins. (Fig. 59.) The china is heat-proof and may have a conventional design, or a splash of bright-hued flowers, as the purchaser chooses. Common bean pots make excellent casseroles, suited to a variety of uses. Shallow, broad bakers give a large surface for browning.

Foods baked in dishes of these wares may be served directly on the table, thus eliminating the cost of an extra container, and saving extra dish-washing and extra storage space. Often the cover is flat on top so that it may be used separately for a pie plate or an "au gratin" dish. A dish with handles is more easily removed from a hot oven, but the handles do take up a little more space. Casseroles and bakers are frequently set into stands of nickel or chromium, to increase ease of handling and to protect the table from the heat. Casseroles should not be used for surface cookery.

In selecting a casserole, be sure that the surface is non-absorbent. It should be free from tiny cracks and flaws which impair the smoothness of the surface and make cleaning difficult. Glass will crack if subjected to sudden variations in temperature so it is best to let a dish cool before pouring cold water into it. Soaking before washing minimizes the work of cleaning.

Accessory equipment. Measuring cups.—Measuring cups are of tin, aluminum, and glass. Tin cups tend to rust, so that aluminum and glass cups are preferable. Metal cups are to be preferred for use with hot liquids, although heat-proof glass may be used for liquids of moderate temperatures.

There are three kinds of measuring cups: those which measure a cup when full, those which measure a cup about a quarter of an inch below the rim, and the single-capacity cups. (Fig. 60.) The first kind is best for measuring dry materials; the single-capacity cups may be used for either, but are especially accurate for dry ingredients; the second variety is best for liquids. The sides of the graduated cup are commonly marked to indicate ¼, ½, and ¾ on one side, and 1/3 and 2/3 of a cup on the other side, but a few cups are graduated in ounces. The transparency of glass is an aid in determining whether the substance being measured is even with the graduation. The single-capacity cups have four in a set, the full cup, half-cup, quarter-cup, and third-cup.

The Code of Specifications for household measuring cups, formulated by the United States Bureau of Standards, states that the standard measuring cup shall have a capacity of one-half a liquid pint (8 fluid ounces). The Code also specifies that the top diameter of the one-cup measuring cup must not exceed 3 inches; the word "cup" must be marked on the side to indicate the capacity; if a pouring lip is present, it must not interfere with filling the cup to the edge or graduation mark, when the cup is on a level surface; and all graduated cups shall have handles.

Measuring cups of aluminum should be sufficiently heavy to hold their shape without denting or bending. The handle should be welded to the cup or carefully riveted, so that it will not come loose, and should be large enough to allow the use of a holder when hot liquids are measured. A lip on the side of the cup helps in pouring. A distinct groove between the bottom and sides, and deep-cut grad-

FIG. 60.—Measuring cups and spoons.

uations with sharp edges, are to be avoided because of the difficulty of cleaning.

Measuring spoons.—Although other types are found on the market, measuring spoons usually come in a cluster of 3 or 4. The cluster may have a teaspoon, half-teaspoon, and quarter-teaspoon, or these three and in addition a tablespoon. (Fig. 60.) Since there are 16 level tablespoons to a cup, the standard tablespoon may be considered 1/16 of a standard cup. The teaspoon by common usage is 1/3 of a tablespoon. Measuring spoons are most frequently made of aluminum, and a certain amount of care must be taken not to bend the handle of the spoon where it joins the bowl, for aluminum tends to be brittle and cannot be soldered.

Sifters.—Depending upon one's choice of a sifter, flour and other ingredients may be sifted once, twice, or even four or more times in a single operation. The wire screen may be coarse or fine. A fine screen sifts more thoroughly.

The sifter is held in one hand and the sifting mechanism operated by the other, or in certain constructions, one hand may both hold and sift. In this case, sifting may be done with one hand, while at the same time the other hand stirs the mixture. Such a method is very efficient. Sifters, operated by one hand, are shaken from side to side; or a flat metal ring, attached to a spring in the handle, is moved across the screen and presses the flour through the wire.

There are at least two sifters in which four or more sifting operations may be performed without emptying the sifter. One such sifter is an oblong tin can with a removable frame of four screens, $\frac{1}{2}$ inch apart, which hooks over the edge of the container. Flour is sifted through the four screens by shaking the can. The frame of screens may then be removed and the flour emptied out or the can may be reversed and the flour sifted four times again. The other sifter is of the usual cylindrical shape, but it has a solid bottom, and a closely fitting cover. After the flour is put in, the cover is put on, and the flour sifted first in one direction, then in the other, as many times as desired. Sifters of these types would be very useful to the homemaker specializing in angel food cakes or other products which are improved by many siftings of the ingredients. Most sifters will hold a quart of flour at a time. Small ones of a cup capacity are also on the market.

Sifters are commonly of tin. They should be sturdy in construction with substantial, securely fastened handles, when handles are present. Sifters should be washed in warm soapy water, rinsed in hot water, shaken and wiped as dry as possible and left in a warm place until thoroughly dry, to prevent rusting.

Strainers.—Wire strainers may also be used for sifting, as well as for the numerous other operations for which they are intended. The wire screen must be carefully fastened to the solid metal edge, and two or three pieces of heavy metal ribbon beneath the bowl will serve as extra support and tend to increase the life of the strainer.

A type of strainer called a colander, made of tin, aluminum, or graniteware, has perforated sides and bottom. The holes are drilled, and are larger than the individual meshes of a wire screen.

Metal sieves, or fruit and vegetable presses, also have drilled holes. The holes are smaller than in the colander and much closer together. Vegetable and fruit sieves are often conical in shape, and are used with a conical wooden mallet which is revolved against the inner surface of the sieve to force the product through in a finely divided condition. Such an appliance is used for making purées or

Fig. 61.—A fruit or vegetable press used in making purées.

preparing fruit for whips. These sieves are made of tin and of aluminum. The tin sieve seems to be somewhat more efficient because this metal can be used in a thinner sheet, and the edges of the drilled holes are very sharp. One press on the market is of steel. The perforated seamless bowl is spherical in shape, and a revolving spiral pressure-blade with beveled edges presses the food through the bowl. (Fig. 61.) A metal scraper, which may be attached below the bowl, scrapes off the food as it comes through the holes.

Beaters.—Few pieces of small equipment have more constant and varied use than beaters. They are used to mix ingredients, to develop a fine texture, to clump fat as in whipping cream, and to incorporate air, in the beating of egg whites.

Three different types of beaters are found on the market; the whisk, the wheel or rotary, and the turbine. (Fig. 62.)

The whisk is effective in incorporating large amounts of air and gives maximum volume, though a somewhat coarse texture. The

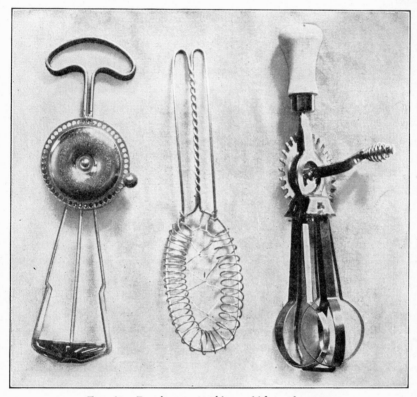

FIG. 62.—Egg beaters; turbine, whisk, and rotary.

whisk may be made of many fine wires, each wire forming a long oval, and all the wires brought together at the top to make a handle; or it may take any one of many spoon shapes. The outer edge of the spoon is of fairly heavy wire, with a mesh center of fine wires or flat metal ribbon, looped, interlaced, twisted, or coiled. One model has a mesh stamped out of a flat sheet of metal. Fine wires give greatest volume. Wires should be fastened smoothly and securely to the frame to make cleaning easier, and to increase the durability of the beater.

The handles may be an extension of the frame, or the ends of the frame may be fastened into a wooden handle. In this case the ends must be firmly fixed or they will pull out. All handles should be shaped to fit the hand comfortably. Whisk beaters require a good deal of energy, for all the work is done by the operator.

Wheel or rotary beaters are often called Dover beaters because the first one was made by a Mr. Dover more than 65 years ago. At the present time many different firms manufacture the wheel beater. The first rotary beater was of cast iron with two agitators; the usual modern rotary beater is of steel with four circular or elliptical agitators which revolve in a vertical plane. Other beaters have two circles, and occasionally five circles are found, one being stationary. To be efficient the metal blades should have thin cutting edges.

The agitators are fastened around a support of heavy metal wire, which carries the small pinions. The wire is riveted or welded to the main shaft, to which the large cog wheel and handle are attached. The thickness of the wire determines how closely the beater will fit to the bottom of the container. The more closely it fits, the more effective, since all food is brought into better contact with the blades.

The efficiency of the beater depends in part upon the ratio of the gears in the pinions to the gears in the drive wheel. A ratio of 1 to 4 and 1 to 5 is most commonly found. The larger wheel makes one revolution while the beating circles make four or five, in other words, the beater itself will do four or five times as much work as the housewife. A central drive wheel makes better contact with the pinions, the supports on either side preventing it from running "out of mesh." Ball-bearings greatly increase the ease of operation.

Four-agitator beaters produce greater volume than two-agitator beaters, for they throw the food over a greater space and incorporate more air. If the blades are held rigidly in position, the volume seems to be increased. In some beaters rigidity is procured by metal bands around each group of blades. The wheel beater produces the finest texture.

Handles are of various designs. A handle should fit the hand, preferably project slightly beyond the hand to prevent cramping the muscles. The shank should be sufficiently long to eliminate any danger of contact with the cogs. The same thing is true of the small handle on the drive wheel, which should be easy to grasp and long enough to keep the hand from the gears.

The turbine beater is less widely known and used. Some appliances made specially for whipping cream include a turbine beater.

The turbine has an almost-flat, slotted, circular metal disc fastened to the end of a central shaft which carries a pinion and is attached to a drive wheel. It is, therefore, manipulated in the same manner as the Dover-type beater, and the general rules of construction are the same for both. The slotted disc revolves in a horizontal plane, and is effective in general mixing, but there is no lifting action, so that the volume obtained is smaller than with the whisk and rotary beaters.

A combination wheel and turbine beater is also on the market. It possesses the advantageous characteristics of both types.

All beaters should be durable in construction, with a smooth, rust-resisting finish. Agitators of steel which have been electroplated with copper and then with nickel have proved most satisfactory. Gears should mesh accurately. Ball-bearings increase the ease of manipulation. Light weight beaters, if they are at the same time durable and efficient, are to be preferred. Thin blades and wires cut the mixture into more minute particles than do thick blades and heavy wires, and consequently give greater volume and finer texture. For efficiency, any beater must fit closely to the bottom of the container, so that it will pick up all the material, and beat and mix it thoroughly.

Since the beater is always used with some kind of a platter or bowl, it may be well to consider types of containers at this time. The efficiency of a beater often depends upon the shape of the bowl.

Bowls.—Broad shallow bowls or platters are used with whisk beaters, narrow deep bowls with the rotary or turbine. All bowls should have a smooth, rounded interior surface, with no creases to retain some of the mixture.

Bowls are made of enamelware, tin, aluminum, earthenware, glass, and china; occasionally, also, of wood. Most metal and enamel bowls are light in weight, a valuable characteristic for many uses, but they tend to slide around and have to be held in position when used with a beater, and this is difficult when both hands are needed for the operation. Bowls of these materials scratch easily and may discolor; when they are used for mixing, the stirring should be done with a wooden spoon. The use of chipped enamel bowls should be avoided since a slight blow of the spoon or beater may cause additional pieces of the enamel to scale off into the food.

Bowls of glass, china, and earthenware are heavier, and scratch and mar much less readily. Sometimes earthenware bowls have a ridged outer surface by which they may be firmly held. It is a good practice, however, to let the bowl rest on a table of the proper height instead of using energy to hold it.

At the present time bowls may often be purchased in sets of three or five and in a variety of attractive hues. Such sets offer a diversity of sizes, suited to many uses, and add a bright bit of color to the kitchen.

Can opener.—Small accessory equipment is too frequently purchased at the dime store. It looks and behaves well when new, but does not stand up under continuous hard service. The can opener is no exception. Most can openers which require two hands for manipulation are inefficient. They take a lot of energy to use, and they leave a jagged, hazardous edge on the can. A good can opener should remove the cover from a round, square, or oval can with the minimum of effort and leave a smooth even edge. Openers which fasten to the wall or table-edge usually do this. The can to be opened is held mechanically between two wheels, one with a knife-blade rim; or, in another model, the can rests on a metal shelf and a sharp knife-point is pressed from above into the edge of the top cover. In either case the cutting is done by turning a crank, which takes only a moderate amount of energy, uses only one hand, and cuts the cover cleanly from the top of the can. Usually only the flat metal support is permanently fastened to the wall; the rest of the can opener may be removed and placed in a drawer.

Knife sharpener.—Some can openers of this type have as a second attachment a knife sharpener, which may be put in place of the can opener. The knife sharpener may be two finely corrugated steel wheels or two wheels of emery or sandstone turned by a handle. Sandstone wheels are preferred to emery, because they do not wear away the steel as rapidly. A tapering steel rod, fitted with a handle and held in the hand, is also used. If a knife becomes heated in the sharpening process, the temper of the knife may be drawn, in which case the knife loses its ability to keep an edge. Wetting the emery wheels or grindstone prevents this misfortune.

Cutlery.—Knives, forks, spoons, and spatulas of good quality are a worthwhile investment. Stainless steel has eliminated much of the drudgery of scouring which once followed every meal, but all stainless steel is not necessarily good steel or even steel at all. It may be stainless iron, and iron knives will not take or hold a keen edge. Since good steel cannot be recognized at a glance, the purchaser should buy cutlery from a reliable manufacturer. It is not so much the number of knives which the housewife has, but rather the careful selection of a knife to meet a definite need, which will make her kitchen well equipped and her work easier. (Fig. 63.)

A study of the time taken and motions made in preparing three meals a day for ten days disclosed the interesting fact that the housewife performs some task with a knife on an average of 129 times a day. It may well be said that "the use of the household and kitchen knife in its varied and improved forms marks the dividing line between savagery and civilization; and the more skilled a nation becomes in the preparation of foods, the more attention it pays to the design and workmanship of its cutlery."[4]

Knives are forged or blanked from a flat or double-bevel steel. The forged knife will give longer service and take a superior cutting edge because forging develops a finer grain in the steel. After forging, the blade is tempered and ground. Frequently blades are ground under water to prevent drawing the temper.

A knife should have good balance and proper "spring." If a knife has balance it is easily manipulated without any strain on the muscles, the weight of handle and blade is properly adjusted. A blade with spring is ground tapering from handle to point. When such a blade is bent, about one-third of it next to the handle remains rigid, the other two-thirds to the point is flexible enough to form a slight curve. (Fig. 64.) A cross section of the blade, cut perpendicular to its length, should be a flat-sided wedge. This shape is most easily ground to a desirable edge. (Fig. 65.)

Good knives are often recognized by the manner in which the

[4] The Most Important Tool in Your Kitchen. p. 3. Harrison Cutlery Company.

blade is fastened into the handle. In a cheaply constructed knife, the shank of the blade is narrowed to a point, which is pushed into the handle and held there by a small nail or brad, or sometimes merely

FIG. 63.—Select knives carefully to meet a definite need.

by a metal collar. The nail or collar may work loose if the wood becomes softened in water, and the blade pull out.

A better method is to have the broad shank of the blade extend the entire length or at least half the length of the handle and be fastened in by two or three good-sized rivets. The wood is more likely to split when small rivets are used.

Handles are now made of Bakelite, or of rubberized wood. The blade shank is molded into the Bakelite by heat, and forms with it a solid piece. These handles are very strong and durable, there are no cracks to collect dirt, and the material is practically moisture proof, but they will break with rough usage. Some cutlery manufacturers use rosewood for handles. It is a very hard, close-grained wood, which is resistant to moisture and will not stain or warp.

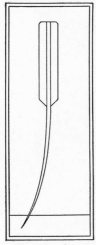

FIG. 64.—A tapering blade has "spring."

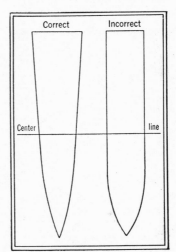

FIG. 65.—Correct and incorrect grinding of blade.

Knives are classified according to the shape and length of the blade. At least four different knives find a use in most homes. The paring knife has a short blade, which gives leverage for operating, without undue strain on the finger muscles. (Fig. 66.) Blades of paring knives are of three forms; the straight-edged knife is useful in paring where the product is held in the hand, the pointed knife is best where eyes must be removed; another type, known as the "rocker" or "sheep-foot" blade, may take the place of the other two.

The utility knife is of medium size and may have a straight or curved cutting edge. It has many uses: cutting up large vegetables, trimming meat, slicing cold chicken, cleaning fish, in fact almost any kind of food preparation.

The carving knife is used principally at the dining room table, but is also often needed in the kitchen. It has a fairly long sturdy blade, not too pliable, that it may cut hot, yielding meats with ease, and sever joints. The point has a long, rather thin curve, to assist in getting around the bones. (Fig. 63.)

The fourth member of the quartette is the slicing knife. (Fig. 67.) This knife has a long flexible blade, tapering slightly at the point. The straight edge affords an even cutting surface, which will give the thinnest of slices of cold meat, bread, or cake.

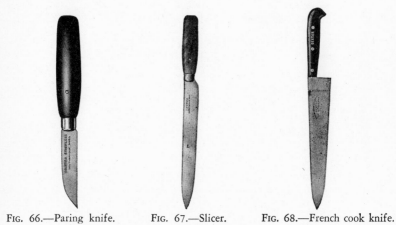

FIG. 66.—Paring knife.   FIG. 67.—Slicer.   FIG. 68.—French cook knife.

To this list, if desired, may be added the butcher knife with its thick, heavy, curved blade for strength; the grapefruit knife, curved and double-edged, to cut the sections of the fruit from the rind and the enclosing membranes (Fig. 63); and the French cook knife, with its straight edge and firm but tapering point. The handle of the French knife is placed in line with the back of the blade instead of in line with the edge, that the hand may not interfere when the knife is used for quantity chopping of nuts and small fruits and vegetables. (Fig. 68.)

Another most useful knife is the serrated- or scalloped-edged bread knife. (Fig. 63.) Cutting bread rapidly dulls a slicing knife. The blade of a knife should never be heated in a flame to aid in cutting fresh bread or cake, since this treatment spoils the temper of the steel. The serrated bread knife has groups of fine ridges, running first in one direction, and then in another. These ridges are self-sharpening and always cut satisfactorily. One of the newest knives has two edges, a slicing edge on one side, and the serrated edge on the other. The scalloped-edged bread knife is also very efficient and easily cleaned.

Kitchen forks are of various sizes and have two, three, or four prongs, depending upon the use to which they are to be put. A long-handled fork is helpful when the kettle is deep, or the product to be handled large and heavy. Smaller forks are needed to hold meats when they are cut, and potatoes or other vegetables for skinning.

FIG. 69.—Long- and short-handled 2-tine forks.   FIG. 70.—Spatula.   FIG. 71.—Broad spatula.

The tines should be firm and sharp. Handles should have the same characteristics as handles on knives. (Fig. 69.)

Spoons for mixing, stirring, and serving are of aluminum, tin, graniteware, iron, inexpensive plated silver, and of wood. Aluminum spoons are brittle and will not stand bending; most tin spoons rust easily, and all metal spoons scratch the container. Wooden spoons do not mar the bowl or kettle, are easy to hold, and do not become warm when hot mixtures are stirred. One or two wooden spoons should find a place in every home.

The spatula with its flexible rounded blade of stainless steel, riveted into a comfortably shaped handle, has many uses. (Fig. 70.) With it cups of dry ingredients are leveled off, egg whites are folded into mixtures, bowls are scraped clean of batter, and cakes are iced. If the blade is rigid close to the handle, but flexible for the rest of its length, it is more easily manipulated than when flexible for the entire length. The progenitor of the spatula was the artist's palette knife. The broad, more rigid spatula may take the place of a pancake turner, remove cookies from the baking sheet, and perform other useful tasks. (Fig. 71.)

Kitchen cutlery, knives especially, should be stored with care. Putting all kinds together in a drawer tends to nick the edges and break the points. A rack within the drawer or hung on the wall will prevent this damage.

Graters.—Graters may be of various shapes: flat, cylindrical, square, or semicircular, but the shape is of secondary importance to the type of hole. Holes in graters are punched or drilled.

Punched holes have rough uneven edges with four sharp points, and tend to give a mushy product of no definite form and of compact volume. The drilled holes are round or crescent-shaped, and have a smooth, sharp edge which cuts the grated food into a definite shape, each small sliver distinct from the piece next to it. The resulting volume is much larger than with the punched holes.

Graters may be of aluminum, but are usually of tin. They should be of sturdy construction so that they will not bend. Drilled graters are more easily cleaned than punched graters. With either type, care must be taken to hold the product to be grated in such a way that the fingers will not come in contact with the sharp edges of the cutters.

A safely manipulated grater is the rotary grater, which looks a little like a hand-operated meat grinder and may be fastened to a shelf or table. Surrounding the cylindrical cutting surface is an outer shell, with an opening on the top, through which the food is held in contact with the grater by mean of a plunger. The cylinder is turned by a crank. If this grater is to work efficiently the cylinder must be close enough to the outer shell to leave no space in which the food may pack.

A recent flat model which grates, slices, or shreds has a protective device to keep the hand from the cutters. Some graters and shredders which come in a set of different sized cutters have an interchangeable safety guard.

Slicers.—Slicers are commonly of steel. A rotary slicer has blades turned by a crank; and a flat slicer, knife-plates set in a wooden or metal frame. The crank-operated slicer is fastened to the table; the frame of the flat knife-plate is supported by hand. The rotary slicer has two or three blades, and the flat slicer usually only one. The blades should be removable for sharpening, and be adjustable, that different thicknesses of food may be obtained. The size of the blades limits the kind of food which may be sliced. Slicers should be tested to determine how satisfactory a product they give, and whether they show a tendency to scatter the food. Some slicers have a device for protecting the hand.

Molds.—Molds are most frequently used for "cold cookery," although muffins and fancy cakes are baked in certain types of molds. Molds for jellies, blanc manges, and creams are made of glass or china, aluminum, enamelware, and tin. They should be made in one piece, with all corners well rounded to permit easy cleaning.

Molds have many forms. Some are fluted; others have designs of flowers, fruits, or animals. Molds representing special symbols used in fraternal or other organizations are also obtainable. All help to give a fancy shape to otherwise commonplace food.

Juice extractors.—Fruit juice extractors vary in size from small reamers of metal or glass with a slotted rim, placed over a cup or tumbler, to the large ones, patterned after the mechanical juice extractors, which are fastened to the table edge and turned by a hand crank. The housewife should select one which is suited to her needs, is easy to operate, and easy to clean. The larger ones are efficient, and surprisingly inexpensive.

Can sealer.—A can sealer is a most valuable addition to the equipment of the housewife who does much home canning. With it not only is the can sealed, but later the cover is cut off with another attachment, and still other attachments will reflange the can in preparation for a second use. There are several different makes of can sealers on the market, but in all makes the basic principles of manipulation are the same. The can is clamped in position, and metal rolls press the edges of cover and can together in an air-tight joint. The manufacturer's complete instructions come with all sealers, and should be carefully followed.

Tricolators.—Non-electric tricolators may, perhaps, be considered in a class by themselves. The tricolator proper, of aluminum or silver-plated nickel, has a perforated bottom which fits into a vitrified china, glass, or aluminum pot. In making coffee a filter is placed over the perforated bottom, the rather finely ground coffee measured onto it, and a perforated cover set over the coffee. Boiling water is poured into the top of the tricolator, drips through the perforations onto the coffee, filters through it, extracting the value of the coffee, and flows into the pot. The manufacturers recommend a special fiber-silk filter, which holds back, with the grounds, the insoluble fats that injure the coffee flavor and are not easily digestible.

After the water has passed through the coffee the tricolator is removed and the coffee is served from the pot. Pots come in 2 to 9 cup sizes, but the larger capacity tricolators will make small quantities satisfactorily. Tea tricolators are also on the market.

Egg boiler.—There is also a non-electric automatic egg boiler, which may be set for the desired degree of hardness, and when that point is reached, will automatically lift the eggs out of the water.

Limited space does not allow a discussion of the many perforated and lipped ladles and turners, cooking tongs, butter curlers, egg and tomato slicers, and the fancy cutters of all kinds and shapes for garnishes, cookies, and tiny cakes. The same suggestions with regard to fundamentals of selection apply to these smallest of appliances, used chiefly to gain artistic effects, as to the larger pieces of equipment.

Summary.

1. An appliance should be sturdily constructed, of size, shape, weight, and material suited to the purpose for which it is to be used.
2. An appliance should have a smooth, seamless surface, with rounded corners and be free from rough edges. It should be well balanced.
3. Handles should fit the hand, be heat-resistant, and firmly fastened to the utensil with no unnecessary grooves.
4. Lips and spouts should be non-dripping.
5. Surface utensils should have flat bottoms and straight sides, and fit the unit. Covers should be tight-fitting.
6. Oven utensils should be of a size and shape to permit circulation of

heat around and between them. Casseroles suitable for table service save initial cost, cleaning, and storage space.

7. To be efficient an appliance must accomplish the task for which it was made, in a moderate length of time, and with a minimum of effort.

8. Utensils should be reasonably easy to clean.

References

1. Barnett, Nell M., and Aken, Elva V. The Steam Pressure Cooker. Home Ec. Bul. 17. (Rev. by Gertrude Lynn.) Ext. Service, Iowa State College, Ames, Iowa. 1924.

2. Brashear, Vivian. Hand Beaters for the Kitchen. Ladies' Home Jour. Leaflet 226. Curtis Publishing Co., Philadelphia, Pa. n.d.

3. Egg Beaters: Their Creation, Perfection and Manufacture. Unpublished data. United Royalties Corp., New York. 1930.

4. Frank, May C. The Comparative Thermal Efficiencies of Casseroles of Different Materials When Used in a Gas and in an Electric Oven. Unpublished thesis. Iowa State College Library, Ames, Iowa. 1931.

5. Gartrell, Bennie Mae. A Study of the Effect of Different Materials and Finishes on the Thermal Efficiency of Pans. Unpublished thesis. Iowa State College Library, Ames, Iowa. 1930.

6. Gibbons, R., Mason, M. A., and Newberry, R. D. Variations in Pastry Baked on Utensils of Different Materials. Jour. Home Ec. 23:977. 1931.

7. Goeppinger, Katherine. Roasting Equipment. Ladies' Home Jour. Nov. 1931.

8. Good, F. F. Thermal Efficiencies of Stew-kettles of Aluminum Ware and Enameled Ware. Jour. Home. Ec. 15:435-438. 1923.

9. Hart, Mary I. A Study of Various Materials Used in Baking Cookies. Unpublished data. 1931.

10. Home Canning with the Pressure Cooker. National School of Pressure Cooking, Eau Claire, Wis. 1932.

11. How to Tell Good Cutlery. John Russell Cutlery Co., Turner Falls, Mass. 1928.

12. Kendall, Helen W. Approved Measuring Cups. Good Housekeeping 91:94. 1930. (Sept.)

13. Krüger, Gabriele M. The Comparative Efficiency of Electric and Hand Operated Utensils. Unpublished thesis. Iowa State College Library, Ames, Iowa. 1931.

14. Landreth, Catherine, and Hutchinson, Mrs. R. O. Thermal Efficiencies of Aluminum Saucepans. Jour. Home Ec. 21:599-604. 1929.

15. Littleton, J. T. The Efficiency of Pyrex Brand Dishes in Electrical Ovens. Unpublished Ms. Corning Glass Works, Corning, New York. 1921.

16. Loizeaux, A. S. Electric Cooking Aided by Black-Bottom Utensils. Elec. World 99 (Part 2.): 997. 1932.

17. Lowe, Belle. Experimental Cookery. John Wiley & Sons, Inc., New York. 1932.

18. Lynn, Gertrude. The Home-made Fireless Cooker. Home Ec. Bul. 59. Ext. Service. Iowa State College, Ames, Iowa. 1926. (Second reprint.)

19. Monroe, Merna M. A Study of the Effect Upon Muffins of Pans Made of Different Materials. Unpublished report. Kans. State Agric. College, Manhattan, Kans. 1932.

20. Monroe, Merna M., and Smith, Lolie. Thermal Efficiency of Cooking Utensils

as Affected by Variations in the Area of Their Contact with the Heating Surface. Jour. Home Ec. 26:42-45. 1934.

21. Most Important Tool in Your Kitchen, The. Harrington Cutlery Co., Southbridge, Mass. 1924.

22. Nash, Mary A. Kitchen Kettles—Why Has the Hotel Man a Better Designed Kettle than the Housewife? House Beautiful 65:190. 1929.

23. Phillips, C. J., and Nordberg, Mary L. Ovenware and Fuel Economy. Jour. Home Ec. 26:37-41. 1934.

24. Redfield, Gail. Heat Penetration in Glass in Canning. Unpublished thesis, Iowa State College Library, Ames, Iowa. 1927.

25. Sater, V. Enid. The Thickness of Sheet Aluminum as a Factor in Influencing the Thermal Efficiency of a Utensil Used in Surface Cookery on an Electric Range. Unpublished thesis. Iowa State College Library, Ames, Iowa. 1932. Jour. Home Ec. 25:324-326. 1933.

26. Shank, Dorothy. (1) Factors Governing Baking Results in Gas Ranges. Unpublished report. American Stove Co., Cleveland, Ohio. 1931. (2) How Well Do You Know Your Equipment? Bul. 33. American Stove Co., Cleveland, Ohio. 1933. (3) When is an Oven Overcrowded? Better Homes and Gardens 8:43. 1930. (Mar.)

27. Some Ice Cream Freezers. Household Refrigeration Bureau of the Nat. Assoc. Ice Indust., Chicago, Ill. n.d.

28. Summer's Surplus for Winter's Dinner Table. Automatic Canning Devices, Inc., Chicago, Ill. n.d.

29. Swartz, Ve Nona W. Speed and Efficiency of Oven Utensils. Jour. Home Ec. 23:464-467. 1931.

30. Swartz, Ve Nona W., and Jones, Grace. Fuel Economy of Triplicate Pans. Jour. Home Ec. 23:467-470. 1931.

31. Those Green River Knives. Reprinted in part from Indian Notes, Vol. IV, No. 4. Museum of the American Indian, Heye Foundation, New York. Oct. 1927.

32. Whitney, L. D. Baking Pans. Cereal Chem. 6:304-308. 1929.

33. Worthington, Robert. Heat Conductivity of Metals as Factors in Heat Transfer. Chem. Met. Eng. 35:481-482. 1928.

ILLUSTRATIONS: Fig. 53, Geuder, Paeschke & Frey Co.; 54, 56, 57, West Bend Aluminum Company; 60, Good Housekeeping Institute; 63-65, John Russell Cutlery Co.; 66-71, Harrington Cutlery Co.

CHAPTER XI

REFRIGERATION

Refrigeration may be said to date back to very early times, if it is defined as the cooling of food below the temperature of the surrounding atmosphere for the purpose of preserving the food. When primitive man had killed and so procured fresh meat, he probably ate to repletion and then discarded the remains of his feast, and when hungry, killed again. Such a manner of living was only possible when the number of people in a given area was comparatively small, and when the supply of game was abundant. With the gradual increase in the inhabitants of a land, the natural food supply became less, and man was forced to keep food for longer periods. The first refrigerators were doubtless caves or cold springs. They are still used today, and if natural caverns do not exist, artificial caves are dug. The spring-house used later for the storage of milk and butter was a single-room cabin built over a spring, a running brook, or a well, where comparatively cool temperatures might be obtained.

History.—Foods are also cooled to develop flavor. In warmer countries some means of cooling water and wines was an early need. Records tell how the ancient Egyptians filled porous jars with water, covered them with reeds, and left them on the flat house-tops over night. The night breezes caused some of the water to evaporate and this evaporation cooled the rest sufficiently for use. Sometimes slaves fanned the water to make it evaporate. These same methods are used today in parts of India.

Alexander the Great had trenches filled with snow in which to cool wines for his soldiers. And Nero, the Roman Emperor, forced innumerable slaves to bring ice and snow from the higher mountains in Italy. This snow, placed in pits insulated with sod and straw, was used in cooling wines, fruits, and fish for his elaborate banquets.

Later, ice was harvested in the winter from rivers and ponds, and stored for summer use. In the seventeenth century such ice was sold in France under governmental control but this proved unsuccessful—the licensed distributors charged such exorbitant prices that people refused to buy. Ice harvesting is still a common practice in many sections of the world.

The story of Lord Bacon is familiar. He was so interested in the possibilities of food preservation by cold that he stopped his carriage in a suburb of London one winter evening, purchased a chicken at a nearby farmhouse, and stuffed it full of snow. His experiment unfortunately proved fatal to himself for he developed pneumonia and died. His interest in the result seems to have remained keen until the end for just before his death he is said to have asked a servant if the fowl still kept.

Water and milk ices were used in China as early as the thirteenth century, and at about the same time in the Near East, for Sir Walter Scott tells how Saladin, the Mohammedan, sent a frozen sherbet to King Richard of England, when Richard contracted fever during his crusade. But from the time Dolly Madison first served ice-cream in the White House until the present day, frozen desserts have been considered typically American. People of no other country have made frozen creams and ices of such satisfying texture and of such a variety of flavors.

The first home delivery of ice in America was in 1802. This necessitated the building of a form of ice chest, a heavy wooden box large enough to hold both the ice and food, the forerunner of the refrigerator of the present day.

Attempts to bring about refrigeration by mechanical means were made as early as the middle of the eighteenth century. In 1755 Dr. Cullen produced cold by evaporating water under a vacuum. A hundred years later (1850) the air compression system was developed by Dr. Gorrie of Florida. During the Civil War an ammonia absorption machine invented by Carre was used in the South to make the first artificial ice, and a few years later ammonia was also used in a compression type of system both by Linde in Germany and David Boyle in America. It was not until after 1890, however, that artificial ice production and mechanical refrigeration made rapid progress. In that year an unusually mild winter caused a severe ice famine the following summer. As a result ice-making became an established industry. Today more than 42,000,000 tons of artificial ice are manufactured yearly in America alone, three times the amount cut from lakes and rivers. In addition mechanical refrigerators are in use. And yet approximately 25 per cent or more of all families living in the United States have no adequate means of food preservation.

Physical principles.—The theory of refrigeration is based upon certain fundamental laws of heat. Heat is a form of energy due to the vibration of molecules.

Heat transfer.—Heat always passes from the warmer to the cooler body and does so in one of three ways, by radiation, conduction, or convection. Radiation is the transfer of heat from one body to another by vibrations in the ether. When heat is transferred by conduction it passes from one body to another in contact with it, owing to a vibration of the molecules in the body materials. In convection, heat is transferred by moving currents of gas or liquid. Convection currents are the usual means of bringing about cooling in a refrigerator; warmth in food and refrigerator walls is carried by means of these currents to the compartment containing the refrigerant.

Temperature versus heat capacity.—The heat of a body indicates the amount of warmth it can absorb and retain. It is a measure of capacity. Temperature on the other hand merely indicates degree of heat. Two bodies of vastly different sizes may have the same temperature, but the larger one will contain more heat. Temperature is measured by a thermometer; heat, in British thermal units. A British thermal unit, usually written B.t.u., is the amount of heat needed to raise the temperature of one pound of pure water one degree Fahrenheit, usually at the point of maximum density, 39.1°F. (4°C.). Water is taken as the standard because of its large heat capacity.

Specific heat.—Refrigeration also involves a knowledge of specific heat. The specific heat of any substance is its capacity to absorb heat compared to the capacity of an equal weight of water. In constructing the refrigerator cabinet it is necessary to know the specific heat of the materials used, and also the specific heat of the foods to be stored in the refrigerator, in order to determine the size of ice space or of cooling unit to build, to maintain the desired temperatures.

(Fresh) Beef........ 0.75	Chicken........... 0.80	Fish............... 0.80
Berries...... 0.91	Celery............. 0.96	Milk.............. 0.90
Butter....... 0.60	Cream............. 0.68	Watermelon........ 0.92
Cheese...... 0.64	Eggs.............. 0.76	

It is to be noted that the specific heat of those foods containing a large percentage of water approaches more nearly the specific heat of water, 1.0. Since the specific heat of milk is 0.90, it would require 0.9 B.t.u. to raise the temperature of one pound of milk 1°F.

The thermometer measures sensible heat, heat which is apparent to the touch. A body may gain or lose sensible heat without physical change.

Latent heat.—Latent heat cannot be measured by a thermometer. Latent heat accompanies a change of state, from a solid to a liquid, or from a liquid to a gas. It is the heat needed to bring this change of state about, and is used in separating the molecules of the substance. Molecules in a solid are closer together than are the molecules in a liquid, and liquid molecules in turn are more closely packed than the molecules of a gas. It is evident that energy is required to separate these molecules in changing from one state to another. The heat required to change a solid to a liquid is known as latent heat of fusion. For ice the latent heat of fusion is 144 B.t.u.; that is, it takes 144 B.t.u. to melt one pound of ice at 32°F. The latent heat of vaporization of water at 212°F. (100°C.) is 971.7 B.t.u. The latent heat necessary to melt ice in a refrigerator is absorbed from the area of the refrigerator and makes it cool. Similarly in the mechanical refrigerator, when the liquid refrigerant changes to a gas it absorbs heat from the food-box. Conversely, when the gas is again liquefied it gives off an amount of heat equal to what it had absorbed, but this process is carried on outside the refrigerator cabinet. To condense or liquefy a gas, a correct combination of temperature and pressure is essential.

Critical temperature and pressure.—The point at which the density of a liquid and the density of the vapor above the liquid are equal is known as the critical temperature. Regardless of the pressure, no substance can exist as a liquid above its critical temperature. The pressure of the saturated vapor at the critical temperature is called the critical pressure. A refrigerant in the form of a vapor must be cooled sufficiently to be liquefied without excessive pressure.

Change in boiling point.—Water boils and changes from a liquid to a vapor, at 100°C. at sea level. This temperature of boiling decreases 1° for every thousand feet rise in altitude. In changing from a liquid to a vapor at sea level, work has to be done against an atmospheric pressure of 14.7 pounds per square foot of exposed surface. At higher altitudes the atmospheric pressure is less and so the water boils more easily, and, therefore, at a lower temperature. If water is evaporated under a partial vacuum, it will evaporate at a temperature considerbly less than 100°C., depending upon the degree of vacuum present. Dr. Cullen used this principle in a mechanical machine for producing cold as early as 1755. It was successful enough to be used in cooling wines in Paris restaurants. The same principle is made use of in mechanical refrigerators of the present day.

Need for refrigeration.—Our early ancestors recognized the need of preserving food from spoilage, although the cause of the spoilage was unknown. Spoilage is now known to be due to the presence of tiny plant microorganisms—molds, yeasts, and bacteria. Molds and yeasts may be seen, but only when they have multiplied in sufficient numbers; bacteria, which probably cause the most harm, are always microscopic in size. As the organisms grow and multiply they cause certain chemical changes in the food, which alter the flavor and may be detrimental to health. Experiments have proved that in addition to the presence of suitable food, these plants require a certain amount of moisture and warmth for growth. Ordinary atmospheric conditions in most sections of the world supply the necessary moisture and warmth for at least a part of each year. Tests show that bacteria multiply rapidly at high temperatures, and 50°F. has been chosen as a convenient, economical maximum temperature to be permitted in the refrigerator in the prevent development of household equipment. There is no magic in the 50°, however, no evidence that 50° is a critical temperature in the preservation of foods, and certain foods need an even lower temperature for preservation and safety. (Fig. 72.)

Alternate freezing and melting of foods is also to be avoided. Vegetables and fruits and meats are made up of many tiny cells, which contain a watery fluid and are surrounded by a fibrous wall of cellulose. When these foods freeze under ordinary conditions the liquid in the cells expands and tends to rupture the surrounding walls. Upon melting, the texture is no longer firm but mushy and

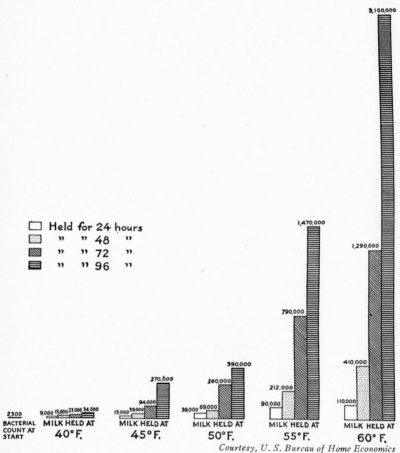

Courtesy, U. S. Bureau of Home Economics

FIG. 72.—Increase in bacteria in milk when held in refrigerators at different temperatures.

undesirable. Foods should, therefore, be kept cold, but at a temperature above freezing; in other words, a temperature below 50°F. but above 32°F. should be maintained for economical food preservation. Records of the United States Weather Bureau show that in the United States there is an average of only 19 days in the year when atmospheric temperatures fall within this range. In Iowa the average is only 15 days. The need for some method of artificial refrigeration is at once apparent.

Ice refrigeration.—At the present time over 90 per cent of the refrigerators in the United States use ice for cooling. There are two principal types of ice refrigerators, the side-icer type and the top-icer type. In addition to these two types there are "ice-chests," having only one door on the top of the cabinet, and with a single compartment in which both ice and food are placed.

Cooling process.—Refrigerators are used to preserve food by cooling and it is, therefore, important to know how this cooling is brought about. It has been noted that heat always passes from a warmer body to a cooler one. When food at room temperature is placed within the refrigerator the warmth it contains tends to flow toward the ice, and the warm air, passing over the ice, melts the ice. During this melting process heat is absorbed (latent heat of fusion) and the air cooled. The cold air drops toward the bottom of the cabinet, and as it becomes warmed, again rises and passes over the ice. In cold air the molecules are packed more closely together than in warm air; hence, a given volume of cold air contains more molecules than an equal volume of warm air and is heavy, whereas the warm air is light. When the refrigerator is properly constructed, these convection currents of air form a continuous cycle.

Ice chamber.—The construction of the ice chamber is important. The rack on which the ice rests should be $1\frac{1}{2}$ to 2 inches above the floor of the compartment to allow unhampered air flow, and there must be a sufficiently large opening in this floor to permit an efficient down-drop of the cold air. This opening in the usual household sizes should be from 6 to 8 inches wide and about 12 inches long, giving a free area of at least one-fourth of the total area of the compartment floor. Around the rack, between it and the walls of the compartment, should be sufficient space to allow the cold air to fall easily to the chamber floor and so through the opening to the food space below. The door to the ice compartment should be sufficiently wide and high to permit the piece of ice to be put in without breaking or chipping.

Baffle.—In side-icers there is a partition in the middle of the chest known as a "baffle," to guide the air currents. The baffle is more efficient if it is insulated. It should reach to within about 5 inches of the floor of the chest, and 6 inches from the top. The cold air falling from the ice chamber is directed downward by means of the baffle to the bottom of the space below the ice, before passing to the other side of the refrigerator and circulating upward.

Efficient circulation.—Anything which hinders efficient circulation retards refrigeration. Ice should not be covered; wrapping the ice in newspapers or burlap is a misguided effort in economy. It is the melting of the ice which cools the food. Foods should not be placed on the ice or even in the ice compartment, since this also hinders air circulation. The cake of ice should have at least an inch of space above it and between it and the side-walls to permit the air currents to pass. When the ice lies against the wall or the baffle, the cold is conducted away and air circulation is hindered.

The air in its circulation gathers moisture from the foods over which it passes and the odors dissolve in this moisture. Cold air can hold less moisture than warm air, and as the warm air passes over the ice and is cooled some of the excess moisture is deposited with the film of meltage from the ice, and the odors are thus carried away through the drain pipe.

Range of temperature.—The coldest place in the refrigerator is in the down-drop of cold air from the ice chamber. In the side-icer this place is at the bottom of the refrigerator in the space below the ice. In the top-icer the coldest place is in the middle of the top shelf of the refrigerator chamber below the opening through which the cold air falls.

The temperature in the coldest location should be 45°F. or below. The warmest location is that through which the air circulates last before again passing over the ice. Some authorities state that the warmest temperature here should not be over 50°F., but others believe that as high a temperature as 55°F. may be reached, without detriment to the food which may be placed in this space.

It is important to know the maximum and minimum temperatures which the refrigerator will keep under varying conditions; the average temperature which will be maintained is of comparatively little importance.

Location of foods.—Milk and butter, and sauces and desserts containing these products, and other protein foods, such as meats, poultry, and meat broths, are most liable to spoilage and should always be kept at 45° F. or below, if they are to be held for more than a few hours. Eggs and small fruits—strawberries, cherries, raspberries—are given the next coldest place. Berries should be picked over, the bruised fruit removed, and the perfect berries placed in shallow containers so that the circulating air may reach all parts readily. Salad vegetables occupy a place near the fruits. In the warmest location strong-flavored vegetables and fruits find their place. These foods have flavors which tend to contaminate the air of the refrigerator, and they should, accordingly, be put in a covered container or wrapped in waxed paper.

A similar arrangement of food should be followed in the mechanical refrigerator. The excess moisture is deposited on the cooling coils, and both it and absorbed odors are removed during defrosting.

Refrigerator specifications.—Shelves should be of rust-resistant metal rods or of enameled slats with wide spaces between, and food containers should be separated sufficiently to allow the air to move freely. The American Standards Association's Sectional Committee on Specifications for Refrigerators recommends that the milk compartment should be not less than 9¾ inches high, the lowest shelf in the food compartment should be 10 inches above the floor of the cabinet, and the other shelves not less than 5 inches apart.

Refrigerators have previously been rated according to the size of the cake of ice which they will hold. An effort is being made at the present time to rate the refrigerators on the basis of food-storage space. The size of the ice chamber varies from about 29 to 36 per cent of the total cubic capacity of the refrigerator; in some cases it is even as high as 40 per cent. This variation in size depends largely upon the amount of space which a given weight of ice will cool, and this in turn depends very directly upon the construction of the cabinet and the amount of insulation. The dimensions of the ice chamber are standardized to coordinate with standard sizes of ice cakes. The ratio of ice space to food space should be such as to obtain the desired temperatures with the most economical use of ice.

Construction of refrigerators.—Refrigerator cabinets are made of wood or of steel. If wood is to be used it must be very well-seasoned hard wood; otherwise it tends to shrink in dry weather and to swell during periods of excessive humidity. Ash, spruce, fir, and oak are good. The joints should be fastened together with tenons, or be braced to maintain rigidity of shape and prevent airleakage. The outside sheathing should be of simple design to be easily cleaned, and should be painted or varnished to preserve the wood. It is well to repaint or revarnish the surface at regular intervals.

Steel frames are more rigid than wood and joints may be welded securely, but steel is a much better conductor of heat than wood and requires added insulation in the walls. When the frame is of steel the outside finish may be vitreous enamel or lacquer. The lacquer exterior is less expensive and is usually found on the lower-priced models.

Lining.—The most satisfactory lining is two or three coats of vitreous enamel. With this enamel for a lining, the steel or iron base may be made in one piece, and joints and seams, which tend to cause air- or moisture-leakage, avoided. The lining should have rounded corners to increase ease of cleaning. Whatever lining is used, it should be stain-proof and impervious to moisture, and should neither crack, chip, nor peel.

Insulation.—The efficiency of the refrigerator depends largely upon the insulation which is between the outer wall and the lining of the cabinet. Insulation is a material which is a poor conductor of heat. Experiments have proved that from 80 to 90 per cent of the heat which gets into a refrigerator comes through the walls. The rest of the heat, insignificant by comparison, comes from opening the door and from the warmth of the food placed within the cabinet. Good insulation, therefore, is a true economy. Refrigerators are graded upon the thickness of the insulation, the highest class cabinets having at least 2 inches of insulation. An efficient insulating material must be heat-resistant and moisture-resistant, non-destructible, and odorless. Moisture is a good conductor of heat. The insulation must also maintain its position between the walls, and not settle or sag, leaving air pockets to conduct heat. So-called dead-air spaces or layers of paper are not satisfactory insulators. The dead-air spaces usually contain some moving air caused by the difference in temperature between the inner and outer walls, and moisture is deposited when the air cools. Paper does not stay in place.

Cork board is the insulation used most frequently in the better ice refrigerators. It is made up of many tiny cells closely wedged together. These cells are very poor conductors of heat and practically non-absorbent.

As a further precaution against any possibility of moisture being absorbed the insulation may be sealed into the walls with an odorless asphalt mixture which will protect the surface of the insulating material. Hydrolene is commonly used.

Vegetable fiber is being extensively used in mechanical refrigerators under various trade names. It is a very satisfactory insulating material when made into slabs, otherwise it tends to sag. Vegetable fiber insulation is also usually treated to a coating of some waterproof substance. When the cabinet is of steel a layer of wall-board

Courtesy, U. S. Bureau of Home Economics
Fig. 73.—A well-filled ice chamber means lower temperatures.

½ inch thick is frequently placed next to the outside wall to improve the insulation.

Amount of ice necessary.—Tests carried on at Purdue University on ice refrigerators have shown that the temperature of the refrigerator rises much more rapidly after the cake of ice which is of the correct size for any given ice chamber has melted to less than one-half. The ice chamber should, therefore, always be kept more than half full to maintain the low temperatures necessary for the safe preservation of food. (Fig. 73.)

Dr. Pennington has pointed out that "if the insulation in the walls of the box is as efficient as it should be, from 48 to 72 hours, or even longer, will be needed for enough heat from the outside to struggle through to melt more than one-half to two-thirds of the ice which the ice compartment will hold in a well balanced refrigerator. If meltage and the ice used for household purposes reduce the ice supply in 24 hours to less than half the capacity of the ice chamber the family needs either a better insulated box, or a larger one."[1]

An exception to this requirement of at least a half-full ice chamber is a new ice refrigerator recently placed on the market. In this model the air does not circulate over the ice, but simply across the bottom surface which covers practically the entire width of the cabinet. The ice melts horizontally owing to the way in which the ice compartment is constructed, and the air is adequately cooled as long as a thin sheet of ice covers the large opening into the food chamber. (Fig. 74.)

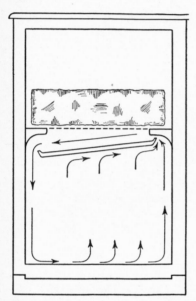

FIG. 74.—The air circulates across the bottom of the cake of ice.

High external temperatures affect the temperature inside the cabinet making necessary more frequent replenishing of ice, or causing the mechanical unit to run a larger percentage of the time. The unit has reached the limit of its performance-ability when it runs continuously. Adequate insulation diminishes the effects within the cabinet of variations in the outside temperature.

Door.—Doors may be regarded as part of the wall and should have the same insulation as the walls. Wooden doors are frequently built with rabbet joints, which fit into each other and give a tighter closing. Steel cabinets have wedge-shaped doors, the wedge often insulated with a composition material and the outer edge furnished with a rubber gasket to make the door fit more closely. The latches and hinges on the doors should be of first class construction, to hold the door securely. It is convenient to have the latch not require hand

[1] Pennington, M. E. The Care of the Child's Food in the Home. p. 12.

manipulation, but hold when the door is pushed shut with the arm or knee, in case the hands are filled with supplies which have been removed from the cabinet. The hardware should be finished in nickel or chromium to be rust-proof and easy to care for.

Drain pipe.—The drain pipe of the ice refrigerator should be held securely in place, but at the same time be easily removable for cleaning. It is usually more convenient to have this pipe connected with the sewer, though the problem of cleaning is thereby increased. The drain pipe should have a trap to prevent undesirable odors or insects finding a way into the refrigerator by this path, and to lessen the leakage of heat.

Refrigerators should sit flat on the floor or be "broom-high" to facilitate cleaning beneath them. It is a saving of energy if the bottom of the food compartment is of such a height that it is not necessary to stoop in taking supplies from the refrigerator chamber.

Food space.—The properly constructed and insulated ice refrigerator should have food space in proportion to its ice capacity. If the insulation is of equal thickness, a refrigerator built to hold 100 pounds of ice can cool a larger food space than one built to hold 50 pounds. That is to be expected. But more significant is the fact that a refrigerator of 50 pounds ice capacity, having 2 inches of efficient insulation, can adequately cool almost twice as much food space as the same size refrigerator with only 1 inch of good insulation.

Classification of ice refrigerators.—Ice refrigerators have been classified on construction durability, amount of space a given weight of ice will cool, and on thickness of insulation. Class A has 2 inches or more of pure cork board insulation, or its equivalent; Class B, 1½ inches; and Class C, 1 inch. The table on p. 178 shows the amount of food space in refrigerators of the three classes, cooled by 100, 75, and 50 pounds of ice. The larger cabinets have more cubic foot capacity in proportion to the surface of the boxes than the smaller ones. When properly iced, a cabinet of any class should maintain temperatures which will protect food.

Mechanical refrigerators.—Mechanical refrigerators may be run by electricity, gas, or kerosene oil. The largest number of types is electric. In all types refrigeration is based primarily upon the two fundamental physical laws previously referred to: (1) when a liquid changes to a vapor or gas, heat is absorbed, and (2) when the vapor

Ice compartment* of size to receive	Food Space in Minimum Size		
	Class A refrigerator	Class B refrigerator	Class C refrigerator
lb.	cu. ft.	cu. ft.	cu. ft.
100	8	6	5
75	6	5	4
50	5	4	3

* Pennington, M. E., Buying a Refrigerator, p. 7. (With slight modification.)

is again liquefied it gives off the heat it had absorbed. Electricity or gas or oil supplies the energy which starts the cycle. In the gas or oil refrigerator Dalton's law of the partial pressures of gases is also utilized.

The discovery that certain substances would undergo these changes of state was first made by Faraday in 1824. He found that if he compressed ammonia vapor and then cooled the vapor, he could obtain liquid ammonia. When he removed the pressure from the liquid it boiled and changed back to a vapor, absorbing heat in the process.

Compression system.—These three steps take place in electric refrigerators in a more or less continuous and controlled cycle. The system is closed so that the refrigerating substance may be used over and over. Since the vapor is compressed by means of a motor, the system is called the compression system to distinguish it from the absorption system, which uses gas or kerosene oil instead of electricity. The size of the motor varies usually from 1/3 to 1/8 horsepower. In the household refrigerators of the compression type, sulphur dioxide is most commonly used for the refrigerant. Occasionally, however, methyl chloride is used. Ethyl chloride, butane and isobutane, and more recently dichlorodifluoromethane have also been used for refrigerants, but less frequently in household refrigerators than the other two.

Fig. 75 shows in diagrammatic form the essential parts of the compression system: (1) the compressor, (2) the condensing coils, (3) the liquid receiver containing the expansion or float valve, and (4) the cooling unit or evaporator. In addition to these parts there are the motor which drives the piston in the compression cylinder, the thermostat which regulates the operation of the system according to the temperature of the refrigerator box, and in some types a storage tank of brine surrounding the cooling unit.

When the piston is drawn by the motor to the left, the pressure is reduced in the cylinder, the valve on the pipe line from the evapo-

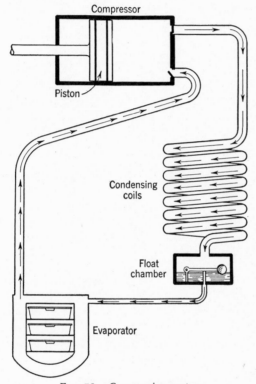

Fig. 75.—Compression system.

rator is forced open, and the vapor is sucked from the evaporator coils into the cylinder. As the motor pushes the piston to the right the gas is compressed, the evaporator valve closed, the valve into the condensing coils opened, and the compressed gas discharged into these coils. The condensing coils may be cooled by direct radiation, by forced air-circulation by means of a fan, or by water. When the coils are air-cooled they are often supplied with "fins" to increase the surface area exposed. When the compressed vapor is sufficiently cooled—for a given pressure there is a definite temperature at which condensation will take place—the vapor liquefies and collects in the receiver. From the receiver it is discharged into the evaporator either through an expansion or float valve.

Dry system.—The type of refrigeration using the expansion valve is known as the "dry" system. In this system the refrigerant is sprayed through the expansion valve into the evaporator, and enters the evaporator in a semi-liquid form.

Flooded system.—With the float valve, or "flooded" system, the amount of liquid flowing into the cooling unit is regulated by the float. In this case a fairly large amount of liquid refrigerant is always held in the evaporator, and comparatively continuous evaporation takes place. As the movement of the piston sucks the vapor from the cooling unit, the pressure is further reduced in the evaporator and a more rapid evaporation is possible at a lower temperature. This change to a vapor causes the cooling of the food chamber, owing to the absorption of heat of vaporization.

Sealed-in unit.—The unit of the compression system may be hermetically sealed in, or it may be the "conventional" or "open face type." In the sealed type the motor and compressor are within the same housing, and the whole system is so connected that there is comparatively no possibility of leakage.

Conventional unit.—In the conventional type the motor and compressor are separate and the compressor shaft is driven by an exposed belt connected to the motor. It is necessary to surround this shaft by a packing, a stuffing-box, so called since there is a tendency for the refrigerant to leak out around the piston shaft when the pressure inside the cylinder is greater than atmospheric pressure, and for air, probably containing moisture, to leak in, when the atmospheric pressure exceeds the pressure in the cylinder. This packing-box must be flexible, and it is sometimes difficult at the same time to make it sufficiently tight to prevent leaks. The conventional system does, however, lend itself to easy servicing in the home. If the hermetically sealed unit gets out of order, it must be returned as a whole to the factory.

Rotary compressor.—Some types of electric refrigerators use a rotary compressor instead of the piston. Otherwise the system is similar to the conventional type.

Brine tank.—The expansion coils of the evaporator or chilling unit may be exposed directly to the surrounding atmosphere in the cabinet, or the evaporator may be surrounded by a tank filled with brine or other suitable liquid. In the first case the refrigerant as it changes from a liquid to a vapor absorbs heat directly from the box; in the other case, the changing refrigerant absorbs heat from the brine in the storage tank, and the brine in turn absorbs heat from the atmosphere of the cabinet. The brine tank in storing the heat or the cold usually cuts down the number of times the motor starts. The brine tank has certain disadvantages, however, in that the brine solution frequently has a corrosive effect upon the metal of the unit.

High and low side.—The part of the refrigeration system between the valve where the vapor enters the compression cylinder and the float or expansion valve is known as the "high side"; the rest of the system is called the low pressure side, or often only the "low side."

Thermostat.—The thermostat, which controls the temperature, is usually placed at the point where the suction line leaves the evaporator. The thermostat contains a kind of bellows which contracts or expands according to the temperature in the refrigerator box, and so breaks or makes an electric contact, which causes the motor to stop or start operating.

Temperature range.—Just as it is necessary for a radiator to be hotter than the temperature of a room, so it is essential for effective cooling that the evaporator be colder than the atmosphere in the cabinet. The thermostat is usually set at the factory where the refrigerator is manufactured for the evaporator to maintain a maximum temperature of 28°F., and a minimum of 10°F. to 20°F. At this setting the motor operates from 25 to 33 per cent of the time, or from 6 to 8 hours out of the 24. Lower temperatures may be obtained by setting a manually controlled dial. In certain refrigerator models low temperatures are obtained automatically in some sections of the chilling unit.

Automatic quick freezing.—The automatic control permits quick freezing without affecting the temperature of the rest of the cabinet. There is no danger of excessive cooling of foods in the food chamber; and it is to be remembered that too low a temperature is as detrimental as too high a one.

In these models there is a storage tank and "isothermic" tubes. "The first section of the evaporation coils is wound pancake fashion and soldered fast to the bottom of the lowest single depth freezing sleeve. This gives direct metallic contact between anything placed in this freezing tray and the evaporating refrigerant. This causes a concentration of refrigeration on the one point, while the cooling tank maintains the temperature of the other freezing trays, and of the cabinet itself, without appreciable fluctuation."[2]

Ice trays.—Ice trays are commonly made of aluminum and rubber in various sizes and shapes. Some of the newer trays mold triangular-shaped ice bars instead of the more common cubes. The rubber trays are flexible and usually permit an easy removal of the ice cubes but are somewhat slower in freezing, since rubber is not as good a conductor of heat and cold as metal. The trays may be used for freezing a variety of salads and desserts.

Location of unit.—In some refrigerators the unit is placed above the food chamber; in others, below the chamber. There are arguments for both locations. Manufacturers who place the unit on top call attention to the fact that heat rises, and when the unit is above the cabinet the heat is carried away from the cabinet. They also show how the condensed liquid-refrigerant follows the natural course of gravity in passing into the evaporator and the resultant vapor again rises to the compressor.

Manufacturers of the types where the unit is below the food chamber point out that the unit is placed where the temperature of the room is lowest, and so the heat given off from the condensing coils most easily dispersed. This position also makes for a more elevated food box which eliminates stooping. Finally, if it is desired, the unit may be removed and placed in the basement, and the space used for other storage purposes.

Absorption system.—In the absorption system, where gas or oil is used to help bring about the necessary changes in the refrigeration cycle, an additional part is needed, the absorber, and this gives the name to the system. Ammonia is the refrigerant commonly used.

[2] Sawyer, Marion. The Science of Refrigeration.

The action depends upon the ease with which ammonia gas dissolves in water, and the fact that the combination is at best an unstable one, easily broken down by heat.

A simplified diagram of the absorption system is given in Fig. 76. The liquefied ammonia passes from the condensing coils into the evaporator or cooling unit. To hasten the change into a vapor the

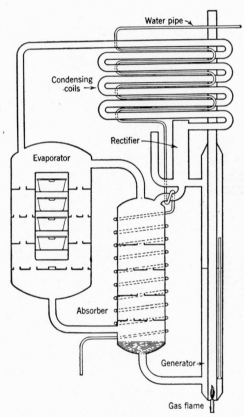

FIG. 76.—Absorption system.

liquid is allowed to drip through perforated shelves in the evaporator. The raised edges around the holes permit some of the ammonia to collect on the shelves before trickling through. In this way more surface is exposed, and evaporation takes place more rapidly. To hasten the action still further, the evaporator contains an atmosphere of hydrogen, the lightest gas, which reduces the pressure to a minimum. The total pressure in the evaporator will be the sum of the pressures exerted by the ammonia vapor and the hydrogen gas. In the generator the ammonia has a pressure of 180 pounds per square inch. The hydrogen in the evaporator has a pressure of 150 pounds per square inch. As the liquid ammonia enters the evaporator where the pressure is 150 pounds, it needs to exert a partial pressure of only 30 pounds per square inch to equal its former pressure of 180 pounds. (Dalton's law of partial pressure of gases.) Evaporation at this greatly reduced pressure is, therefore, very rapid. This change of the liquid ammonia to a vapor is accompanied by absorption of heat, which is removed from the refrigerator cabinet.

Absorber.—The saturated vapor sinks to the bottom of the evaporator and passes from it into the absorber. This cylinder also contains perforated shelves over which a spray of distilled water falls. Hydrogen is insoluble in water, but the ammonia vapor readily dissolves in the water, forming ammonium hydroxide, which collects at the bottom of the absorber. The light hydrogen gas rises to the top of the cylinder and passes back through a connecting pipe to the evaporator where it is again used.

Generator and condensing coils.—The ammonium hydroxide next passes to the generator. Here the heat from a gas or oil flame starts the separation of the hydroxide into ammonia and water. A percolator form of siphon raises the ammonia, water vapor, and some unchanged weak hydroxide to the upper level of the generator where the separation continues. The water flows by gravity back into the absorber and the ammonia is driven into the condensing coils where it again becomes a liquid under pressure, at reduced temperature. The whole system is run at a uniform pressure sufficiently high to permit the ammonia to condense. There is no high and low side as in the compression system. In all but the most recent type, circulating air will not cool the condensing coils sufficiently, and the coils are, therefore, surrounded with a pipe containing running water. The pipes of the water coil and condensing coil are soldered together to hasten cooling by contact. The water pipe is also extended to cool the distilled water flowing back into the absorber, and the absorber itself. The ammonia vapor will unite with the water in the absorber more readily if the water is cool. Heat, as has been seen, tends to separate the ammonia from the water. The temperature of the cooling water should not be over 80°F. and the pressure of the water should be reduced to about 15 pounds.

Added features.—As in the compression system, certain other features are added to the absorption cycle to increase the efficiency. A rectifier condenses any water vapor mixed with the ammonia vapor leaving the generator, and returns it to the generator. The rec-

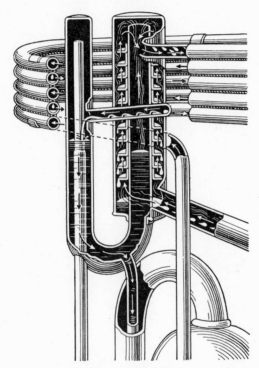

FIG. 77.—Rectifier.

tifier is a series of small steel baffle plates surrounding one arm of the U-tube which is the storage chamber for the condensed liquid ammonia. The cool liquid ammonia aids in the condensation of the water vapor. When a predetermined level of liquid ammonia is reached in the U-tube, it flows into the evaporator. (Fig. 77.) There are also two exchangers; in the gas heat exchanger the hydrogen and ammonia mixture entering the evaporator is cooled by the vapor leaving the evaporator; in the liquid heat exchanger the ammonium hydroxide flowing into the percolator is preheated by the liquid leaving the generator and, therefore, needs less heat in the generator.

The evaporator is covered with radiating fins which help in the absorption of the heat from the food chamber. Within these fins is the receptacle containing the trays for ice cubes.

Gas burner.—The gas burner is fitted with an automatic cut-off, a "Klixondisc," made of a metal which contracts as it cools, and so shuts off the gas, if the flame should be accidentally extinguished. When lighting the gas burner the disc must be heated before it will open the gas inlet and permit the gas to flow. The amount of heat generated by the burning gas, i.e., the height of the flame, is regulated by a thermostat, which controls the flow of gas. A higher flame speeds up the refrigeration cycle and gives greater cooling of the food chamber. The thermostatic control also shuts off the gas if for any reason the cooling water is unexpectedly cut off.

The latest model of gas refrigerator uses air for cooling the condensing coils, and cools the absorber with a separate system, containing methyl chloride. In this refrigerator another chamber is also added to equalize undesirable variations in the pressure of the refrigerant.

Oil-burning refrigerator.—When electricity and gas are not available kerosene oil may be used to supply the necessary heat for starting the refrigeration cycle. Ammonia is the refrigerant employed. In one oil refrigerator, ammonium hydroxide (ammonia + water) in the generator is heated by an oil burner which burns until the oil in the fuel tank is exhausted (from $1\frac{1}{2}$ to 2 hours), when it is automatically extinguished. The vaporized ammonia is driven into cooling coils immersed in a water tank on the top of the refrigerator, where it liquefies, and the liquid ammonia drops into the evaporator within the refrigerator cabinet. When the oil burner goes out and the generator cools, the pressure is reduced, causing the liquid ammonia in the evaporator to change to a gas which slowly passes back to the generator and dissolves in the water, making the process continuous for 24 hours or more. (Fig. 78.) A patented arrangement forces any small amounts of water carried over with the ammonia to return automatically to the generator shortly after the burner is again lighted. A special housing encloses the fuel tank and burners.

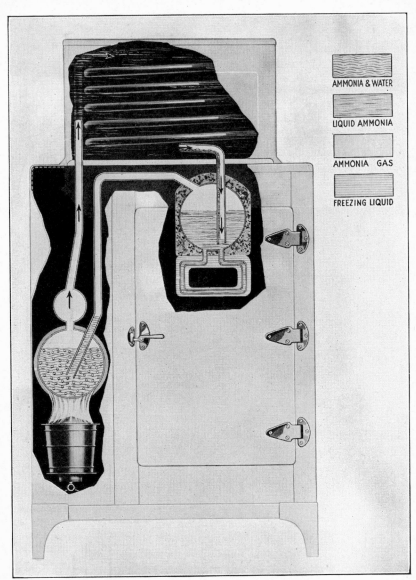

AMMONIA & WATER

LIQUID AMMONIA

AMMONIA GAS

FREEZING LIQUID

FIG. 78.—Unit of oil-burning refrigerator.

Tests carried on at Rhode Island State College indicate an average daily running cost of two cents, when kerosene is eight cents a gallon. The oil-burning refrigerator tested maintained temperatures varying from a low of 23.0°F. to a high of 48.2°F., at room temperatures averaging as high as 71.9°F.

Advantages of each system.—The absorption system is sealed; so there is little possibility of leakage. The condensing pressure of ammonia, however, is high and heavy steel cylinders and pipes of one-piece construction are necessary. This type of refrigeration is noiseless, because of the absence of moving parts. Only a very tiny stream of water is needed to cool the condensing coils and absorber, but the water must be running and requires connection to a source of supply and to a drain; and in sections where the local water is hard, i.e., contains various minerals, some trouble may occur from the gradual deposit of mineral within the pipes, even clogging them sufficiently to stop the water flow. The new gas refrigerator eliminates the need for water. When oil is used in place of gas, it is necessary to fill the oil tank from time to time.

The compression system is more flexible in that the refrigerator may be plugged into any wall outlet. The expense of running an electric refrigerator is greatly reduced, however, if the refrigerator is connected to the so-called "power line," on which there is a lower rate. There is always some noise when the motor is running, but recent research by manufacturers has reduced this to a minimum.

Special features.—Different makes of refrigerators feature certain specialties which add to the convenience or attractiveness of the machine but are not essential. The door may be opened by a foot control as well as by hand; an interior light may be automatically switched on as the door is opened; sliding shelves which do not tip when pulled out permit easy access to foods. A wire egg basket, a covered pan for succulent vegetables, and a reservoir for drinking water are other accessories. Cooling units which defrost automatically are found in some makes.

Size.—The size of cabinet needed depends upon the number in the family, the amount of entertaining done, and the necessity of keeping extra supplies on hand. It is estimated that from one to two cubic feet per person will supply sufficient space for ordinary use.

Defrosting.—Whatever the type of mechanical refrigerator, occasional defrosting of the cooling unit is usually necessary. Frost is deposited when the circulating air, laden with moisture, passes over the unit. The amount of frost may be diminished by keeping foods of high water content in covered containers or wrapped in wax paper or aluminum foil. Defrosting is advisable whenever the thickness of the deposit is greater than ¼ inch. Ice on the coils acts as an insulator, rapidly cuts down the efficiency of the evaporator, and forces the motor to run a higher percentage of the time.

Units may be defrosted by shutting off the current or gas for the night, or by filling the ice cube trays with hot water and placing them inside the evaporator sleeve. The latter method is more rapid, but should not be followed unless advised by the manufacturer of the model in question. Either method does not greatly increase the temperature of the cabinet, since ice in melting absorbs heat. It is estimated that the temperature in the box does not change more than 4 or 5 degrees when defrosting takes place over night. Some recent models have a special circuit to which the machine is switched when defrosting is necessary. Defrosting takes place somewhat more slowly in this case but the temperature inside the food chamber never rises above 50°F.

Refrigerants.—Sulphur dioxide, ammonia, and methyl chloride are the refrigerants most widely used in household refrigeration units. The query arises as to why these refrigerants were selected, in other words, what characteristics are desirable in a refrigerant, and how nearly do the ones in use meet the requirements.

A refrigerant should be

1. Non-toxic under all conditions.
2. Non-inflammable.
3. Non-explosive by itself or in any mixture with air.
4. Of a characteristic, but non-irritating odor.
5. Easily detected in leaks by a simple test.
6. Stable, to avoid disintegration during repeated compression, condensation, and evaporation.

The refrigerant should have

1. A non-corrosive action on metals.
2. A fairly high latent heat.

3. Comparatively low condensing pressure.

4. Evaporating pressure close to atmospheric pressure.

5. Little or no effect on lubricating oils.

None of the refrigerants under discussion, or any of the others which have been used, entirely approach the ideal. Sulphur dioxide is used in about 90 per cent of the household compression type of refrigerators in operation in the United States. It would seem, therefore, to be considered superior to the others.

Sulphur dioxide.—Sulphur dioxide is non-inflammable and non-explosive. Some authorities also rate it as non-poisonous because it is so suffocating that a person would not remain in an atmosphere containing it. In concentrated amounts it is certainly dangerous, and even in small amounts the irritation it causes to mucous membranes may be sufficient warning to adults of normal mentality, but not to infants or small children, and it may not be possible for the insane or invalids to heed the warning even if they receive it. Fortunately leaks practically never occur, and the quantity of the refrigerant used in a single unit is so small that a serious accident would be nearly impossible.

Sulphur dioxide is stable. Leaks are easily located by a fume test, when ammonium hydroxide is applied to the suspected spot. Sulphur dioxide does not corrode iron, copper, or copper alloys, unless moisture is present. In this case sulphurous acid is formed, and the acid will react with metals. Copper is preferable for unit construction because it has a thermal conductivity seven or eight times that of iron and steel.

The boiling point of sulphur dioxide under atmospheric pressure is 14°F. The boiling point to a large extent determines the operating pressure required in the system. With sulphur dioxide the pressure in the evaporator on the low side of the system is practically atmospheric. (—2.88 lb. gauge at 5°F.) There is, therefore, almost equal pressure on both sides of the stuffing-box in the models where the box is used, and less probability of leakage.

Condensing coils cooled by air operate at a pressure 10 to 20 lb. higher than when cooled by water. Air-cooling, however, reduces the initial and installation costs and increases the simplicity of the system and is used by preference whenever possible. Sulphur dioxide has a condensing pressure of 51.75 lb. gauge at a condensing temperature of 86°F. This is a comparatively low operating pressure.

If a vapor has a very high latent heat of vaporization a small quantity will bring about the desired amount of cooling. On the other hand, if only a small quantity of the refrigerant is allowed to circulate, the float or expansion valve must be very sensitive to control the amount which passes. A moderately high latent heat is, therefore, preferable. At 5°F. sulphur dioxide has a latent heat of vaporization of 169.38 B.t.u. per lb. There are from 2 to 3 lb. of the refrigerant in the unit.

Sulphur dioxide tends to absorb certain lubricating oils, but there is no chemical reaction between them. Separation is fairly simple because sulphur dioxide is heavier than the oils. Light colored oils are less easily absorbed than the darker colored ones.

Methyl chloride.—Methyl chloride is a colorless and practically odorless liquid or gas. Leaks are detected with an alcohol lamp, the methyl chloride imparting a greenish tinge to the alcohol flame. Methyl chloride is inflammable and will explode, but only under conditions which would be rarely met with in the home.

When methyl chloride is present in concentrations of more than 10 per cent, it produces first a form of intoxication, then anesthesia, and may cause death through suffocation. The probability of such high percentages occurring in the home from leakage of a single unit is decidedly remote, if not wholly impossible.

Methyl chloride has no corrosive action on copper or its alloys, or on iron and steel. It dissolves most oils, but white mineral oils and glycerine are not affected, and are generally used for lubricants. Care must be taken to reduce any moisture to a minimum, since glycerine readily absorbs moisture, which may freeze and stop the circulation of the refrigerant.

Methyl chloride boils at —10.66°F. at atmospheric pressure, has a condensation pressure of 0.83 lb. gauge at 86°F., a vaporization pressure of 6.19 lb. gauge at 5°F., and a latent heat of vaporization of 178.5 B.t.u. per lb. at 5°F. The increase in pressure over that of sulphur dioxide makes a somewhat sturdier construction of the system necessary, and there is more tendency for leakage through a stuffing-box.

Ammonia.—Ammonia is a colorless gas of characteristic odor, is inflammable and explosive under certain conditions, but not commonly under conditions found in the home; it has no corrosive action on iron or steel, but does corrode copper, especially in the presence of moisture. Leaks may be detected by a sulphur candle.

Ammonia boils at —28°F. at atmospheric pressure, has a latent heat of 565.0 B.t.u. per lb. at 5°F., a vaporization pressure of 19.57 lb. gauge at 5°F., and a condensation pressure of 154.5 lb. gauge at 86°F. Ammonia is very soluble in water, about 900 volumes of ammonia being soluble in one volume of water at ordinary temperatures. By weight, water absorbs about 40 per cent of its own weight of ammonia. The ammonia and water form an unstable union, and are readily separated again by heat. Its reaction with water causes it to be used in the absorption rather than in the compression system in the household types of refrigerators. The fairly high condensation pressure required necessitates cylinders and pipes of heavy construction.

Care.—Since the preservation of food is the main purpose of the refrigerator, it must be kept spotlessly clean at all times. When the external finish is varnished wood, it may be dusted whenever other pieces of furniture are; if of lacquer or porcelain enamel, it may be wiped off as frequently as the range or kitchen table is wiped.

The inside of the refrigerator should be kept clean and dry. No dirty containers or foods should be placed in the cabinet, spilled food should be wiped up immediately, and the shelves and walls should be wiped dry from any deposited moisture.

The ice refrigerator should be completely cleaned once a week. Remove the ice rack, shelves, and drain pipe, wipe the entire interior with a cloth wet with soda or borax water (2 tablespoons to a quart of water), wipe again with a cloth wrung from clear cold water, then dry thoroughly. Wash the rack and shelves in warm soapy water, rinse in clear water, and dry. Pour hot soda or borax water through the drain pipe. If necessary use a stiff long-handled wire brush to remove any deposit of slime. In a similar manner clean the water seal and drip pan beneath the cabinet. Replace all parts as quickly as possible to conserve the cool temperature.

Mechanical refrigerators usually have a drier interior atmosphere than the ice refrigerators and may require less frequent cleaning.

Cleaning at the time of defrosting is recommended. Wipe the unit as well as the inside walls with the soda or borax water. Empty the ice trays, wash in warm soapy water, rinse, and refill.

Summary.

1. Refrigeration is essential for the adequate preservation of food.
2. Refrigeration is based on fundamental physical laws of heat transfer, latent heat, and specific heat.
3. Food spoilage is caused by the growth of yeasts, molds, and bacteria.
4. The air circulation in the refrigerator carries the cold air to all parts of the cabinet and removes excessive humidity and undesirable odors.
5. Cakes of ice should be left uncovered. No food should be placed in the ice chamber.
6. Protein foods are placed in the coldest location.
7. There are two types of mechanical systems, the compression and the absorption. The compression system is electrically operated; the absorption system, by gas or kerosene.
8. Sulphur dioxide, methyl chloride, and ammonia are the refrigerants most commonly used in household refrigeration systems.
9. Economical operation of any refrigerator depends upon sturdy construction and efficient insulation.
10. The refrigerator must be kept clean and dry at all times.

References

1. Ackerman, W. T. Electric Household Refrigeration. Agric. Expt. Sta. Bul. 244. Univ. of New Hampshire, Durham, N. H. 1929.
2. A. M. A. Safety Requirements. Refrig. Eng. 20:238-239. 1930.
3. Broadhurst, Jean, and Van Arsdale, Mary B. Food in the House Refrigerator. Teachers College Record 26:230. 1924.
4. Code for Testing Domestic Refrigerators Using Ice. Unpublished report. Electrical Testing Laboratories, New York. 1930.
5. Danner, B. G. Cold Facts. Bul. 433. Georgia State College of Agric., Univ. of Georgia, Athens, Ga. 1933.
6. Electrolux Educational Series. No. 1 and No. 2. Electrolux Refrigerator Sales, Inc., Evansville, Ind. n.d.
7. Food Preservation in our Daily Life. Frigidaire Corp., Dayton, Ohio. 1929.
8. Hull, H. B. Household Refrigeration. (Third edition.) Nickerson & Collins, Chicago, Ill. 1927.
9. Jordan, Ruth. Factors in the Management of the Ice Cooled Refrigerator in the Home. Agric. Expt. Sta. Bul. 316. Purdue Univ., Lafayette, Ind. 1927.
10. King, W. J. Recent Developments in Heat Transfer. Refrig. Eng. 24:76-80, 158-159, 165. 1932.
11. Kingsley, Margaret H. Home Service Work for the Ice Industry. Nickerson & Collins Co., Chicago, Ill. 1931.

12. Lewis, E. B., and Brunig, M. P. Fitting the Mechanical Refrigerator into the Home. Agric. Expt. Sta. Circ. 45. Univ. of Nebraska, Lincoln, Neb. 1933.
13. Lindsay, H. B. Insulation. Refrig. Eng. 19:9-11. 1930.
14. McBride, R. S. How Dangerous are Refrigerating Gases? Elec. Merchand. 1929. (Aug.)
15. McCord, C. P. (M.D.) Household Mechanical Refrigeration. Jour. Amer. Med. Assoc. 94:1832-1838. 1930.
16. Moyer, J. A., and Fittz, R. U. Refrigeration. McGraw-Hill Book Co., Inc., New York. 1928.
17. Murray, Eleanor M. Bacteriological Tests on the Efficiency of Various Types of Household Refrigerators. Unpublished thesis. Iowa State College Library, Ames, Iowa. 1925.
18. Patty, R. L. Cost of Electricity for the Home Electric Refrigerator. Agric. Eng. Expt. Sta. Bul. 241. South Dak. State College, Brookings, S. D. 1929.
19. Pennington, M. E. (1) Where to Place Food in the Household Refrigerator. 1924. (2) Care of the Home Refrigerator. 1924. (3) Care of the Child's Food in the Home. 1925. (4) Why We Refrigerate Foods. 1926. (5) Cold is the Absence of Heat. 1927. (6) Romance of Ice. 1927. (7) How to Use a Good Refrigerator. 1929. (8) Home Refrigeration of Fresh Vegetables. 1929. (9) Buying a Refrigerator. 1930. Household Refrigeration Bureau, Nat. Assoc. Ice Indust., Chicago, Ill.
20. Porter, M. B. Temperature and Ice Consumption in an Ice Cooled Refrigerator as Affected by Room Temperature. Refrig. World 65:19-22. 1930.
21. Rating of Mechanical Refrigerators. Refrig. Eng. 20:94-101. 1930.
22. Refrigeration Study. Unpublished data. Home Ec. Dept., Agric. Expt. Sta., Rhode Island State College, Kingston, R. I. 1932.
23. Refrigeration Tests. Bul. 106. Electrical Testing Laboratories, New York.
24. Roe, Charles H. Electrical Refrigerators and Electrical Refrigeration. Address given at Second Home Service Conf., Chicago, Ill. Mar. 17, 1931.
25. Roe, Charles H., and Thompson, Gordon. Testing Iced Refrigerators Under Two Codes. Refrig. Eng. 21:106-117, 136. 1931.
26. Sawyer, Marion. The Science of Refrigeration. Unpublished report. Kelvinator, Inc., Detroit, Mich.
27. Schuchart, Bertha. Energy Consumption and Air Circulation in Some Mechanical Refrigerators. Unpublished thesis. Iowa State College Library, Ames, Iowa. 1932.
28. Stanley, Louise. Refrigeration. Ladies' Home Jour. Leaflet 200. Curtis Publishing Co., Philadelphia, Pa. 1929.
29. Stevenson, A. R., and Boyer, H. L. Transient Flow of Heat through Insulation. Refrig. Eng. 20:23. 1930.
30. Ward, D. A. Household Refrigerators. Ice and Refrigeration 72:286. 1927.

ILLUSTRATIONS: Fig. 74, Duluth Refrigerator Corp.; 77, Electrolux Refrigerator Sales, Inc.; 78, Perfection Stove Co.

CHAPTER XII

LAUNDRY PROCEDURE

It seems a long way from the days when the family washing was done at the village stream to the modern equipment of the present home laundry, and yet today probably two-thirds or more of the world's housewives still wash in the primitive way, beating and rubbing clothing clean on the smooth rocks by the side of a river or pond and spreading the clothes to dry on the nearby bushes or grassy bank. However clean the clothing may be when washed by this method, it is usually far from sanitary, and when the same water is also used for drinking, spread of disease is inevitable.

First public laundries.—An epidemic of cholera in London in 1832 led to the establishment of the first public laundries where clothing might be sterilized. A few years later in the United States the rush to California in search of gold brought together a great many single men with no women to care for the washing. One far-sighted man started a laundry and built a crude type of machine which would wash a fairly large amount of clothing at one time. This machine consisted of a water-tight box, in which a wagon wheel, turned by hand, agitated the clothes. Six or seven years later it occurred to one of the workers that it might be possible to turn the wheel by power instead of by hand, the wheel was connected to a discarded donkey engine, and the first power-driven washing machine had been made.

A Pittsburgh man, H. E. Smith, was the first to invent a machine with self-reversing gears, the principle upon which all modern washers are built. Ten years later (1873) he designed an ironing machine for flat work. This equipment was used in hotel and hospital laundries. It was not until almost the close of the nineteenth century that any public laundries were established for the family wash. Thirty years later these laundries were doing an annual business valued at half a billion dollars.

Motor.—Washers and most ironers are motor driven. A motor is similar in structure to the generator (p. 39). In the generator the armature is revolved in a magnetic field by means of mechanical power, and electromotive force is built up; in the motor the armature itself is connected to a source of electricity, and the attractions

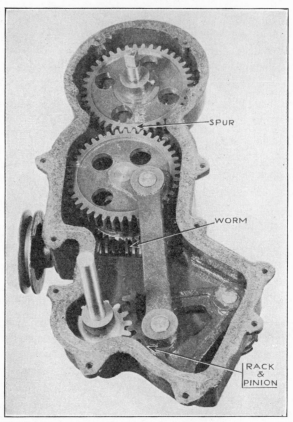

FIG. 79.—Gears transmit the energy of the motor to the mechanism of the washer.

and repulsions between the field of force set up by this current, and the magnetic field between the poles of the surrounding field magnets, cause motion. This motion is transmitted directly or by means of gears to the mechanism of the appliance.

Gears.—Gears used in washing machines are usually of four common types: the spur, rack and pinion, bevel, and worm. In spur gearing the axes of the toothed wheels are parallel. The wheels may be the same size or may vary in size. When the radius of one of the wheels is greatly increased, so that only a small portion of the toothed circumference is used, and the teeth mesh along a line which tends to become straight, the gear is the rack and pinion. A bevel gearing has intersecting axes and the pitch surfaces are cones, with a common apex at the point where the axes intersect. In the worm gear a screw rotates tangentially to a toothed wheel and in so doing imparts a continuous motion to the wheel. The axis of the worm is at right angles to the axis of the wheel. (Fig. 79.)

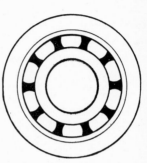

FIG. 80.—Ball bearings.

Bearings.—In changing the electrical energy of the motor into the mechanical energy of the washer there is a certain loss due to the friction of the brushes and revolving shafts and gears. To reduce this friction to a minimum, bearings are used. Depending upon the type of bearing, point, line, or surface contact is obtained. The ball bearing is formed of two concentric rings with a number of metal balls between them. (Fig. 80.) Ball bearings make point contact, since a surface can be tangent to a sphere at only one point, and point contact reduces the friction to a minimum. Roller bearings, which are in the form of cylinders, have line contact with tangential surfaces. When the shaft rotates in a bushing or sleeve there is surface contact. (Fig. 81.) Friction is greatest in this case and is minimized as far as possible by using one kind of metal for the shaft, another for the sleeve. In many washing machines the

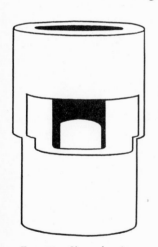

FIG. 81.—Sleeve bearing.

sleeve bearings in which the wringer shafts rest are of wood, which may be successfully lubricated with soapy water. In other cases oil is used to lubricate the bearings, but is not used on the wringer shaft because of the likelihood of damage to the clothing.

Surface tension.—Removal of soil from clothing depends upon the reduction of the surface tension of the water by soap or other cleaning agent, and the emulsification and adsorption of the soil by the soapy solution. Surface tension is the force which causes a liquid to take a form that will give the least surface area; that is, a sphere. Liquids of low surface tension form small drops and wet surfaces with which they come in contact more readily than do liquids of high surface tension. Millard found that sodium carbonate was the most effective alkali in reducing the surface tension of soap solutions and that soap-soda solutions have the lowest surface tension of any liquids. Although it is true that the detergent value of a solution is not wholly dependent upon the surface tension, nevertheless, according to several investigators, there seems to be a close relationship between surface tension and removal of soil.

Adsorption.—Adsorption is the adhesion of the soil particles to the surface of the soap bubbles. Millard believes that "The chief function of soap is that of an emulsifying agent for the greasy material which surrounds the dirt, holding it in suspension until it is removed by the mechanical agitation of the solution."[1]

In this discussion of surface tension both water and soap are important factors, and they are the factors upon which the efficiency of the washing process depends. Hot water is a prerequisite, not alone for cleaning action, but also for sterilization. A discussion of hot water heaters is given in the chapter on plumbing (p. 283).

Hard water.—The ease of the washing operation depends not only upon the temperature of the water but also upon its softness. Temporary hardness may be removed by boiling the water, but permanent hardness must be treated in some other way. Soap itself is a water softener, and some soaps contain added ingredients such as borax, soda ash (Na_2CO_3), or sodium silicates to aid in softening the water. Extremely hard water requires so much soap that the operation is expensive, and delicate fabrics are injured by the use of any but neutral soaps. Soap reacts with the minerals in hard water to form a scum which tends to deposit in the fibers of the cloth and is rinsed out with difficulty, so that in time the clothes develop a gray or streaked appearance.

[1] Millard, E. B. Surface Tension of Alkaline Soap Solutions. p. 810.

The following table,[2] based on a U. S. Geological Survey of 300 cities, shows the distribution of areas of varying degrees of hard water over the country:

0 TO 3 DEGREES (GRAINS PER U. S. GALLON) "SOFT"

Requires 0.12 to 1.75 ounces of neutral soap to soften 16 gallons of water.

Maine, Vermont, New Hampshire, Massachusetts, Connecticut, Rhode Island, New York, New Jersey, Delaware, Maryland, Virginia, North Carolina, South Carolina, Georgia, Alabama, Mississippi, Louisiana, Washington, Oregon.

3 TO 6 DEGREES ("MODERATELY HARD")

Requires 1.75 to 3.0 ounces of neutral soap to soften 16 gallons of water.

Pennsylvania, West Virginia, Kentucky, Tennessee, Montana, Idaho, Nevada.

6 TO 12 DEGREES ("HARD")

Requires 3.0 to 5.3 ounces of neutral soap to soften 16 gallons of water.

Ohio, Michigan, Wisconsin, Chicago, Ill., Minnesota, Missouri, Arkansas, North Dakota, Texas, Wyoming, Utah, Colorado, New Mexico, California.

12 TO 30 DEGREES ("VERY HARD")

Requires 5.3 to 11.4 ounces of neutral soap to soften 16 gallons of water.

Florida, Indiana, Illinois (except Chicago), Iowa, South Dakota, Nebraska, Kansas, Oklahoma, Arizona.

Soap.—Soaps may be purchased in the form of flakes, chips, beads, and powders, as well as in cakes. Chips are similar in form to flakes but thicker. Both flakes and chips are made by running liquid soap over cooling rolls and scraping off the thin hard layers. Flakes are usually of the same composition as pure neutral cake soap; chips frequently contain builders which tend to increase the detergency of the soap. Chips or flakes may be pulverized to form powdered soap. A careful distinction should be drawn between powdered soaps and soap powders, the latter usually containing washing soda or silicates.

Rosin is used in soap to increase the lathering properties. It unites with a part of the alkali. Satisfactory laundry soaps do not have more than about 20 per cent of rosin in the form of rosin soap and not more than 0.02 per cent of free alkali (calculated as NaOH). Larger proportions of rosin tend to make the soap sticky. Rosin

[2] From The Problem of Hard Water. Bul. 9. The Easy Washing Machine Corp.

soaps are yellow in color and are purchased in bar form. White bar laundry soaps often contain silicates as builders. Hard water soaps have from 20 to 30 per cent of cocoanut oil and usually some sodium silicate or carbonate.

As has been noted, the kind of soap selected is determined in part by the hardness of the water. Another essential factor in the choice of a soap is the fabric to be laundered. In general, that soap should be chosen which will restore the fabric to its original state without impairing its appearance, texture, or color.

Effect of washing on fibers.—Fibers of the fabrics commonly laundered are of vegetable or animal origin, and more recently, of synthetic make. Cotton and linen are plant fibers; silk and wool, animal fibers. Vegetable fibers are injured by the strong acids sometimes used in bleaches. Wool and silk are easily damaged by strong alkalies; the fibers are weakened and turn yellow. Too hot water has a similar effect, causing silk to yellow and streak and wool to shrink and mat. Wool contains a natural oil, linolin. When this is neutralized by alkaline soap or dissolved out by too hot water the fibers become hard and brittle and tend to shrivel. Wool fibers are also very sensitive to scrubbing or any hard rubbing; the tiny barbs on the fibers interlock and give a firm felted effect instead of the desired fluffiness. Loosely woven woolens should be washed as rapidly and as gently as possible in water of moderate temperature and should be rinsed in water of the same temperature as the wash water.

White cottons and linens are not damaged by hot water and can stand considerable rubbing, but colored materials tend to fade. Inexpensive fabrics often have the surface finished with starch or other dressings to give an appearance of firm weaving and good body. During washing such finishes are removed, leaving a flimsy material.

Synthetic fibers are of several different kinds depending on the method of manufacture. Viscose and acetate fibers are most widely used, the acetate fabrics being best known under the names "Celanese," "Acele," etc. They are made from cotton or wood pulp, which is treated chemically to form a solution. The solution is forced through tiny holes under pressure to form filaments, and these filaments are used like silk filaments. All rayons lose a large percentage of their strength when wet and must be handled with care during the washing process. Acetate is easily melted and cannot be ironed with a hot iron. Silk garments should be washed frequently, in fact after each wearing is a good rule to follow, for silk absorbs perspiration which weakens the fibers, causing them to disintegrate.

Soil.—Soil from mud and dust is inorganic in nature. Organic soil consists of food spots and stains, body excretions of oil or waste epithelial cells, and bacteria. The character of the washing varies with the kind of soil; soil on overalls differs from soil on a tablecloth, and that in turn from dirt on a neck-band.

It is apparent, therefore, that no one type of treatment is equally efficacious in all cases. In some instances pure neutral soaps must be used; in others, a laundry soap to which supplementary detergents have been added is preferable. Rhodes and Brainard found that a concentration of soap in the wash solution of approximately 0.25 per cent gave optimum results; in higher concentrations there was little increase in cleaning efficiency. But whatever the problem with regard to soap and water, the washing itself is completed most efficiently and with the smallest expenditure of time and energy if a mechanically operated washing machine is used.

WASHING MACHINES

Types.—In 1931 there were about seventy companies in the United States manufacturing washing machines, and each company made from two to seven different models. All of these models, however, may be classified into about five different types: the dolly, cylinder, oscillator, vacuum cup, and gyrator. (Fig. 82.) In small washers clothes are sometimes washed by air pressure which forces the water through the fabric. The present trend is toward the gyrator type, although gyrator washers may differ very greatly from one another.

The dolly resembles an old fashioned three-legged stool and may float at the top of a central shaft, around which it oscillates, or it may be attached to the cover. Clothing is caught on the projections of the dolly and is pulled back and forth through the water. In some dolly washers, a single switch controls the dolly mechanism and the wringer, and the dolly must, therefore, be removed for convenience and safety in wringing.

The cylinder type has a perforated cylinder of wood or of metal which revolves several times (commonly 4 to 7) in one direction, and then in the reverse direction, inside of an outer tub which holds the water. The clothes are carried through the water. Three or four projections or baffles on the inside of the tub catch the clothes, lift them from the water, and permit them to drop back into the water again. At the same time the wash water is forced in and out of the perforations, causing considerable agitation.

In the oscillator type there is a tub or tank within an outer shell. The tub revolves through part of a revolution and then reverses.

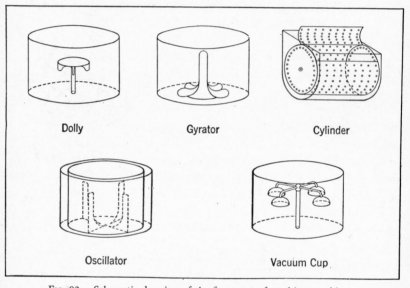

Fig. 82.—Schematic drawing of the five types of washing machines.

Blades project from the side of the tub and help to hold the clothes in position. Another type is in the form of an old-fashioned cradle which rocks back and forth between the supporting frames. In either type the water is agitated and forced through the clothes.

The vacuum cup model has inverted hemispherical cups attached to the top of a central shaft. The cup mechanism moves around the shaft and at the same time up and down in the tub, forcing the water through the clothes in an action similar to that obtained with the hand "stomper."

The gyrator, often called the agitator type, resembles an inverted dolly and fits over a central shaft. The blades or vanes vary in number and shape; some gyrators have short thick blades extending horizontally, others are high and thin. One model has very broad blades; another, blades of two different sizes. No experimental work as yet reported has proved that one type is superior to another.

Small portable washers for use in the sink or bathtub where space is limited and the home washing small in amount may be of the oscillator or vacuum cup type, or they may have a motor-driven turbine which agitates both water and clothes by air suction. (Fig. 83.) One small washer has no motor; the hot water is forced, by the pressure of the steam generated in boiling, up through a central hollow cylinder and out through perforations at the top, from where it sprays down over the clothes. The action is mild but it sterilizes satisfactorily.

Between the larger washers and the portables is a medium-sized machine, suitable for apartments or the laundry of a small family. The height is usually adjustable; by means of a crank the tub may be raised for washing and lowered for storage. When not in use the wringer may be dropped at the side. The wringer is turned by hand but with a minimum of effort; the gyrator is operated by electricity.

FIG. 83.—Clothes are washed by air pressure in this portable machine.

In place of a separate washing machine it is possible to launder the clothes mechanically in any type of tub by the use of suction cups operated by a motor on a movable base.

Optimum time of washing.—Investigations carried on in the equipment laboratory would seem to indicate that all types of washing machines have approximately the same cleaning ability. For each machine, however, there is an optimum washing time, depending somewhat upon the nature of the soil. This optimum washing period varies for different models of the same type; not all gyrators require the same running period. Tests carried on at the University of Nebraska and at Cornell University gave similar results. If the washing is continued beyond the optimum time the clothes become less clean rather than more so; with the continued agitation the dirt is apparently broken up into very fine particles which are absorbed by the fibers of the cloth. As a result the clothes acquire a grayish tinge.

If this explanation is correct, it is a strong argument against using the same water for portion after portion of the family wash. Frequent changes of wash water will give more satisfactory results.

FIG. 84.—Washing machine with wringer.

Wringers.—After the washing process is completed the water may be extracted by any of several different methods. The wringer is the most commonly used extractor. (Fig. 84.) Until within the last few years the rolls were of hard rubber, but now rolls are made of soft or semi-soft rubber, or the wringer may have one hard and one soft roll. Tests on wringers with these different kinds of rubber rolls have shown that a maximum extraction of water of about 32 per cent occurs with all types of rolls regardless of the pressure, so that although it is not possible to obtain the degree of compression with soft rubber rolls that is obtainable with hard rubber rolls, apparently a high degree of compression is not necessary. With soft or semi-soft rolls there is a larger area of contact between the rolls. Soft rubber rolls cause less injury to the clothing; buttons are not removed, for the soft rubber adapts itself to irregularities in the fabric; creasing is less evident, and ironing, therefore, easier. It is true that clothing seems to cling more readily to the soft rubber. The semi-soft rolls have the good qualities of both soft and hard rubber; hard rubber stands up under the strain of use, and soft conforms to the variations in thickness of material being wrung.

Controls.—The wringer controls should be within easy reach from any position at the machine. A centrally located safety release, easily manipulated and instantaneous in action, is essential. The wringer usually swings into and locks in at least four different positions. The direction of the rotation of the rolls and of the drainboard is reversible. The drainboard should be of rust-resisting material, and have rounded corners to prevent the catching or snagging of clothing; it should be wide enough to direct the passage of the clothes, but not so wide as to interfere with them. It is an advantage to have the tension on the rolls automatically controlled.

Centrifugal dryers.—Some machines are made with a centrifugal dryer instead of a wringer. (Fig. 85.) The dryer may be a removable basket attached to the central shaft within the washer tub, or it may occupy a separate tank beside the tub. In some models the dryer is a perforated basket or cylinder, in others a smooth-surfaced conical container with the openings only around the top rim. The speed of revolution varies in different makes; if the number of revolutions per minute is high, the cover to the dryer chamber must be fitted with a locking device to prevent its opening during the whirling process.

The dryer may be whirling while a second tub of clothes is being washed, and in some models rinsing may be done in the centrifugal basket. The dryer does not remove buttons, and is a satisfactory way to extract the water from filled comforters, pillows, and blankets, leaving a soft, fluffy product. If desired, the whirling may be continued until a large percentage of the water is removed. On the other hand the clothing must be entirely lifted from the tub into the basket, and if the material is very bulky and heavy, this is difficult; the wringer helps in the lifting of the material. Clothes must be

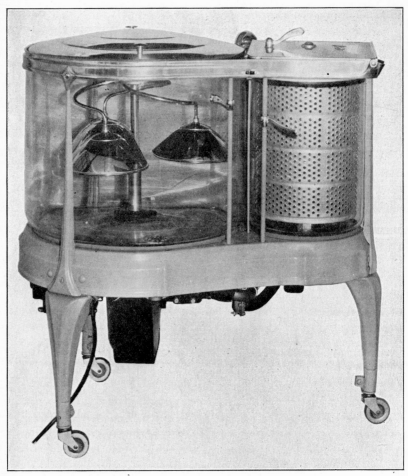

FIG. 85.—One type of centrifugal dryer.

packed evenly into the basket, or considerable vibration occurs. There is no danger of catching the fingers in the dryer.

Pressure extractor.—A recent addition to types of water extractors is the air-pressure extractor. A very recent model has a rubber-lined compartment beside the tub. After clothes have been placed in the compartment, air is pumped into the space between the rubber lining and the walls of the well, forcing the clothes upward against the cover and extracting the water. This method eliminates vibration and noise.

Materials used for washing machines.—Washing machines range in price from about $58 to $165, the price depending somewhat upon the materials used and the workmanship. The materials commonly used in the construction of the tub are aluminum, steel or galvanized iron, nickeled copper, Monel metal, and porcelain enamel. A study made at the University of Nebraska, on the relation of heat retention to kind of material and finish, showed little difference in cooling rate. "In no case was the cooling rate high enough to be of significance in the selection of a washing machine."[3]

The material selected should be light in weight, durable, rust-resisting, non-warping, resistant to alkalies, easy to clean, and should have a smooth hard finish.

Aluminum is light in weight and durable, but discolors with strong soaps and alkaline water-softeners used in hard water regions. It is, therefore, difficult to keep clean. Galvanized iron is inexpensive but heavy, and also difficult to clean where hard water is used. Many of the first mechanical washers were made of galvanized iron, and were usually bulky and clumsy to operate and move.

Nickeled copper is very strong and durable, is little affected by alkalies, and is fairly easy to clean. Monel metal, found in some of the more expensive models, is durable, rust-proof, easy to clean, and its appearance improves with use.

Porcelain enamel on steel is used frequently for the newer moderately priced washers. It is attractive in appearance, rust-resistant, and very easy to clean, but may chip unless handled with care. Exposed screw heads inside the tub are usually objectionable, because of their tendency to rust or to catch the fabric.

Protective devices.—Washing machines may be driven by hand power, gas engine, water power, or electric motor. The motor on household washers is usually of ¼ or 1/6 horsepower and is connected to the mechanism of the washer by shaft or belt; the belt is somewhat less durable, but is more easily and less expensively replaced than a broken shaft. All moving parts should be enclosed, as

[3] Snyder, E. B., and Brunig, M. P. A Study of Washing Machines. p. 4.

a protection to children and to the worker herself. The motor is placed beneath the tub to shield it from water, and is either grounded or insulated from the metal framework of the machine. The electric cord is rubber-covered. A switch independent of the gear switch is a convenience in starting the motor; such a switch should automatically protect from overloading. The washer should be well braced to prevent excessive vibration.

Gas attachment.—Some washing machines have a gas burner beneath the machine tub to heat the water and to maintain the desired temperature during the washing process. The burner is covered in such a way that the machine is protected and contact with the flame is not possible.

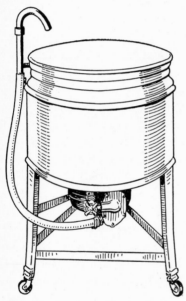

FIG. 86.—Washer with electric pump for emptying.

Emptying the tub.—The t u b is usually so constructed that it will drain quickly and completely when a good sized drain pipe is provided. A threaded drain valve permits the tub to be connected to a piece of flexible hose for emptying, but if the washing machine can stand in a permanent position, it may be connected to the sewer pipe. When no floor drain is available the tub may be emptied by an ejector, a two-armed hose, one arm of which is connected to a faucet so that it works by suction, but this method is not successful unless there is good water pressure. Some washers have an electric pump attachment, run by the motor, which empties the tub mechanically. (Fig. 86.)

Filling the tub.—The tub should also be filled with the least possible expenditure of energy by using a hose attached to the faucet. A mixing hose fastened to both hot and cold water faucets is a convenience. A pail of water weighs from 15 to 20 pounds, and since it takes from 6 to 8 pails to fill a tub, much energy is unnecessarily expended if the tub is filled by means of pails.

Legs, lid, controls.—A washing machine of adjustable height is recommended. The legs should be fitted with casters so that the machine may be easily moved from place to place. The lid is attached in some models, in others, separate. An attached lid is never misplaced, and when turned back may be used as a table top. All controls should be centrally located, at a convenient height to make stooping unnecessary, and should be easy to grasp and manipulate with wet hands. A compact machine, light in weight, but rigid in construction, is desirable.

Washing process.—Before starting the washing process clothes are sorted according to fabric, color, and amount of soil. Stains are removed (see pp. 210-212 on methods of removing some common stains) and, if possible, rents and tears mended. The washer is filled to the water line with warm water (120°-125°F.) if the clothes have not been soaked, and if previously soaked, with somewhat hotter water (150°-160°F.). Soaking is preferred by some homemakers, because it loosens and dissolves the dirt, opens the meshes of the fabrics, and permits the use of hotter wash water. Other housewives wish to avoid the extra labor of soaking and use a second suds instead.

In either case before putting in the clothes the soap shavings or chips are added to the water and the washer operated until a good strong suds is obtained. If the water is hard and the clothes are put into the tub before the soap is added, the hard water curd will form inside the meshes of the cloth instead of on the surface. Since such curds are insoluble, they are removed with difficulty, and tend to harm both texture and color.

The clothes are added gradually so long as free water action is obtained. A greater quantity of small pieces may be added than of larger ones. Overloading hinders agitation and lessens the proportion of water. Tests show that underloading also is not desirable. "A possible explanation is that underloading provides too little friction between clothes, and between water and clothes."[4]

The length of the washing period will depend in part upon the nature and amount of soil. Slightly soiled clothing requires only a short washing period. Silks and woolens should be washed more rapidly than cottons. Loosely woven materials wash more quickly

[4] Snyder, E. B., and Brunig, M. P. A Study of Washing Machines. p. 32.

than those of fine close weaves. Some gyrator washers have a variable speed control; fine fabrics may be agitated at the low speed. In machines of one speed, the agitator usually rotates at a medium rate, and the washing period is shortened or lengthened as required.

At the end of the washing period the wash water is removed with the type of extractor provided on the machine and the clothes are rinsed. If the clothes have been washed in luke-warm water the first rinse is of hotter water (140°F.), to aid in the removal of soap and any remaining soil held in the meshes of the clothes. Some investigators advise against too high temperature for the rinse water. On the other hand too low a temperature, less than 100°F., has been found to cause the yarns of the cloth to shrink, holding in the soap and soil. A machine rinse is about twice as effective as a rinse by hand. The hot rinse may be followed by a cold rinse, and bluing, if desired, except in the case of silks and woolens, where moderately warm water is used for the washing process and all rinses.

Care of machine.—When the washing is finished, the tub should be drained immediately, the cylinder, vacuum cups, or agitator rinsed, removed, and wiped clean and dry, and the tub rinsed and dried before the units are replaced. Remove any lint from the drain pipe. Do not scour the tub with harsh abrasives to remove any deposit from hard water; such scouring will tend to roughen the finish of the surface and make it more difficult to keep in condition. A cloth dipped in vinegar water will often remove a water coating. Wipe the wringer rolls with a damp cloth and release the pressure.

Purchase a washing machine from a reliable manufacturer, one who inspects and tests the materials used in the various machining processes, who uses hardened steel for shafts and gears and matches the gears to assure smooth running. Then carefully follow directions for oil, both as to kind of oil and frequency of use. Different types of motors require different kinds of care, but some care is essential. Upon intelligent use and care depends to a large extent the life of the machine.

Stains.—Most common stains are easily removed if treated promptly. Stains usually penetrate more deeply into the fibers of the cloth than ordinary soil, which clings to the surface, but the majority of stains may be removed by the application of water of one temperature or another, and water should be tried first.

Cold soapy water and gentle rubbing between the fingers will remove many grease stains. Tar and heavy oils may be dissolved by applying lard, rubbing it well into the fibers of the cloth, and then removing it with cold soapy water. Finally wash the material in warm soap suds. If hot water is used before the grease is removed the stain is set in the cloth, and is removed with great difficulty. Fabrics which cannot be washed may be treated with carbon tetrachloride.

Fruit and vegetable stains of a red or purple color, and tea and coffee stains, are removed by pouring hot water through the fabric. Peach stains if treated when fresh will disappear in a cold water bath, but if overlooked will be "set" by hot water.

Mildew is a fungus which grows on clothing allowed to lie around in a damp condition during the warm summer months. In the early stages it may be removed in cold water. More persistent growths are treated with Javelle water (a tablespoon of Javelle water to one quart of warm water), if the material is white. Javelle will bleach colored goods. Careful rinsing is essential, otherwise Javelle water weakens the fibers.

Blood stains soak out in cold water. Many fresh ink spots will also disappear in cold water. Ink made from iron compounds and iron stains may be removed by a solution of oxalic acid. After the use of oxalic acid, use a weak solution of household ammonia to neutralize the acid, and then rinse carefully. Grass stains may be removed by warm soapy water, or if that is unsuccessful, use denatured alcohol.

When stains are caused by chewing gum or colored candles, remove any particles adhering to the fabric, moisten with turpentine, and wash in warm soap suds. When the garment is non-washable, sponge with gasoline. Use gasoline preferably out-of-doors, since it is highly inflammable.

Sugar and sirup stains disappear in warm water. Water spots may often be removed by rubbing the spot with another piece of the same material. If this method is not efficacious, the garment will have to be completely sponged. Before making up silk goods, they should be tested for dressing which will cause water spotting. To prevent this spotting in wools, dressed wool materials should be sponged and shrunk before they are made into garments.

Try to fit the method of stain removal to the type of stain and the kind of fabric. Use a clean soft cloth for sponging. Label all bottles and store them out of the reach of children. Use inflammable solvents out-of-doors, and avoid excessive friction. Severe burns have resulted from the hard rubbing of materials soaked in gasoline.

Dryers.—Portable dryers may be used in private homes with great convenience. They eliminate the need of yard space for clothes, and are independent of weather conditions. There are two types, the rack and cabinet types, the cabinet type being used more widely in the average-sized home. It has a drying rod capacity of about 60 feet. The rods are usually at least ¾ of an inch in diameter, of rust-resistant material, and strong enough to carry a weight of 25 pounds at the center of the rod.

The heating may be direct, where the burner is in the drying chamber, or indirect, where there are two separate compartments. When the burner is in the drying compartment a protective screen is placed above the burner to prevent clothing from coming in contact with the flame. This screen must be at least 3 inches above the heating unit. A thermostat on the burner maintains the temperature between 200°F. and 250°F. since clothes will scorch at 300°F. Some dryers have a control by which the gas is shut off when the clothes are dry. The dryer should be connected to a flue.

IRONS AND IRONERS

Probably our long-ago ancestors were so glad to have clean clothes that wrinkles passed unnoticed. A similar feeling animates the present-day housewife when it is a choice between a few wrinkles and several hours of hard work over the ironing board. The new electrically and gas heated irons and especially the motor-driven ironer have greatly reduced the time and energy required.

The earliest irons were undoubtedly stones. The ancient Romans used wooden mallets, but even at a very early date devised a kind of press in which the clothing was smoothed beneath a weighted cover. Later the cover was screwed down to increase the pressure.

In Scotland in the tenth century a linen smoother of black glass was used. It was brought to the country by the Vikings and resembled a large inverted mushroom. A hundred years later heated irons were used in France, the heat being produced by charcoal or a small hot iron bar placed on a shelf inside the iron.

Later still the wooden ironer came into use, a roller which was moved back and forth across a flat board. These hand ironers were often beautifully carved by the young men who presented them to their brides for wedding gifts. Following this type came the ironer with two rolls, manipulated like a wringer, the immediate predecessor of the present-day ironing machine.

At the same time, the hand iron was evolving from the sad iron, in one piece or with a detachable handle, to the gas, gasoline, and electric iron. The first electric iron had a permanently attached cord and was without its shiny nickel finish or heat-resisting handle, so that a holder was needed to protect the hand. Only within the last 20 years has the convenient modern electric iron been available, and even now improvements are added from year to year.

Types of irons.—Irons vary considerably in price, depending upon the type of element, and the finish of the iron. The least expensive irons have a coiled wire element placed in the grooves of a porcelain insulating brick. These coils wear out comparatively soon under frequent heatings and coolings. The soleplate on this iron is not very thick and the iron has only a thin plating over the casting, which does not take a very high polish. The area of the soleplate is smaller than in the more expensive irons.

Mediumly priced irons have a metal ribbon element wound on mica sheets; often they carry a 3- to 5-year guarantee, but usually last longer. In the highest priced models the wire element is embedded in the insulating material and may carry a lifetime guarantee. (Fig. 87.) The casting of the soleplate is as far as possible without flaw, giving a smooth, flat surface, and the iron is heavily plated and highly polished.

Characteristics of a good iron.—A good iron has tapering sides with beveled edges and a narrow point to get around buttons and into gathers. Some irons have a special indentation on the side of the sole for ironing under button edges. The handle should be of a size and shape which is comfortable for the hand, of heat-resistant material, and far enough away from the body of the iron to eliminate any danger of burns. Occasionally a thumb rest is attached to the handle. If the iron is well balanced the point will not dig into the material. Until recently the standard home iron has weighed about 6 pounds, but new 1,000 watt light-weight irons weighing only 3 or 3½ pounds have been found to be fairly efficient. When the light-weight iron is used in ironing heavy linens, the operator must exert a good deal of pressure if creases are to be entirely removed, and the time required is apparently longer than with the heavier iron.

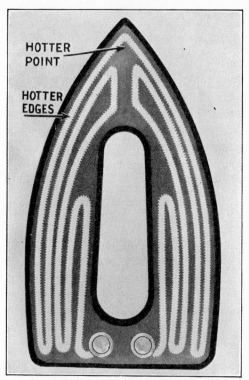

FIG. 87.—Heat element of electric iron.

Cords.—Cords used with irons must have an insulation of asbestos beneath the fabric covering. Cords are flexible and sometimes tend to kink. A wire spring attached to the plug holds the cord away from the iron, and there are attachments for the end of the board which will keep the cord away from the clothing. The latest type of cord uncoils or coils automatically as the iron is pushed back and forth. The iron and wall plugs should be of a type easily detached, without pulling on the cord.

It is preferable to attach the iron to a service outlet, since irons are commonly rated at 660 watts. The light socket is designed to carry not over 250 watts. If it is necessary to attach the iron to a light socket attach the cord to the socket first and then to the contact pins on the iron, and in disconnecting, pull the iron plug off first and then disconnect at the lamp socket. One thousand watt irons should never be attached to light sockets.

Heat control.—Irons may or may not have automatic heat control. The automatic control shuts the electricity off above a certain

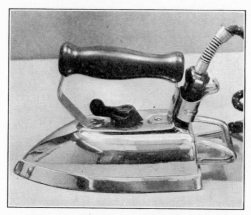

FIG. 88.—Iron with automatic control giving a range of heats.

temperature and turns it on again as the iron cools. Some automatic controls have a range of heats suitable for different types of materials. (Fig. 88.) Such a control reduces the cost of electricity by supplying only the heat needed; it reduces the fire hazard, since the iron cannot reach an excessively high temperature; and it greatly reduces the wear on the element. Overheating is very detrimental to a heating element. A difference of not more than 80°F. between the "on" and "off" of an automatic control is recommended. If the iron does not have an automatic heat control, it is an advantage to have a switch on the cord or in the iron plug, by which the heat may be turned on and off and so regulated without disconnecting. Irons should heat evenly, that is, without any noticeably cold or hot spots. The point is always somewhat hotter than the rest of the iron, the heat gradually lessening toward the heel, which is coolest.

Temperatures suitable for different fabrics.—Linens and cottons require a fairly high temperature, silk and woolen materials a comparatively low one. Viscose rayons and unweighted silks use a heat suitable for wool, but weighted silks and especially Celanese rayon require even lower temperatures. Celanese is melted with a hot iron.

Iron rest.—The iron is placed on a separate stand or has an attached heel rest. If the iron is well balanced the latter is somewhat more efficient, since it requires less energy to tip the iron onto this heel rest than to lift it to a raised stand. The iron should be kept clean, the soleplate free from rough places, stains, and rust.

Ironing board.—The hand iron is used with an ironing board. The board has also developed; at first a table top covered temporarily with a blanket and sheet, then a shaped board placed across the flat tops of two chairs or between a table and a chair (a type still in use in many homes), now often a collapsible folding board or one which folds into a shallow wall-compartment. These folding boards should have a well-supported framework to prevent swaying. The average board is about 54 inches long with one end narrow enough to permit double clothing to be slipped on and off. The height of the collapsible board is often adjustable and should be fitted to the height of the individual.

The ironing board is padded to allow a certain amount of "give" under the pressure of the iron; this increases the ease of ironing. The outer cover should be removable for washing. It may be fastened onto the board in any one of several ways: by tapes across the back of the board, by a draw-string run through a hem, or by metal catches, which fasten into the edges of the cover and hold it tightly in place.

Ironing machines.—Ironing machines or ironers, as they are frequently called, may be classified in several different ways, but the main division is into the roll and press-board types. (Fig. 89.) Each type has certain advantages, and the choice will depend upon the individual. The roll requires fewer manipulations, but the inexperienced worker usually finds it easier to iron shirts, dresses, and similar clothing on the press-board. The roll may have closed ends because of the manner in which it is attached to the framework; or one or both ends may be open with a frame attachment in the center; or one or both ends may be semi-open. Flat work is ironed satisfactorily on any type of roll; double clothing, however, is more easily handled on rolls or press-boards with open or semi-open ends, which permit the garments to be slipped over the end. The ironer is heated by electricity, by gas, either manufactured, natural, or portable, or occasionally by kerosene or gasoline. At the present time, these last two methods are seldom used. In the gas-heated ironer the shoe is stationary and roll movable.

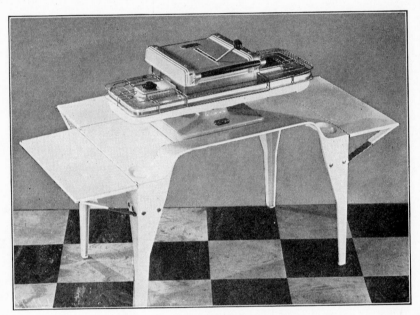

FIG. 89.—Press-board type of ironer.

The ironer roll or board corresponds to the ironing board. It is evenly padded and covered with a muslin cloth to give a smooth, resilient surface. When the padding becomes packed down the roll is too hard; the padding should, therefore, be removed occasionally and fluffed up or reversed in position, or new padding may be added. When the muslin cover is soiled, it should be laundered. The roll varies in length from 26 or 28 inches to 42 inches or more.

The ironing surface, a heated metal strip called the shoe, is made of aluminum, cast iron, steel, or a metal alloy. It should be smooth and rust-resisting. Any starch sticking to the shoe may be scraped off with a knife and the final particles gently removed with a piece of emery cloth. An occasional rubbing with paraffin when the shoe is warm will keep the surface smooth, in the same way that the iron is kept smooth.

An ironer is expected to give a smooth, dry, unscorched ironed product, with a glossy sheen or not, as desired. It should do this in the least time, with the least effort on the part of the worker, and at the smallest expense possible. Various factors contribute to this end. The pressure exerted by the shoe on the roll or board should be uniform throughout, except at the extreme ends. The pressure exerted by the average shoe is from 100 to 200 pounds. The heat should be even without any excessively hot spots; it is an advantage to have the heat thermostatically controlled. Amount of pressure and heat very definitely influences the speed of the ironing operation. The American Gas Association's approved requirements for gas-heated ironers require the shoe to reach a temperature of 200°F. above room temperature in not more than 10 minutes. The manufacturer's heat input rating in British thermal units per hour must be recorded on the name-plate. Shoes heated by electricity will probably take somewhat longer; 15 minutes is the time given by most manufacturers. Linens require a temperature between 430° and 450°F. With a few exceptions the ironer is operated by an electric motor. Ironers should never be attached to a light socket, but when of medium size, 1,000 to 1,200 watts, may be plugged into the convenience outlet on the light circuit. Larger sizes requiring more current must be heated by gas or connected to an appliance circuit fused with a 20 ampere fuse, or to a power circuit. (Fig. 90.)

The switches for the motor and for heating the shoe, and the controls on the roll, should be conveniently located where they are easily accessible. The roller controls are operated by the finger tips, by the knee, or by foot. There is also a safety release, manually operated, which is used in case of need. This manual release may be used to separate the shoe and roll if the current shuts off while the ironer is in operation, for cleaning purposes, or for the arranging of some special material for ironing, as in pressing pleats. When the shoe has been pushed away by the hand release it must be brought back into position before the mechanical controls will function.

Ironers may be purchased in various forms. Perhaps the most common type has the roll attached to a permanent framework base with the legs fitted with casters so that it may be easily moved around. Some ironers have a hinged table top which provides an additional work surface when the ironer is not in use. When the storage space

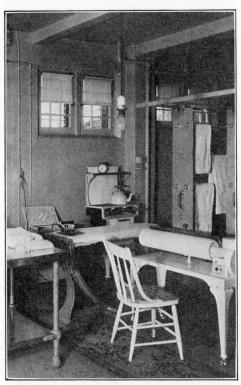

FIG. 90.—Corner of modern home laundry. Note clothes dryer and open-end roll ironer.

is limited purchase an ironer which folds on end and rolls into a corner or closet. In a similar class is the portable ironer which may be used on any table top. There is also the ironer which may be attached to the washing machine in place of the wringer. (Fig. 91.) It requires a certain amount of energy, however, to make the change.

The ironer usually has a flat table-like surface below the press-board or roll to hold the fabrics as they are ironed, so that they will not get wrinkled or soiled. This surface should extend several inches beyond the roll or board. An attached rack or table top for holding ironed pieces is a useful addition.

The shoe should be thoroughly heated before the ironing is started, but the motor need not run while the shoe is heating, unless the same control is used for both heat and motor. Some ironers have a pilot light to indicate when the current is turned on. Warm the roll by rotating it against the shoe for some minutes before ironing. It is also well to allow the roll to rotate against the shoe between pieces, to dry out any dampness from the roll and to keep it warm. The roll usually makes about 6 revolutions per minute. Most rolls

Fig. 91.—Ironer used in place of wringer. Intial cost and space are saved.

may be used for pressing by holding the roll stationary and bringing the shoe against it.

To maintain the evenly padded surface, distribute the ironing over the roll, using different parts of the roll for different pieces. This method will also utilize all the heat and prevent the scorching of the pad cover.

Flat work is easily ironed even by a beginner. More complicated clothing requires experience which is only acquired, as in all other kinds of operations, by repetition. Do not attempt to iron on the mechanically run machine articles which may be ironed more quickly and more satisfactorily with the hand iron.

All moving parts on the ironer, as on other household appliances, should be enclosed. Oil the motor according to the manufacturer's directions. If the washer or ironer is stored in a cold room in winter the packing of grease around the gears will harden, and the appliances must be allowed to stand in a warm place for the grease to become soft again before starting the motor.

Summary.

1. Motor-driven washers and ironers were first used in public institutions and laundries and only comparatively recently in the home.
2. Gears are necessary in transforming the electrical energy of the motor into the mechanical energy of the moving parts of the washing machine and ironer.
3. Friction is reduced by the use of bearings.
4. Removal of soil depends upon the emulsification and adsorption of the soil by the soapy solution.
5. Soft or softened water is prerequisite for adequate removal of soil.
6. Choice of soap is largely determined by the type of fabric to be laundered. Fabrics are made of vegetable, animal, and synthetic fibers.
7. Five types of washing machines are used: the dolly, cylinder, oscillator, vacuum cup, and gyrator type. Portable washers sometimes employ air suction.
8. Each washing machine seems to have an optimum washing period. With a longer period the dispersion of the dirt is increased, resulting in the redeposition of the soil in the fibers of the cloth.
9. Water may be extracted by the wringer, centrifuge dryer, or air pressure.
10. The washer should be built of durable, rust-resisting material, light in weight, resistant to alkalies, and easy to clean.
11. Stains should be removed before washing.
12. Hand irons may be heated on top of the range, or by gasoline, gas, or electricity. The electric iron is more easily handled and the heat is more easily controlled. Automatic heat control is an aid in using the iron with different kinds of fabrics.
13. Electric iron units are of coiled wire, flat metal ribbon on mica, or embedded elements.
14. The ironing board should be sturdily constructed with an open end over which clothing may be slipped, and with a padded surface for resiliency.
15. Ironers are of the roll or press-board type with the shoe heated by gas or by electricity.
16. Ironers with at least one end open or semi-open are to be preferred for most kinds of ironing.
17. Washers may be connected, if necessary, to a light socket, though a

convenience outlet is preferred. The ironer must be connected to a convenience outlet.

References

1. (1) A. G. A. Approval Requirements for Gas Heated Ironers. 1930. (2) A. G. A. Approval Requirements for Hot Plates and Laundry Stoves. 1929. American Gas Association, Inc., New York.
2. Cassels, Lillian. More Power to the Home: Ironing. National Electric Light Assoc., New York. n.d.
3. Griffith, Marion E. The Influence of Laundering and Exposure to Light Upon Some Wash Silks Used for Outer Garments. Ohio Agric. Expt. Sta. Bul. 506. Wooster, Ohio. 1932.
4. How to Get the Most out of a Trip through the Maytag Factory. The Maytag Company, Newton, Iowa. n.d.
5. Ittner, Martin H. Soaps. Jour. Home Ec. 17:189-194. 1925.
6. Johnson, Geo. H. (1) Textile Fabrics. Chaps. IV and XIV. Harper and Brothers, New York. 1927. (2) Laundry Standards. Laundryowners National Association of the United States and Canada. Joliet, Ill. 1930.
7. Lutes, Della T. Laundry Bulletins. Home Economics Dept., The Easy Washing Machine Corporation, Syracuse, N. Y. n.d.
8. McGowan, F. R., Smither, F. W., and Schoffstall, C. W. Performance Tests of a Liquid Laundry Soap Used with Textile Materials. Bureau of Standards Technologic Paper 273. Dept. Commerce, Washington, D. C. 1924.
9. Methods of Equipment for Home Laundering. U. S. D. A. Farmers' Bul. 1497. Washington, D. C. 1926.
10. Millard, E. B. Surface Tension of Alkaline Soap Solutions. Ind. & Eng. Chem. 15:810-811. 1923.
11. Modern Home Laundry. Home Economics Dept., The Procter and Gamble Company, Cincinnati, Ohio. 1930.
12. Pfautz, Lila W. Some Factors Involved in Water Extraction in the Home Laundry Process. Unpublished thesis. Iowa State College Library, Ames, Iowa. 1930.
13. Rhodes, F. H., and Brainard, S. W. The Detergent Action of Soap. Ind. & Eng. Chem. 21:60-68. 1929.
14. Roberts, Evelyn H. Efficiency of the Home Laundry Plant. Agric. Expt. Sta. Bul. 248. State College of Washington, Pullman, Wash. 1931.
15. Snyder, Edna B., and Brunig, Morton P. A Study of Washing Machines. Agric. Expt. Sta. Research Bul. 56. Univ. of Nebraska, Lincoln, Neb. 1931.
16. Soap. Bureau of Standards Circ. 62. Dept. Commerce, Washington, D. C. 1923. (Third edition.)
17. Sommerfeld, Esther. Correlation of Moisture Content, Free Alkalinity, and Washing Performance with Cost in Twenty Commercial Laundry Soaps. Unpublished thesis. Iowa State College Library, Ames, Iowa. 1931.
18. Spear, Abby J. Soap in Everyday Life. Colgate-Palmolive-Peet Company, Jersey City, N. J. 1929.
19. Textile Research. A Survey of Progress. Compiled by the United States Institute for Textile Research, Inc. Chaps. VII, XI, XV, XVII. Technology Press, Institute of Technology, Cambridge, Mass. 1932.

20. Vaughan, Lela M. Time of Washing as a Factor in the Cleaning Efficiencies of Electric Washing Machines of Various Types. Unpublished Thesis. Iowa State College Library, Ames, Iowa. 1931.

ILLUSTRATIONS: Figs. 79, One Minute Mfg. Co.; 82, Lela Vaughan; 83, 86, from material presented at 1931 Home Service Conf., National Electric Light Assoc.; 84, 91, Hurley Machine Co.; 85, 90, Easy Washing Machine Co.; 87, Coleman Lamp and Stove Co.; 88, Westinghouse Electric & Mfg. Co.; 89, General Electric Co.

CHAPTER XIII

ELECTRICAL CLEANING EQUIPMENT

Dust and dirt are common household annoyances, but modern electrical cleaning equipment has done much to diminish the time and labor required for their removal. A vacuum cleaner is a device designed primarily for removing dirt from floor coverings. By the use of the dusting tool attachments of a vacuum cleaner or by using the small hand cleaners, dirt and dust may be removed from radiators, moldings, ceilings and walls, mattresses, upholstery, draperies, and other household fabrics. Wood, linoleum, and composition floors may be scrubbed, waxed, and polished with electric floor machines, and, when necessary, wood floors may be refinished by the use of the attachments to the machine.

Rug structure.—In order to understand the problem of dirt removal, some slight knowledge of the structure of a rug or carpet is essential. Yarns which produce the pile are grouped together to form tufts. In many rugs the tufts are entirely separate from one another and are held in place by the interweaving of the warp and filler threads which form the body of the rug. In some rugs, however, the pile yarn is carried underneath between the tufts as a part of the rug body. Filling materials are also used with the warp to increase the thickness and firmness of the body of the carpet. The spaces between the individual tufts and between the rows of pile make pockets and furrows in which dirt easily collects and from which it is removed with difficulty.

Dirt.—Dirt as found in carpets and rugs may be divided into three kinds: surface litter; dust containing organic matter, grease, and bacteria; and grit with sharp cutting edges. Surface litter includes pieces of thread, hairs, lint, bits of paper, tiny scraps of cloth, etc. Beneath the surface, but in the upper portions of the pile, are dust and sand which have not yet settled to the base of the carpet; in the furrows and pockets is the embedded dirt which is so difficult to remove. If the dirt is gritty in nature it tends to cut into the yarn fibers under the friction of use, and destroy the pile. Grease mixed with the dust clings closely to the yarns or forms solid cakes in the crevices and pockets at the base of the tufts. (Fig. 92.) In selecting an electric cleaner, an effort should be made to choose a model which will not only remove the surface litter and upper layers of dust and dirt, but will also be effective in reaching the infiltrated

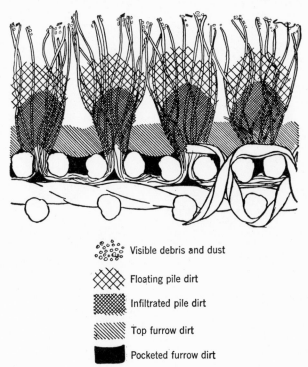

○ Visible debris and dust

Floating pile dirt

Infiltrated pile dirt

Top furrow dirt

Pocketed furrow dirt

FIG. 92.—Analysis of rug dirt.

dirt, which is deeply embedded in the pockets and furrows. No vacuum cleaner is 100 per cent efficient, but if a rug or carpet is not allowed to become too dirty, it may be kept in a comparatively clean and sanitary condition by the use of a reliable cleaner at regular intervals. (Figs. 93 and 94.)

VACUUM CLEANERS

The term vacuum cleaner is usually applied to the electric vacuum cleaner, in which the fan is driven by an electric motor, but there is also a non-electric cleaner in which the fan is driven by the friction of the wheels on the floor. The non-electric cleaner is a straight-air suction type. It has a limited use and will not be considered in the present discussion.

Types.—Electric cleaners are classified, according to the mode of cleaning action, into the straight-air suction type, the motor-driven brush type, and the motor-driven agitator type.

Parts of cleaner.—The electric cleaner has four major parts— the nozzle, fan, motor, and bag. The nozzle is the part which makes contact with the floor covering, the edges of the nozzle, known as

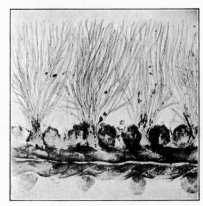

Fig. 93.—A very dirty rug may become

Fig. 94.—a well-cleaned rug, by using an efficient electric cleaner.

the nozzle lips, forming a seal with the carpet. The lips are usually smooth, but some nozzles have toothed or corrugated edges. Nozzles are of two types, those which are a part of the frame of the machine, and those mounted at the end of a hollow rigid tube which is connected to the fan chamber by rigid or flexible tubing. The construction of the nozzle determines the method of cleaning.

Straight-air suction cleaners.—Straight-air suction cleaners have a long narrow nozzle with no moving parts, so that a large portion of the cleaning action is dependent upon suction; hence, the degree of suction must be high. The removal of dirt is somewhat furthered by a slight pile agitation produced by the movement of the nozzle lips across the floor covering. (Fig. 95.)

Straight-air suction cleaners are usually classified according to the type of nozzle support which is present. The nozzle may be completely supported by wheels, partially supported by wheels, or entirely unsupported.

In order to secure the most efficient results with any cleaner the lips of the nozzle must form a seal with the floor covering. In the unsupported and partially supported types the weight and the design of the nozzle are such that a seal is supposedly maintained at all times when the cleaner is in an operating position. In the supported type the weight of the machine is carried upon wheels, usually two in front and one, or two close together, in the rear. The adjustment between the nozzle lips and the floor covering is made by a screw or cam which lowers either the rear or the front of the machine.

Most suction cleaners of this type are equipped with a brush for picking up threads, hair, and other surface litter. Brushes have one

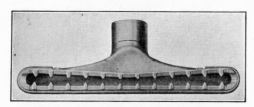

Fig. 95.—Straight-air suction nozzle.

or two rows of heavy bristle tufts and are of three kinds: detachable stationary brushes, permanently attached brushes which may be thrown in or out of operating position, and floating brushes. Regardless of kind, any brush used with the straight-air suction cleaner is mounted outside the nozzle lips.

With the exception of the floating brush, brushes are not used for ordinary cleaning. With the stationary and adjustable brushes the bristles have a tendency to dig into the pile of the carpet and as a result increase the amount of energy required to push the cleaner. The brush may also weaken the seal between carpet and nozzle. A floating brush rides upon its own weight, so that very little additional effort is required; this type is, accordingly, not detachable.

Motor-driven brush type cleaners.—The motor-driven brush type cleaner depends upon suction and a certain amount of pile agitation, sweeping, and beating for dirt removal. The beating and sweeping are produced by a motor-driven brush mounted between the lips of the nozzle. (Fig. 96.) The brush consists of a wooden or metal cylinder, upon which are mounted one or two rows of stiff bristle tufts, rotated by a belt which passes over the shaft of the motor. The suction of the cleaner raises the carpet against the lips of the nozzle, and the rotating rows of bristle tufts have a tendency to depress the carpet as they pass over it. This continuous raising and depressing produces a slight beating action which dislodges the dirt in the carpet, and the stream of air passing into the nozzle car-

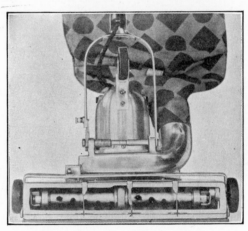

Fig. 96.—Motor-driven brush type.

ries this dislodged dirt with it through the fan chamber and into the bag.

The nozzle of the motor-driven brush type is completely supported. Until very recently the two front wheels have been placed at the ends of the nozzle in line with the revolving brush. Wheels so placed hold the carpet in contact with the floor at the ends of the nozzle and thus prevent the suction of the cleaner from lifting the carpet the full length of the nozzle. For effective beating it is necessary for the carpet to be lifted from the floor and be supported by a cushion of air. Some manufacturers secure the lifting of the carpet the entire length of the nozzle by placing the wheels directly behind the nozzle.

Since the efficiency of this cleaner depends to a large degree upon the beating action of the revolving brush the brush should always be adjusted for maximum efficiency with the bristles extending the proper length beyond the nozzle lips. After a cleaner has been used for a period of time the brush bristles become worn and the beating effectiveness decreases. If this condition is allowed to continue the brush is finally so worn that the cleaning action is dependent almost entirely upon suction. To eliminate this difficulty all cleaners with revolving brushes are provided with an adjustment by which the brush may be lowered as the bristle tufts wear down. The number of adjustments varies from 1 to 5 with different makes of cleaners; the greater the number of adjustments possible, the longer the life of the brush. In addition to the beating action, the motor-driven brush, because of its speed, also has a very effective sweeping and pile-raising action.

FIG. 97.—Motor-driven agitator type.

Motor-driven agitator type cleaners.—The motor-driven agitator type cleaner employs the same cleaning principles as does the motor-driven brush cleaner, but owing to the construction of the agitating device, beating is increased to a high degree.

The agitator consists of a metal cylinder on which are mounted two highly polished beater bars and a soft brush. The agitator is placed within the lips of the nozzle, and driven by a belt attached to the shaft of the motor. (Fig. 97.) The rigidity of the metal bars on the revolving cylinder not only produces greater beating action than is obtainable with a flexible brush but their effectiveness remains constant. The pile fibers are separated so that the suction may reach and remove the embedded dirt.

The nozzle of a cleaner of this type is completely supported by wheels. The front wheels, however, are placed back of the nozzle lips so that the suction of the cleaner is able to raise the carpet the full length of the nozzle. This placement of the wheels makes possible effective cleaning action over the entire area of the nozzle.

Because the motor-driven brush and agitator type cleaners do not wholly depend upon suction for their cleaning action, the suction of these cleaners is not as high as in the straight-air cleaner.

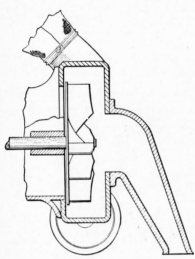

FIG. 98.—Fan and fan chamber.

Fan.—The suction of a vacuum cleaner is produced by a rotating fan, mounted on the shaft of the motor and revolving with the same speed as the motor. The fan is surrounded by what is known as the fan chamber. In most cleaners the fan chamber is slightly above and back of the nozzle and terminates in an opening to which the bag is attached. (Fig. 98.) The fan is usually built on the centrifugal principle, i.e., the rotation of the fan throws the entering air toward the periphery and produces a region of low air-pressure at the center of the fan. This low pressure area in the fan chamber is directly connected with the nozzle of the cleaner and, as a result, the air pressure in the nozzle drops below atmospheric pressure, and the difference in pressure without and within the nozzle forces the outside air through the rug or carpet into the cleaner. Because of the closely woven warp and filler threads of most carpets, only a small percentage of the air entering the nozzle passes through the body of the rug from the back; instead the larger percentage flows through the top of the pile and under the lips of the nozzle.

In one type of cleaner, in which the nozzle is separate from the frame of the machine, a turbine is used in place of a fan. In this machine the bag, turbine, and motor are housed in a hollow metal cylinder, the metal cylinder is mounted on skids, and the nozzle is attached to the cylinder by means of a flexible tube.

Motor.—Practically all household electric cleaners have a universal motor which may be used on either direct or alternating current. "Most motors are of the series type. This means that the magnetic field and armature windings are connected in series. The current from the cord comes into the field coil from one of the poles, passes through the coil and goes to one of the carbon brushes. Then it is carried into the commutator bar, through it and into and through the coils of the armature winding. Finally it reaches another commutator bar on the opposite side of the commutator and is collected by the other carbon brush. It completes the circuit by going through the second field coil and thence back to the connecting cord."[1] The motor shaft is furnished with bearings of the ball or sleeve type (p. 197).

The vacuum cleaner motor should not heat to a high temperature nor should the carbon brushes spark. Sparking may be caused by worn carbon brushes, by an irregular surface on the commutator, or by both. Sparking once started tends to roughen the commutator bars, and the rough surface to wear away the ends of the carbon brushes, so that a "vicious circle" is produced. Old carbon brushes are easily replaced with new ones, and the surface of the commutator may be smoothed in a lathe. The motor with the largest number of commutator bars usually has the longest life, because of the lower voltage difference between adjacent bars.

Bag.—The bag is attached to an opening in the back or to one side of the fan chamber. All the air passing into the bag by way of the fan chamber must be emptied through the bag fabric, which serves as a filter to remove all the dirt and dust; hence the fabric must be closely woven. The meshes of the cloth are, therefore, very small and offer resistance to the air-flow, known as "back pressure." Back pressure will counteract part of the suction at the nozzle, and is reduced as far as possible by the use of a fairly large-sized bag.

Dirt in the bag increases the back pressure and hence decreases the efficiency of the cleaner. For a cleaner to operate at its maximum efficiency the bag should be emptied and thoroughly cleaned frequently. The fact that the cleaner bag is large does not mean that it was designed to hold a large quantity of dirt but to provide a large filtering area. A few cleaners are equipped with a destructible

[1] Electric Cleaners. p. 12. The Hoover Company.

bag which may be discarded without opening, thus eliminating the unpleasantness of cleaning the bag.

Handle, switch, and cord.—In addition to the four major parts of every electric cleaner, the cleaners have a handle, a switch, and a cord.

The handle of the cleaner is usually attached to the back of the frame and is used for moving the cleaner over the rug. The handle grip should be of a size and shape to fit the hand comfortably and, for maximum convenience in the use of a cleaner, should lock in three positions, a vertical position for storing, a normal range position for general cleaning, and a horizontal position for cleaning under low furniture. The cleaner should be well balanced so that the handle may be left in any position without the cleaner overturning.

For changing the handle position, three types of controls are used, an automatic adjustment operated by the hand, a foot control, and a control which requires the tightening of a nut. The automatic type calls for the least effort on the part of the operator.

The most convenient location for the switch which controls the electric motor is on the handle near the handle grip. If the switch is of the trigger type it can be easily turned on and off with the first finger or the thumb of the hand used in operating the cleaner. When the switch is located farther down on the handle or on the frame of the machine unnecessary energy is required to reach it.

The cord of the cleaner should be of adequate length, 20 feet or more, and should be flexible and durable. Flexibility decreases kinking in the cord, and as a result increases the wearing qualities. A rubber covering aids in decreasing kinking and from the standpoint of durability, appearance, and cleanliness is preferable to a fabric covering. Regardless of the type of cord selected it should have the approval of the National Board of Fire Underwriters.

The operation and care of the electric cleaner.—Efficient and durable construction in a vacuum cleaner is essential, but the operator determines to a large degree the efficiency of operation. For maximum dirt removal the four major parts of the cleaner must operate at their highest efficiency, and the operator should thoroughly understand the use and care of these parts.

Cleaners with partially and totally supported nozzles raise the carpet off the floor in the cleaning process. Different lengths of pile make it impossible for a cleaner to be constructed with the nozzle adjusted to one proper height. The nozzle must, therefore, be adjusted by the operator in order to secure a good nozzle seal on different types of rugs. When the nozzle is adjusted too high it will not pick up the carpet, and if too low the cleaner is hard to operate. With the motor-driven brush and agitator types not only does too low an adjustment increase the energy required to operate the cleaner, but practically all cleaning action due to agitation or beating is lost. A distance of approximately ⅛ inch above the carpet pile has been found to be the proper nozzle height in these types. With the straight-air cleaner, approximately 1/16 inch distance gives the best results. In the unsupported type of nozzle, no adjustment is possible and the operator cannot affect the efficiency.

It is also important that the operator watch the wearing of the bristle tufts in the motor-driven brush type of cleaner and adjust the brush height when necessary. When all the adjustments have been used the old brush must be replaced with a new one.

The suction of the cleaner is contingent upon the correct running of fan and motor. Sharp metal objects such as hair pins, nails, coins, and pins should not be picked up with the cleaner because of the possibility of their nicking the fan. Nicks on the fan destroy its proper balance and, hence, its efficient operation. The motor should be oiled according to directions and kept as free as possible from excessive dirt.

Although nozzle suction is dependent primarily upon the fan and the seal between the lips of the nozzle and the floor covering, the effective suction is the nozzle suction minus the back pressure of the bag. If dirt is allowed to accumulate in the bag, the back pressure increases and the efficiency is diminished. The bag should be easily removable for emptying without liability of spilling dirt, and should be emptied and cleaned with a minimum of effort.

Select a cleaner which may be run into corners, up close to walls, and under the ordinary low furniture. The attachments should be easily and quickly connected and removed.

Tests conducted at the Hoover Testing Laboratory indicate that approximately 1¾ feet per second is the best rate of speed for operation. Experiments on energy costs show an actual waste of energy if a machine is operated faster than 2 feet per second. The cleaning time required depends upon the type of cleaner and the size and condition of the rug. Time studies seem to indicate that when an efficient cleaner is used regularly, approximately 10 minutes per week is adequate for a 9 by 12 foot rug.

Small hand cleaner.—It is also possible to purchase miniature vacuum cleaners known as hand cleaners. Hand cleaners are of two types, straight-air and motor-driven brush. These cleaners usually weigh from 3 to 6 pounds, have a handle for ease in manipulation, and are used for cleaning automobiles, upholstered furniture, and other cleaning for which it is inconvenient to use the large cleaner.

Dusting tools.—Practically all electric cleaners are equipped with dusting tools. These usually consist of a flexible hose fitted with extension tubes; a flat nozzle used in suctioning dust from the tufts of upholstery, in aerating pillows, and in reaching into crevices as in radiators; brushes for cleaning draperies, high moldings, under low built furniture, and for most of the common dusting tasks. The structure of the brush to be used on the hose attachment is most important. It should be constructed in such a way that the point of maximum air-flow occurs near the tips of the bristles. If this is not true the air passes through the brush at the base of the bristles and the suction does not function at the point desired. This type of construction is usually obtained by having a narrow rubber band mounted inside the rows of bristle tufts. This band extends for a short distance beyond the nozzle lips.

In addition to the standard attachments, some cleaners are equipped with a spray for spraying light liquids, a hair dryer, a disinfecting attachment, and a floor polisher.

ELECTRIC FLOOR MACHINES

Instead of a carpet entirely covering a floor, the present-day practice is to use rugs of various sizes and leave a larger or smaller portion of the floor bare, or covered with linoleum. Wax has proved an excellent preservative for wood and linoleum, increasing the wearing qualities and adding to the appearance.

The electric floor machine used for waxing and polishing is similar to the vacuum cleaner. A $1/4$ or $1/3$ horsepower motor is connected to a revolving brush by a belt or a system of gears, a handle attached to the frame guides the machine, a cord makes connection with the convenience outlet, and a switch turns on and off the current. The cord is usually 40 feet in length. (Fig. 99.)

FIG. 99.—Floor machine—with various attachments it may be used for scrubbing, polishing or refinishing.

Brushes.—Some floor machines have only one brush, others have two. The brushes rotate vertically on a horizontal shaft, or horizontally around a vertical pivot. (Fig. 100.) Brushes are made of different kinds of fibers depending upon the use to which they are to be put. Stiff fibered Palmetto brushes are used for scrubbing floors and linoleum with water and scouring powder; the softer Tampico brushes for polishing. Wax may be applied to the floor by another brush attachment, by a special wax mop, or by hand with a cloth.

Preparatory to refinishing a floor it is often necessary to remove accumulations of dirt, or old varnish and paint, with the aid of a steel wire brush. The wire brush is used with a pad of steel wool at least ½ inch thick. After the removal of the varnish and dirt, the floor may be smoothed with a sandpaper disc before applying the new coat of paint, varnish, or shellac.

The Tampico brushes usually give a satisfactory polish, but if a higher luster is desired, it may be obtained with the polishing pad. By these processes the wax is thoroughly worked into the wood and any excess wax is absorbed by the brush, so that the danger of slipping is decreased or entirely eliminated. Wax should be allowed

FIG. 100.—Easily assembled two-brush floor machine.

to dry on the floor for a half hour before polishing. Never attempt to polish wet wax. It is not necessary for the operator to bear down on the handle, as the weight on the brushes is sufficient to accomplish the work. The machine requires only guidance.

Care of machine.—The floor machine should be cleaned after using. Dust and surplus wax are easily wiped from the frame when it is warm. Scrubbing brushes may be cleaned in ammonia water, wax-encrusted brushes with turpentine. Then wipe the brushes until they are dry. Oil the machine at regular intervals, carefully following the directions of the manufacturer.

Summary.

1. Carpet dirt consists of surface litter, of dust, containing organic matter, grease, and bacteria, and of grit.
2. Vacuum cleaners are classified into three types; straight-air suction, motor-driven brush, and motor-driven agitator.
3. Straight-air cleaners have a long narrow nozzle free from moving

parts. The motor-driven brush type has a rotating brush mounted between the lips of the nozzle. The agitator type cleaner has a motor-driven agitator within the nozzle.

4. For maximum dirt removal the nozzle, fan, motor, and bag must operate efficiently. The nozzle lips should form a seal with the carpet. The rotation of the fan produces the suction. The bag filters the air and must be kept clean to reduce back pressure to a minimum.

5. Small hand cleaners and dusting tool attachments are used for various kinds of dust removal.

6. The electric floor machine is used for waxing and polishing floors of wood, linoleum, and composition materials.

References

1. Carpets and Rugs. Home Economics Bul. 1. The Hoover Co., North Canton, Ohio. n.d.

2. Dahl, Jean. How Best to Clean Carpets, Rugs and Composition Floor Coverings. Hotel Management 17:549-554. 1930.

3. Electric Cleaners. Home Economics Bul. 2. The Hoover Co., North Canton, Ohio. n.d.

4. Faraday, Cornelia B. European and American Carpets and Rugs. Dean-Hicks Co., Grand Rapids, Mich. 1929.

5. Instructions. The Kent Co., Inc., Rome, N. Y. n.d.

6. MacLeod, Sarah J. Housecleaning Made Easier. Farmers' Bul. 1180. U. S. Dept. Agriculture, Washington, D. C. 1926. (Revised.)

7. Operating Instructions. Finnell System, Inc., Elkhart, Ind. n.d.

ILLUSTRATIONS: Figs. 92, 93, 94, 96, 97, Hoover Co.; 95, Landers, Frary and Clark; 99, The Kent Co., Inc.; 100, Finnell System, Inc.

CHAPTER XIV

HOME LIGHTING

Mere lighting of the home is not enough. Comfortable seeing is what counts. To our prehistoric ancestors, any light, however inadequate, which kept back the boundaries of obvious darkness and offered even partial protection from the terrifying dangers lurking in the shadows, was welcome. Today light must do more than protect. Adequate illumination means light so placed and shaded that it is sufficient for carrying on any occupation after dark, without strain upon eyes or nerves. It means making the house a pleasant place where the family and friends may find rest and good cheer. Soft light is often desirable but should not be confused with insufficient light.

History.—Until the last century the improvement in artificial light was so slow as to be scarcely noticeable. It is not possible to know the origin of the first fire. According to legend, Prometheus stole a coal from the Olympic gods, and in consequence suffered a lamentable punishment. Lightning may have set the first fire, or a spark have been accidentally struck from two rocks or two dry sticks rubbed together. Undoubtedly it was obtained in different ways in different lands. Regardless of how it was discovered it proved a boon to the early inhabitants of the earth, a source of warmth, of protection, and of light. Roy Chapman Andrews and his party found the remains of an ancient fireplace in the Valley of the Flaming Cliffs in the Gobi Desert. Here men had built their fires twenty thousand, perhaps even an hundred thousand, years ago.

Then one night someone pulled a burning stick from the fire and used it to light the way to a dark corner of the cave, and man had his first torch. Or perhaps fat from a roasting animal dripped into a hollow of the rock at the edge of the fire, a dry piece of moss or a bit of rag acted as a wick, and the possibility of a saucer lamp was suggested. Lamps of this type were at first of stone or clay and crude in workmanship, but in the Greek and Roman eras the saucer lamps used by wealthy families were made of metal and often beautifully decorated with carvings of animals and flowers. Until within the last twenty years the mosques of Constantinople were illuminated by tiny, lighted wicks floating in cups of olive oil.

The use of rush torches, fagots saturated with fat, and grease lamps, has continued in some parts of the world down to the present time. Primitive people in Alaska burn fish stuck on a stick. Less than a hundred years ago street lighting was almost unknown, people as a rule remaining in their homes after nightfall. If one ventured forth, he carried a lantern or was accompanied by a link-boy with his rush torch.

Candles were first used extensively in the twelfth century, though they must have been known before this time for there are occasional references to candles in earlier literature. The use of candles continued for hundreds of years. Even today candle-lighted dining tables have a charm all their own, but present-day man would regret to have to depend upon them entirely for artificial light. Candles are inexpensive and easy to handle, and are often carried on camping trips, but care must be taken to avoid fires, and the electric flash light is usually preferred.

About 1775, Argand, a French chemist, invented a burner with a central air-draft, which gave a round hollow flame, but this lamp burned animal or vegetable oil. Not until after the discovery of oil in Pennsylvania in the middle of the nineteenth century was kerosene commonly used. Gas was used in England somewhat before 1800 and in America shortly afterwards, at first for street lighting and later in private homes. Light from the fish tail burner was not very bright and tended to be flickering even when the flame was protected from drafts with a glass shade, but with the invention of the Welsbach mantle in 1885, steady light of sufficient brilliance was at last obtained. The Welsbach mantle is made by soaking cotton in salts of thorium and cerium, and burning off the cotton, which leaves a fabric of metallic oxide.

Before this time, however, men of science had been experimenting with electricity. Various electric lamps had been made but had proved impractical. The first successful lamp was demonstrated by Thomas Edison in 1879, followed, in 1882, by the first central station for generating electricity for incandescent lighting. For the first time in the long history of lighting a flame was not the source of the light. Since that time both the lamps and the generation and distribution of electricity have been greatly improved. The carbon lamp was followed in 1905 by a metallized carbon lamp, this so-called gem lamp by a tantalum lamp, and it in turn was soon succeeded by the present tungsten filament lamp. The tungsten filament gives three times as much light as the carbon filament for the same cost, and Ernest Greenwood has estimated that "the electric lamp in common use today with the improved electric service available is 700 per cent more efficient than that of 30 years ago."[1]

Physics of light.—Even in very early times the thoughtful observer must have noted that light traveled in straight lines, since it was not possible to see around a corner, but it was not known that light had velocity. Galileo made the first attempt to determine whether or not light had velocity and was unsuccessful, so that until 1676 light was thought to be instantaneous. In that year Römer, a Danish astronomer, studying the eclipses of the moons of Jupiter, found unexpected variations in the time the eclipses occurred, depending upon the position of the earth in its orbit. Römer suggested that these discrepancies might be due to the fact that light had velocity, and by determining the difference in time when the eclipses took place, calculated the velocity of light as 186,000 miles per second. Later methods used stationary and rotating mirrors to reflect light between two spots on the earth's surface. Using these types of mirrors on two mountain tops in California, Michelson, in 1924, found the velocity of light to be 186,300 miles per second.

The sense impression formed by the eye, which is known as light, does not come as a rule from a self-luminous body; the eye sees almost entirely by means of light reflected from the body. There are two theories as to the manner in which the light is transmitted. The corpuscular theory, the first one suggested, assumed that the lighted body shot off particles at high speed and in straight lines. This theory fitted in with many of the laws of reflection and refraction, but required that light travel faster in water than in air which Foucault proved to be contrary to fact. The corpuscular theory also failed to explain diffraction, polarization, interference, and the apparently constant speed of light.

[1] Greenwood, Ernest. Modern Electric Service in the American Home. p. 18.

The other theory for the propagation of light is known as the wave theory. Faraday, Maxwell, and Hertz, each building on the work of his predecessor, developed a theory of electromagnetic waves transmitted through space. These waves were refracted and reflected in the same manner that light waves were, and it was therefore concluded that light waves were probably a form of electric waves. Light waves show a transverse motion, the waves traveling in a direction perpendicular to the path of the light. Like an ocean wave, the light wave has a series of crests and troughs, which travel forward, but the medium itself is not carried along by the wave.

The theory of light propagation by waves presupposes a medium. This medium is known as ether, but just what ether is has never been definitely determined. After the discovery of electrons it was suggested that light waves were formed by oscillating electrons in the source of the light.

The modern theory of relativity, and the quantum theory advanced to explain some of the phenomena of radiation and absorption, are best explained by a modified corpuscular theory. Apparently neither method of light propagation has as yet been found to agree with all the known facts.

Terms. Measurement of light.—Just as a unit is necessary in measuring volume or distance, so a unit is essential for the measurement of light. The oldest standard light unit was a sperm candle of specified size and rate of burning. The illumination given by a horizontal beam from the standard candle was known as candle power. The present light standards are a set of incandescent lamps of known candle power kept by the U. S. Bureau of Standards in Washington. France and England have accepted the same standards so that the fundamental unit is named the "international candle."

Intensity of illumination.—It is a basic law of light that the intensity of illumination of any surface varies inversely as the square of the distance of the surface from the source of the light. This law is strictly true only when the light source is so small that it approaches a point in size. This may be written as an equation.

$$\text{Intensity of illumination} = \frac{\text{candle power of lamp}}{\text{square of distance from lamp}}$$

Foot-candle.—The surface illuminated must be at right angles to the beam of light. If the distance is given in feet, the intensity of illumination is measured in foot-candles. The illumination on any surface or the distribution of light around a source may be determined by a photometer. The foot-candle meter is a portable photometer, often used to make illumination intensity measurements in the home.

An even more accurate light-measuring instrument is the Weston Illuminometer. By means of one or two "photronic" light-sensitive

FIG. 101.—Illuminometer for measuring light.

cells, which are independent of the personal error of the investigator, light energy from any direction is converted directly into electrical energy. The current operates the indicator instantaneously. The scale, which is calibrated in terms of tungsten filament standard lamps, has three ranges, by means of which light intensities varying from 1/10 of a foot-candle to 250 foot-candles may be measured. (Fig. 101.)

Lumen.—At the present time light output is measured in lumens. The lumen is the unit of light flux or flow of light. It tells how much light comes from a lamp, and is, therefore, a measure of the quantity of light which may be used. If light from a standard candle falls upon a screen, one square foot in area, every point of which is one foot distant from the candle, the screen is said to receive a lumen of light. Incandescent lamps commonly used in the home give about 10 lumens for each watt of energy consumed. A photometer is used to measure the lumen output, in establishing the rating of any lamp.

Reflection and transmission of light.—Light falling on a surface may be partly absorbed, partly reflected, and in part transmitted. Reflection may be of three different kinds: controlled reflection where the rays are thrown back along a path similar to the path of the incident rays; spread reflection, when there is a scattering of the rays, but the extent of scattering is limited to a more or less definitely defined area; and diffuse reflection where there is no limit to the scattering. Daylight undergoes diffuse reflection from sky and landscape, and so does artificial light when it is reflected from mat-finished ceilings and walls. As has been previously noted, the eye generally sees a body by means of the light which the body reflects. When light is transmitted it passes through a material which may be either transparent or translucent. Transparent materials transmit a sufficient number of unscattered rays of light so that bodies on the other side of the material may be distinctly seen. Translucent materials are only partially transparent; they transmit rays of light but the rays are diffused, so that objects may not be seen through the material. Opaque materials do not even transmit the rays of light. Transmitted light, like reflected light, may be diffused, if the rays are scattered by being passed through an opalescent or irregular surface. Hall globes and porch lanterns often have such a surface.

In the reflection and transmission of light it is important to know the distribution of that light in the horizontal and vertical planes. The distribution of any given light in these planes may be measured by a special type of photometer. The results are plotted in a curve which indicates the candle power of the light in the various directions, the form of the curve depending upon the type of unit used. (Fig. 106.)

Glare.—When the light is transmitted or reflected in such a way that an unpleasant sensation affects the eye and fatigue is increased and attention distracted, the cause is usually glare. Glare is light wrongly directed. Direct glare comes from unshaded or insufficiently shaded lamps which shine directly into the eyes. Reflected glare results from a bright light falling on a polished or glossy surface, which reflects the light into the eye. Very shiny paper in a book or magazine may cause reflected glare. Spotty light in a room gives another type of glare. This happens when one or two floor or table lamps make bright spots of illumination in a room and the rest of the room is in comparative darkness. The eye must constantly readjust itself to the brightness and the darkness, and fatigue results.

Daylight in the home.—Except in very gloomy weather, the home depends upon light from outside during the daytime. How adequate this light is would seem to be determined by the number of windows. Glass, however, may absorb or reflect as much as 35 per cent of the light which falls upon it. The thickness of the glass does not seem to have much effect, but the smoothness does, a smooth surface transmitting light very much better than a rough surface. According to Higbie and Bull, if frosted glass is used in the window, as much as 7 per cent more light comes into the room when the smoother side of the glass is toward the light source. From 15 to 20 per cent of the total light available may be absorbed by dirt on the glass, and in very dirty, smoky localities this may amount to as high as 25 or even 50 per cent—sufficient argument for keeping the windows clean. Glass has, nevertheless, an important part to play because it diffuses the light. Although glass reduces the available light, it is not an advantage to have the windows open, for the glass distributes the light and so gives more illumination at the farther side of the room than would be obtained if no glass were used.

Other conditions, such as the use of shades and draperies, also greatly influence the amount of daylight which is available in a room. Randall and Martin have studied these conditions and report the following rather startling facts. Drawing the roller shade so that the upper half of the window is covered, cuts off 60 per cent of the usable daylight, but if the shade covers only the upper fifth of the window 14 per cent of the daylight is lost. This great difference is due to the difference in the light transmitted by the upper and lower halves of the window. Except in congested districts of a city, the light coming through the upper half of the window is largely reflected from the sky. By contrast, the light transmitted through the lower panes is reflected from the ground, other buildings, and shrubbery, all of which are so much darker than the sky that they may absorb more light than they reflect. Dark green shades may cut off 98 per cent of the light, whereas light green shades usually transmit as much as 17.6 per cent. Fly screens covering the entire window reduce the available daylight 50 per cent, but if the screen is only on the lower half of the window, 15 per cent of the light is lost. The custom of painting the screens reduces the light still further, 9 per cent on an entire screen, 3 per cent on a half screen; and when the painting is repeated year after year to keep the screens from rusting, the usable light is likewise further reduced. For these reasons bronze or copper screens which do not require painting are preferable.

The windows are regarded as one of the most satisfactory means of decorating the room. The use of curtains and draperies, however, may cut off as much as 75 per cent of the light. Only the thinnest of curtain material should be used. Removing the valance may double the available daylight at the farther side of the room. Moreover, many heavy drapes and curtains increase the shadows in a room and tend to produce a spotty condition which may result in glare, while a clean window and very light materials diffuse the light and soften the shadows. If drapes are desired for purposes of decoration the windows must be more numerous and larger in size to make up for the loss in light. A window area equivalent to one-fourth of the floor area is desirable.

Further experiments proved that the illumination on a vertical plane parallel to a window was twice that on a horizontal plane at the same place. A simple trial will convince anyone of the truth of this statement and show the need for holding the book or magazine at the proper angle when reading, instead of allowing it to lie on a table.

Artificial light.—Although primitive man was limited in his activities largely to the daytime, modern man may continue his work or his recreation long after nightfall, by means of artificial lighting. In many homes artificial light is used for more than one-half the time the family is together. If the home is to be given an adequate number of windows to furnish the needed daylight inside the rooms it may cost as much to produce this inside daylight as it would to use artificial light; in congested cities daylight may be even more expensive. Artificial light has the advantage of being steady in amount and uniform in quality. Although various fuels are used as sources of light, there is probably no person who would not prefer electric lights, if the location of the home made them possible. Electric lights are safer, more easily cared for, and give illumination instantaneously. The electric light is the first and only light not dependent upon a flame for its origin. The first use, and for some time the exclusive use, of electricity was for lighting.

The development of the electrical industry is of such recent date, however, that at the present time the electric wiring in most homes is below standard. A survey in 1926 of 12,000,000 homes showed that these homes were only about half-adequately lighted, and had only about one-third of the needed convenience outlets. Approximately 80 per cent of all house wiring is insufficient. A conservative estimate shows that it averages a dollar a day at a minimum to run an automobile, and yet a bill of $4.50 a month for lighting—an average of only 15 cents a day—is considered excessive.

Adequate wiring.—An adequate wiring system should provide comfortable lighting, conveniently controlled, with a sufficient number of well-placed outlets to allow for the satisfactory connection of portable fixtures and appliances. The type and quality of the wiring installation are regulated by the Electrical Code of the National Board of Fire Underwriters (p. 42). This code specifies the size of wire to be used in the different circuits, the number of outlets allowed on the circuit, and the size of fuse used for protection.

Distribution center.—Wires to the house from the main street-circuit pass through the air to a convenient place for attaching to the house, and then through a vertical or horizontal conduit to where the wires enter the house; or the wires may be carried to the house in an underground conduit (p. 42). It has been suggested that the distribution center should be placed in the kitchen since this is now the load center—"90 per cent of the load will be used within 10 feet of some point in the kitchen." The electric range is in the kitchen; small electrical appliances are used here or in the adjacent breakfast alcove or dining room. In the cellar beneath the kitchen is the laundry with its equipment; on the second floor above, the bathroom, where an electric heater, curling-iron, etc., may be used. If this suggestion is followed the fuse panel will be located in the kitchen. The "Nofuz" panel board is especially suitable for a kitchen installation. In this arrangement fuses are not used, but protection against an overload is obtained by the unequal expansion of a sensitive bimetal strip which breaks the switch and so cuts off the current. When the cause of the overload has been removed the switch may be reset by two simple movements, similar to tripping a toggle switch. The use of "Nofuz" panel boards tends to reduce the length of lightless periods.

Systems of house wiring.—Conduits may be also used for the house circuits, but because of the expense, metallic or non-metallic sheathed cable is more commonly used. The "B X" cable is the best known. The insulated wires in "B X" metallic-armored cable are protected by a steel covering, which is spirally wound to make the conductor sufficiently flexible to bend around corners. Nails will not penetrate this covering, nor can mice or rats gnaw through it. This security from mechanical injury makes "B X" preferable to the non-metallic cable which is sometimes used. In this latter cable the separately insulated conductors are covered with a non-metallic outer sheath, which, is, however, treated, to render it waterproof and fireproof. Sometimes wiring is by the so-called "knob-and-tube" system, in which the wires are fastened to porcelain insulators, except where the wires pass through the wood, and in these cases porcelain tubes, running through holes, carry the wires and insulate them from contact with the wood. In general this method is not as efficient or as safe as the other systems. Back of the fixture and wall outlets are small metal boxes inside of which the wires are connected to the fixture or outlet sockets. These boxes prevent any bare wires from coming into touch with inflammable materials.

Sizes of wire.—The regulations of the National Board of Fire Underwriters specify that wire no smaller than the size known as No. 14 shall be used for lighting circuits. Size No. 12 is probably even more satisfactory if some convenience outlets are to be placed on this circuit. Twelve outlets for fixtures or appliances are allowed on No. 14 wire, and the circuit is fused with a 15 ampere fuse, which at the customary voltage of 110 volts allows a maximum of 1,650 watts.

Waffle irons, toasters, and laundry irons use about 600 or 650 watts apiece, and any of these, but not all at the same time, may be plugged into a convenience outlet on a No. 14 wire.

If several appliances are to be used, however, it is well to have an appliance circuit, wired with No. 10 wire and fused with a 25 ampere fuse. This allows 2,750 watts, and there is, therefore, less danger of overloading the circuit. The range or any other appliance using more than 2,000 watts must have a separate circuit of No. 6 wire, and be fused with a 50 or 60 ampere fuse. Definitions of terms will be found in the chapter on electricity. (Chapter III.)

Circuits.—The number of circuits needed in a house depends upon the size of the house. It is usually preferable to have two circuits in each room, with some of the lights and convenience outlets on one circuit and some on the second circuit. This does not mean twice as many circuits as there are rooms in the house, for both circuits may run through several rooms. Such an arrangement distributes the load more evenly and prevents all the lights from going out when a fuse is blown.

Red Seal Plan.—The Electric Code is a standard of safety, not a standard of adequacy. The wiring of a home may comply with the code and yet be inadequate. To provide for minimum adequacy, and so for convenience and comfort in the use of electricity in the home, the Society for Electrical Development, Inc., has developed the Red Seal Plan. Under this plan a house must be provided with a certain minimum number of fixture and wall outlets, as set forth in the specification sheet. Upon completion, the wiring is inspected, and if satisfactory, the Red Seal Emblem is affixed to the fuse box.

Symbols.—With some slight variations, most architects and electrical contractors use the following symbols in indicating the wiring layout for a house:

-$\bigcirc$- ceiling outlet $=\bigcirc_2$ double convenience outlet

-$\bigcirc$- floor outlet S_1 single pole switch

$\vdash\bigcirc$- wall bracket outlet S_3 three-way switch

-$\bigcirc$- drop cord S_4 four-way switch

$=\bigcirc$ single convenience outlet

The floor plans (Figs. 102 and 103) show typical wiring layouts.
Light may be used to give general illumination, for localized
work, and for decorative purposes. In good lighting the source and
intensity of the light are adapted to its use. Some general rules and
suggestions are applicable to any house.

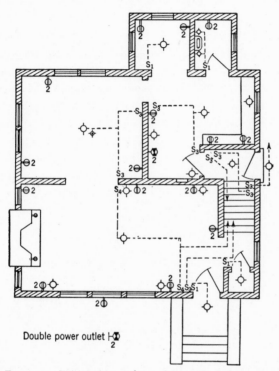

Double power outlet

FIG. 102.—Wiring layout for a house. First floor plan.

Central fixture.—It is preferable to have a central fixture in each
room to give general lighting although the tendency in recently
built homes is to omit the center outlet in the living room. This
outlet may not be necessary if the room is used only by the family,
but social occasions often make such a light desirable. Unless there
is some other source of general illumination, it is better to provide
the outlet even if the fixture is not installed. The outlet may be
covered with an inconspicuous plate, and much inconvenience and
expense will be saved if it is desired to install the fixture at some
future time.

Wall brackets.—Wall bracket outlets may be installed about 5 feet 8 inches above the floor in any room. With the exception of bathroom and kitchen they have chiefly a decorative value, which is increased by using the bracket lights in pairs, and also, if possible, with a balanced effect on either side of a room. (Fig. 110.) In the bathroom a bracket on each side of the mirror illuminates both sides of the face equally. Tasks at sink, stove, or preparation table are carried on more efficiently if there is added illumination from bracket or pendent lights at these work centers.

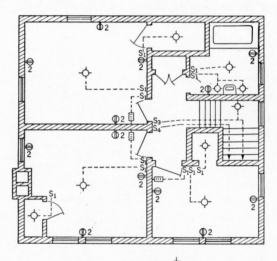

Louvre light

FIG. 103.—Second floor plan.

Light on stairs.—The ceiling outlet in the upper hall should be placed so that no shadow will fall upon the stairs. The same rule should be followed in locating the light for the cellar stairs and for outside front or back porch steps.

Convenience outlets.—Sufficient convenience outlets should be provided to allow any piece of furniture to be placed anywhere in the room, without extension cords crossing doorways or other parts of the room where they will be in the way. It is often desirable to move furniture, and outlets for table and floor lamps should be available at any and all points. Since most extension cords are 6 feet in length it is convenient to have the outlets approximately every 12 feet of wall space. Care should be taken, however, not to place an outlet in the center of a long wall where a large piece of furniture would be placed in front of it.

In the living room additional outlets may be located on the fire-place mantel for connecting decorative lights or a clock. If the living room is large, one or two floor outlets at convenient spots are desirable; they obviate lengths of cord across the floor. Such a floor outlet is also necessary under the dining room table, to which a multiple receptacle may be connected for the attaching of electrical appliances used at the table.

Evergreen trees on the grounds may be decorated at Christmas time, or other decorations used for special outdoor evening festivities, if there are weatherproof outlets at strategic points on the outside of the house.

Convenience outlets are usually installed in the baseboard or in the wall just above the baseboard, with the exceptions noted, where they are on the fireplace mantel or in the floor. In the kitchen and laundry, however, they are installed at a height suitable for connecting appliances. Ordinarily this height is about 42 inches above the floor, but any height desired may be selected by a person building his own home. It has been found more convenient to attach an iron to a low outlet than to a high one unless some other means is provided for keeping the cord off from the board. In the breakfast nook the outlets are often on the end wall just above the table. A high outlet is provided in the bathroom where the curling-iron or electric vibrator may be attached. Outlets 20 inches below the ceiling for electric fans may be included in the wiring of any room. All these outlets are on the lighting or appliance circuits. Special outlets must be provided on the power line for heavy duty appliances.

Switches.—Switches should be sufficient in number and so located that it is possible to light any room as it is entered, and leave it in darkness upon leaving, without retracing steps. To make this possible any room having two doors should have three-way switches at each door; when there are three exits, four-way switches at each doorway are necessary. Some authorities suggest that the switches at both entrances are essential only when the doorways are more than 15 feet apart; other authorities say 10 feet apart. But unless two entrances are practically adjacent, some steps must be retraced in darkness when only one switch is provided. In the lower hall two three-way switches are required, one three-way switch turns on the light in the lower hall and a second turns on the light at the head of the stairs. On the second floor, two similar three-way switches are used to switch either light off or on again.

Every room should have at least one light which is controlled by a switch at the entrance. Sometimes it is convenient to have the outlets used for attaching portable lamps controlled by a switch, and bracket outlets may be switched on, or turned on at each individual socket. When a central fixture contains three or more lamps it may be desirable to have only part of them lighted; a special type of switch, known as an electrolier switch, makes it possible to turn on the lamps in groups. A master switch may be installed in a bed-

Fig. 104.—Types of fixtures for center lights.

room, by means of which all the lamps in the principal rooms may be lighted at one time. This master switch is a protection against burglary. A switch on the hinge side of the door is used to turn a light in the closet on and off, automatically, with the opening and closing of the door.

The switch is placed 4 feet from the floor on the lock side of the door, never behind it. Switch plates may cover several switches grouped together or a switch and single or double convenience outlet. Both switch plates and outlet plates may be of metal or of a non-conducting composition material which may be painted to match the wall.

At the present time toggle switches are preferred to the push button because of their easy manipulation by a slight touch of hand or arm. The location of the switch is often marked by a spot of luminous paint, and luminous balls or cylinders are attached to the end of pull chains. Pilot lights on outlet plates or near the door at the top of the cellar stairs indicate when a circuit is made or broken.

Fixtures.—The well-wired house needs only attractive fixtures to be complete. Fixtures or luminaires, as they are perhaps more correctly called, to be attractive must be suitable. One type of luminaire will be used in a mansion and another type in a cottage, a different luminaire in the drawing or living room from the one in the kitchen. It is always well to remember, however, that the lighting effect produced, i.e., the intensity and uniformity of the light, is more important than the luminaire.

In general, luminaires are classified into three types: the direct, which throws all the light downward on the surface to be illuminated; the indirect, which throws the light on ceiling and the upper part of the walls from where it is redistributed in well-diffused light throughout the room; and the semi-indirect, which may direct most of the light toward the ceiling but send a small part downward on a limited area, or vice versa, distribute the smaller portion over the ceiling, and the larger amount downward. Some authorities recognize a fourth type, the enclosing globe of frosted glass. In this type the light is diffused evenly in all directions. Whatever the type, wherever the location, all lamps should be shaded. (Fig. 104.) If indirect luminaires are used the ceiling and upper walls must be light in color to reflect the light. Dark colors absorb a large portion of the light rays.

Fig. 105.—A floor lamp (shade removed) which gives both direct and indirect light. The central lamp is surrounded by a reflector.

The greatest quantity of light is obtained by the direct luminaire. It concentrates the light at the desired surface and the minimum amount is lost in transmission. The quality, however, is inferior, for the space covered by the light is comparatively small and forms an objectionable contrast with the darker surroundings, so that glare is produced.

The totally indirect light loses most in transmission and absorption, on account of the length of path the rays traverse, but the light is highest in quality. The almost perfect diffusion practically eliminates shadows. The semi-indirect fixtures share the advantages and disadvantages of the other two types according to the proportion of light which is directed to ceiling or floor. (Fig. 105.) Since

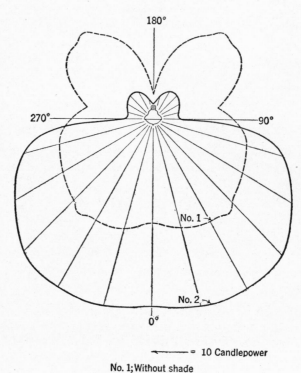

= 10 Candlepower

No. 1; Without shade
No. 2: With shade

FIG. 106.—Distribution of light around lamp, without and with a shade.

the type of fixture largely determines the amount of light obtainable from any source, it is important to know the distribution of light under the various conditions. The curves in Fig. 106 illustrate the distribution of light around a lamp without a shade and after a shade has been placed over the lamp.

Fixtures should be chosen not only for the quality and quantity of light they distribute, but also for their beauty. Their design and color should harmonize with the furnishings of the home.

Entrance fixtures.—At the entrance lanterns or globes may be placed on either side of the door or above the door, to shed light on the steps. An illuminated house number is greatly appreciated by evening visitors. A one-half watt neon glow lamp which gives 3,000 or more hours of service at very slight cost may be used for this purpose.

Hall fixtures.—The entrance hall should be well lighted by a pendant luminaire or an enclosing globe. (Figs. 107 and 108.) If

FIG. 107.—An opalescent enclosing globe   FIG. 108.—one of welcoming cheer. changed this hall from a gloomy entrance to—

the hall is large, bracket lamps on either side of a mirror, or a table lamp on a stand, give added light and attractiveness.

Living room.—The living room is used for so many different kinds of work and recreation that a variety of light is required. As has been said previously, a central fixture is desirable. This fixture should harmonize with the furnishings and decorations. Portable lamps supply needed light beside easy-chairs, at the piano, and the desk. Place floor or table lamps behind and to the left of chairs to give sufficient light and to eliminate shadows. The shades of portable lamps should be light in color; creams or pale yellows give a warm glowing illumination. The lining should be white. Dark-colored shades absorb the light and give spotty effects. If a dark color is desired to fit in with the room color-scheme, use the color in a narrow band or in tiny figures for a border on the shade, or in the lamp base. A shade should be sufficiently thick, however, to conceal the outline of the lamp and deep enough so that the bulb is not visible, even to a person seated nearby. (Fig. 109.)

FIG. 109.—Well chosen shades of semi-indirect type give a diffused illumination which is reflected from the light-colored ceiling and walls.

Brightly colored light should be used only for ornamental pur-poses, in the shaded wall brackets, an illumined figure on the man-tel, or in a lovely vase on a low table. Light for decoration will be discussed more at length later.

Dining room.—In the dining room the dinner table is the center of the lighting arrangements, and it is most attractive when flooded with a well-diffused light. The distance above the table at which the fixture is hung is important. The dome luminaire should be 24 inches above the table; this does not obstruct the view and yet is low enough to prevent the light from shining into the eyes of those sitting at the table. If shower units are used they may be hung 36 inches above the table, remembering always that they must be carefully shaded. Even the candle type of fixture, which became popular during the war because of the scarcity of glass for globes at that time, should be shaded. When a semi-indirect unit is used, it should be of the type with a central indentation at the bottom, which holds a single lamp to give direct light on the table. (Fig. 110.) Cove or

Fig. 110.—The central fixture has a direct light at the bottom to illuminate the table. Note the paired wall brackets, and the ornamental light on tea wagon.

bracket lights may be used for general illumination. A pendent light is often used over the table in the breakfast alcove.

Kitchen.—The central light in the kitchen has a surrounding globe and is hung close to the ceiling to illuminate all parts of the room equally. Local shaded lights at sink and work-centers are desirable to prevent one's shadow from falling on the work. Similar fixtures may be placed in the laundry, or dome-shaped metal reflectors, with a porcelain enamel lining and a "skirt" around the edge to conceal the lamp, will prove satisfactory.

Bedroom.—In the bedroom a central luminaire for general illumination, floor lamps for special locations, and boudoir lamps on either side of the dresser meet the usual needs. The boudoir lamps should be about 15 inches tall and should throw the light on the face rather than on the mirror. Light for reading in bed may be supplied by a floor lamp or a fixture at the head of the bed, high enough to give a wide circle of light on the book or magazine. There is a special type of night light, which uses a lamp of only 2 candle power, is fitted with a small transformer, and screws into the ordinary lamp socket, but the lower Louvre light, placed above the baseboard, which illuminates the floor and does not disturb the sleeper, is even more satisfactory.

Bathroom.—Lights in the bathroom should be placed on either side of the mirror to light both sides of the face equally.

Rehabilitating old fixtures.—It is not always possible to purchase an entirely new lighting outlay for a house already equipped with fixtures, but often the old equipment may be improved at comparatively little expense. All bare lamps may be shaded; dark shades replaced with light-colored ones; a pendent center light in the kitchen may be raised to the ceiling and enclosed in a white diffusing globe (Fig. 111); pendent lights in the bedroom may likewise be raised and shaded; a direct light may be changed to a semi-indirect by turning the fixture around and surrounding the lamp with a translucent shade. Needed convenience outlets may be supplied in the kitchen by attaching to the center-light outlet a pendent convenience outlet which operates separately from the light. If possible, lamp sockets should not be used for attaching appliances. Most electric appliances, irons, toasters, waffle irons, etc., take 500 or 600 watts. When the cord to such an appliance is connected to the lamp socket last, an arc of 600 watts is formed which gradually melts the metal in the socket. Lamp sockets are made for lamps of 200 watts at the largest; some portable lamps have special sockets for 300 watt lamps. It is also a bad practice to turn off a lamp by unscrewing it from the socket, since a little arc is always formed and this gradually wears out the socket.

Types of lamps.—At one time there were forty-five different types of lamps; now there are only six, and four of these are used primarily for decorative purposes. The shape of the bulb is desig-

Fig. 111.—The raised central light and low light over the sink have greatly improved the lighting conditions in this kitchen.

nated by a letter with one of the following meanings: A—frosted inside, S—straight-sided, G—globular (round), F—flame-shaped, T—tubular, PS—pear shaped. (Fig. 112.) The size is measured in eighths of an inch, and a number accompanying the letter gives the diameter. To illustrate, G-20 is a bulb of G shape and 20/8 or 2½ inches in diameter.

Efficiency.—The ratio of light output to wattage consumed gives the efficiency of a light. The amount of light received is proportional to the temperature of the filament. The tungsten filament can be heated to a much higher temperature than the carbon filament without deteriorating and, partly for that reason, shows a higher effi-

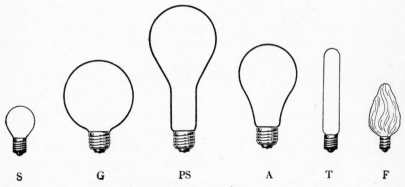

S   G   PS   A   T   F

FIG. 112.—Types of lamps.

ciency, three or four times greater in the sizes commonly used in the home. Since the original cost of the lamp is small compared to the price paid for the electricity which the lamp burns during its lifetime, it is poor economy to buy inefficient types of bulbs or lamps of too small wattage. For example, a 100-watt lamp gives a 105 candle power light; a 25-watt lamp only 18 candle power. It would take approximately six 25-watt or 150 watts to give the same amount of light as that obtained with the 100-watt bulb. Tungsten filament lamps are known as "Mazda" lamps. In ancient Persia Mazda was the god of light. What more appropriate name could have been found for our modern source of efficient illumination!

Tungsten filament.—The tungsten filament has a melting point of about 5,600°F. (over 3,000°C.). It becomes white hot when the electric current passes through it, and so gives a very brilliant white light. The filament for some of the lamps is only 0.003 inch in diameter but is so long that it must be wound in a spiral. In the past, Mazda B lamps had straight filaments, and some of these lamps may still be on the market. The filament wire is joined to two wires which are fused into the bulb at the neck to prevent air from leaking in, and these wires in turn are connected by copper wires to the screw base. The wires which are fused into the glass must have the same coefficient of expansion as the glass.

Mazda B lamps.—There are two types of Mazda lamps. The Mazda B lamp contains a vacuum which prevents the cooling and oxidation of the filament. Lamps of lower wattage are usually of this type because the wires are of smaller diameter than in lamps of high wattage and, therefore, have a relatively large surface area, which tends to cool too much in gas-filled lamps, and consequently give less light per watt. Even tungsten filaments gradually deteriorate. In the common household sizes, 50 or 60 watts, they average 1,000 hours of life. As deterioration takes place in the B lamps the tiny particles of tungsten are thrown off equally in all directions and deposit a thin black film on the inside of the bulb. This film absorbs some of the light, and decreases its efficiency.

Mazda C.—The other type, known as Mazda C, is filled with an inert gas, a mixture of argon (86 per cent) and nitrogen (14 per cent). The pressure of this gas hinders the evaporation of the tungsten, and so gives a lamp of reasonably long life even at the high temperature used. The hot gas tends to rise in the bulb, and carries with it the tiny particles thrown off from the filament. If the lamp is placed base up the blackening will occur largely around the base, and the efficiency of the rest of the bulb will not be reduced. Gas conducts heat better than a vacuum does, and in consequence, the Mazda C lamp is hotter to the touch. All lamps have a certain average lifetime, depending upon the use for which they were designed. Lamps should always be operated at the voltage for which they are marked; operated at too high a voltage they burn out more rapidly, and at too low a voltage they give less light for the wattage consumed.

Frosted lamps.—Frosted lamps are preferable for use where there is any likelihood of the bulb being within the range of vision, because of the better diffusion of the light and elimination of glare.

The brightness of a light depends upon the candle power per square inch. The large Mazda C filament has a brightness of 6,500 candle power per square inch; a frosted lamp, from 50 to 60. According to authorities, the surface brightness of lamps in the line of vision should not be greater than 3.5 candle power per square inch—a further argument for shaded lights.

A lamps are the type used for all general purposes. The A lamp is an improvement made in 1925 in the Mazda C lamp, which was developed in 1913. The A lamp is frosted on the inside, and has a smooth outside surface; it is gas filled, and is tipless.

The inside frosted lamps have been proved more efficient in transmitting the light than the outside frosted lamps previously used. The inside frosted bulbs are also superior in their ability to shed dust. The tipless lamp is more easily handled than one with a tip and is less subject to accident in the home.

Efficiency.—Gloom may be as great a cause of eyestrain as glare. Use lamps of sufficiently high wattage to allow for some loss in transmission and absorption and yet give a high level of illumination. The amount of light which actually gets down to where it may be used on the working plane is important. In cooperation with the physics department, carefully controlled experiments were carried on at Iowa State College in a room $12\frac{1}{2}$ by 13 feet, to determine the effect of the color of the ceiling and walls upon the useful light from a central fixture of five unshaded lamps. Measurements were made on a plane 30 inches from the floor. Mazda B, A lamps, ivory lamps, and flame-tint lamps were tested. The silver-gray paper of the walls was used for one set of experiments, and was then covered with colored hangings of tangerine, red, Yale blue, and black, for a series of tests.

The results of the experiments showed that the A lamps were highest both in installation and utilization efficiencies, ivory lamps ranked next, and the flame-tint lamps were least efficient. Wall coverings of low reflection ability and dark furniture in the room diminished the amount of useful light. Flame-tint bulbs used with a low reflecting background were most irritating to the nerves. The flame-tint lamp is low in blue wave lengths. The interior finish of a room, its furnishings, and the type of lamps are, therefore, of prime importance.

Care.—Keep the lamps and fixtures clean. Dust accumulating over months will absorb as much as 50 per cent of the light otherwise available. The deposit of dust is so gradual that the consumer is not conscious of the dimming until it becomes very bad, but all that time he is paying more and more for light he doesn't get. Clean the fixtures and lamps frequently and at regular intervals. Inverted fixtures should be wiped out every two weeks and the pendent types washed at least once a month. Avoid installing luminaires which catch dust easily and are cleaned with difficulty. Some of the new modernistic styles belong to this class. Bulbs may be wiped off with a damp cloth; they should not be immersed in water. The metal supports of the fixtures are often finished with a protective coating of lacquer, which will be destroyed by acids. Wiping off the dust with a damp cloth and then rubbing with a dry one is usually sufficient to keep the metal in condition. Ceilings should also be kept clean if they are to reflect the light adequately.

It is undoubtedly true that if all the fixtures and lamps in the many homes of the country were washed and the ceilings whitened on the same day, the amount of illumination that night would be doubled. "Water is cheaper than watts."

Light for decoration.—Light may be used for decoration as well as for utility, and the possibilities here are almost limitless. Most of the light ornaments use the tiny 10-watt lamp with the intermediate screw base, so they are not expensive to run. These 10-watt lamps are placed inside lovely china figurines, softly tinted flowers of Kappa shell, and cut crystal balls. Metal figures are silhouetted against a lighted screen, or hold illumined urns. A translucent vase may be lighted from within or from below. Where members of the household wish to rest and listen to the radio, several such light ornaments in a room may give sufficient light. At other times they give life to an otherwise dull corner. One or two of these spots of light may be left, when the family is out in the evening; it is more cheerful to return to a room so lighted than to a dark house.

A lighted figurine in a low bowl of flowers is a lovely centerpiece for the dining table. For special dinners and other parties strings of Christmas tree lights may be used in more elaborate decorations. Such a string may be utilized in making miniature electric candles, for lights inside of colored balloons, for the centers of clusters of artificial flowers, and for a dozen and one other interesting and unique forms of decoration.

The grounds also may be lighted, not only at Christmas time when evergreen trees in the yard are decorated, but during the summer; lights on a pool or fountain or on an interesting piece of statuary with its background of shrubbery will change a garden corner into fairyland. Care must be taken to use non-metallic sockets and weather-proof fixtures.

New notes in lighting.—Modern trends in home lighting have produced some unusual features. A few of these will be mentioned in the following paragraphs.

Cove lighting is fairly new in house lighting and is suitable for both living room and dining room. The 10-watt lamp with intermediate screw base is used in houses already built. These lamps, 6 to 9 inches apart, may be installed above a plate rail and hidden from view by a metal strip painted the same color as the wall, or in the absence of plate rail, a metal trough may be installed. If several circuits are provided, lamps of different colors may be used, and a pleasing variety of effects obtained. Cove lighting costs about a dollar a running foot.

The most recent trend is to build light panels into the room as a part of its construction. These panels may be placed either in the ceiling or in the walls and are made of diffusing glass which gives a most satisfactory uniform light of the desired intensity throughout the room, and almost entirely eliminates shadows. Behind the panels are one or more incandescent lamps backed by a reflecting surface. When installed during the construction of the house, the panels cost little if any more than the regular better grade fixtures.

Many of the modern fixtures are made of a series of glass planes or fan-shaped panels set in metal grooves. These fixtures give semi-indirect lighting, and are effective in the proper setting, but require very frequent washing if they are to remain attractive and efficient.

Eyesight conservation.—All of this discussion of light is important chiefly as it has a bearing on the protection and care of eyesight. Sight is the only one of the senses which is dependent upon an outside agency for its functioning. It is, therefore, doubly important that this agent should be adequate in doing its part. Dr. I. B. Metzger, a president of the Pennsylvania State Board of Medical

Education, is authority for the statement "that 25 per cent of our energy is consumed in seeing with normal eyesight and proper illumination." How much more energy is needed when the eyesight is below normal or the illumination insufficient!

Primitive man lived out-of-doors, did few tasks which required close vision, and went to rest at nightfall. The level of his illumination was high, several hundred times, perhaps at noon-time even several thousand times, the amount of light which modern man receives from artificial sources. Sunlight comes from above and is adequately diffused by sky and atmosphere. The eye is supplied with eye lashes and brows to guard against any discomfort from too much sunlight. Since artificial light at its strongest is but a small percentage of the light found out-of-doors, it would seem impossible to use too much artificial light. Some investigators state that to be 80 per cent efficient the eye requires 100 foot-candles of light, and to be 100 per cent efficient it requires 300 foot-candles of light. In most of the best-lighted rooms there are only 15 foot-candles of light. The important consideration is to have the light properly directed.

The need for superior artificial light is realized when it is known that about 20 per cent of the elementary school children have faulty eyesight. The New York State Health Department found that children living in the country were more subject to defective vision than children in the city, owing perhaps to the better artificial light in city homes. When the children have grown to college age the percentage has doubled and now 40 per cent of them do not see naturally. Over 60 per cent of adults have defective vision, and among people over 60 years of age the percentage has increased to 95 per cent. This condition seems doubly distressing when it is learned that over 70 per cent of all muscular activity needed in work and in recreation is dependent upon seeing.

Insufficient and wrongly directed light causes the child to hold his book too near to his eyes, and doing this habitually leads to near-sightedness. "If you are not able to read easily with the printed page 12 to 15 inches from the eye, there is something wrong either with the light or with your sight."[2] Children's eyes should be carefully protected from unshaded and "spotty" light, where there is too

[2] National Society for the Prevention of Blindness.

great contrast between the illuminated and unilluminated areas of a room.

Eyestrain resulting from the attempt of the eye to adapt itself to unfavorable conditions of gloom or glare may not always show itself in eye trouble. Other ills due to eyestrain may be headaches, nausea, indigestion, sleeplessness, and irritability; and among school children lack of interest, failure to concentrate, and apparent laziness may all be caused by improper sight. A large percentage of accidents are due to abnormal and defective vision.

Health lamps.—The sun is not only our original and still most powerful source of light, but at either end of the visible spectrum are other useful rays not seen by the eye. Beyond the red end of the spectrum, the infra red rays give us heat, and at the opposite end the ultraviolet rays possess certain therapeutic properties. Ultraviolet in wave lengths between 2,900 and 3,100 Ångström units, activates vitamin D in the body. Vitamin D is essential for the proper absorption of calcium in correct bone formation, and its lack causes rickets. The Ångström unit is 10^{-7} mm., or one tenmillionth of a millimeter, in length.

From very early times it has been known that the sun's rays had healing power. A tablet dug up in Egypt shows an early Pharaoh, with his wife and children, and a basket of fruit, enjoying a sunbath. Lest the true meaning be missed, rays from the sun above the group are brought down to strike against each member. The ancient Greeks and Romans had their solaria. The sun porch has been added to the modern home, but glassed in for use in all weathers, and only comparatively recently has it been discovered that ordinary window glass does not transmit ultraviolet rays. Not all the ultraviolet rays are equally valuable; some are even harmful to the more sensitive organs of the body as the eyes, but these harmful rays are absorbed before the sun's rays reach the earth.

In recent years, because of the difficulty of obtaining sufficient sunlight in some latitudes, especially during the winter months, artificial sources of ultraviolet have been developed in the carbon and quartz-mercury arc generator. The carbon arc lamp has been used quite extensively in the home. It has two carbon pencils, which contain cores of a mixture of iron, nickel, aluminum, and silicon, a combination that produces ultraviolet radiations. The pencils are brought together momentarily to cause a short circuit, and are then separated slightly so that an arc is formed between them. A reflector may be used to direct the rays, and since sparks of incandescent carbon are often given off, a screen is usually placed in front of the pencils. The carbon arc lamp takes at least 12 amperes, so is somewhat expensive to run, but it may be plugged into an ordinary convenience outlet. In using these machines smoked or brown goggles must be worn to protect the eyes.

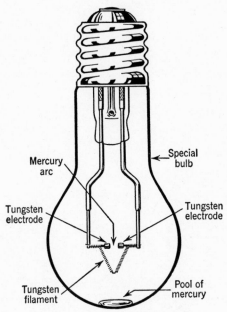

Mercury arc — Special bulb — Tungsten electrode — Tungsten electrode — Tungsten filament — Pool of mercury

Fig. 113.—Sunlight Mazda lamp.

Very recently a sunlight Mazda lamp has been placed on the market. The bulb of this lamp is made of a special kind of glass which screens out the undesirable waves, so that a person may use it without wearing glasses. The lamp is fitted with a transformer which allows it to be connected to the 110- or 115-volt, 60-cycle alternating current circuit, commonly found in the home. The light bulb, of special ultraviolet-transmitting glass, contains two tungsten electrodes, a V-shaped tungsten filament, and a globule of mercury. (Fig. 113.) When the current is turned on the V-shaped filament is heated to incandescence, the heat vaporizes some of the mercury to form an arc between the tungsten electrodes, and ultraviolet radiations are given off. The Mazda sunlight lamp gives sufficient light to be used for play, or reading and sewing, so that it may serve a dual purpose. Care must be taken not to use the lamp at a short distance too long at a time, until the body has become accustomed to the exposure. Erythema does not usually appear during the exposure, but develops afterwards, and will be as painful as a severe sunburn acquired out-of-doors, if the exposure is too long. According to the findings of the Council on Physical Therapy, "It is understood that at a distance of 30 inches directly below the bulb (Type S-1) or 2 feet (Type S-2) the ultraviolet effectiveness is about equal to the midday summer, midlatitude, sea level, natural sunlight. Increasing this distance decreases the effect quite rapidly."[3] The S-2 model is somewhat less powerful, and is the type commonly used in the home. Two new models G-1 and G-5 have recently been put upon the market. These lamps are about 20 per cent richer in ultraviolet output and consume somewhat less electricity than the S-1 and S-2 models.

Cost.—Adequate wiring of the house usually costs from 2 to 3 per cent of the total cost of the house, and the fixtures another 2 to 3 per cent. Compared to the cost of plumbing and plumbing fixtures, which runs from 10 to 15 per cent, the lighting cost is small. When the benefits and comforts derived from efficient lighting and sufficient number of convenience outlets are considered, it should be quite unnecessary to urge the builder not to seek to economize on his electric installation. The most satisfactory way is to employ an expert to lay out the wiring plan, and then personally supervise the installation to guard against any changes.

Other sources of light.—Regardless of personal desires in the matter, a good many homes are so located that it is not possible to have electricity for lighting. Practically any illuminant will supply good lighting, if used in sufficient amount and if properly directed. The simplest system which will give the needed light is to be preferred. All light sources other than electricity are of the flame type, and, therefore, have to be kept away from inflammable materials. Fixtures must be within reach for ignition and control. The location of lights of these types is further limited because flames usually have

[3] Council on Physical Therapy. Jour. Amer. Med. Assoc. 99:32. 1932.

an upright position and need the oxygen of the air for complete combustion. Improper combustion causes a deposit of soot on the chimney and blackening of walls or ceiling. The use of the Welsbach mantle with the gas flame and the mantle in the Aladdin coal oil lamp gives a steady clear white light. A flickering light is injurious to the eye. For an equal amount of fuel consumed, the amount of light is quadrupled by using a mantle.

Rules for the proper shading of light sources are as applicable to these lights as they are to electric lamps. Since the possible positions for most of the flame lamps are somewhat limited, the shade is essential in directing the light where it is needed. Reflectors placed behind or over lights will often increase their efficiency.

Summary.—The essential points brought out in this consideration of the various phases of home lighting may be summarized as follows:

1. A ceiling outlet in every room.
2. Bracket lights, when used, should be placed in a balanced arrangement.
3. At least one light in every room operated by a switch at the entrance to the room.
4. Sufficient switches to enable the home owner to turn on lights as he enters and turn off lights as he leaves a room without retracing steps.
5. A double convenience outlet on every wall space large enough to hold a piece of furniture, usually about 12 feet apart.
6. Sufficient lights, conveniently located to supply all needs without eyestrain. This is about one watt of light per square foot of floor area. "Light is cheaper than vision."
7. All lights shaded; shades deep enough to conceal the lamp, broad enough to give a wide circle of light, light enough in color to transmit light well, thick enough in texture to give well-diffused light. Shades have a fourfold function. They protect the eyes, direct the light, soften shadows, and serve to decorate.
8. Lamps of sufficient wattage to compensate for light lost in transmission and absorption.
9. No strong contrasts of light and shadow, so-called "spotty" light.
10. No glare from reflection. Good reflecting surfaces in ceilings and walls. Light-colored mat surfaces are the most satisfactory.
11. A source of steady light.

12. Clean lamps and fixtures. "Water is cheaper than watts."

13. Light ornaments to give charm and express individuality.

References

1. Adkins, Arthur L. The Romantic Evolution of Light. Pacific Gas and Electric Co., San Francisco, Cal. 1929.

2. Artificial Light and Its Application in the Home. Prepared by Com. on Residence Lighting of Illuminating Engineering Society. McGraw-Hill Book Co., Inc., New York. 1932.

3. Butterfield, W. J. A. Historical Development of Gas Lighting. Illum. Eng. 24: 8-10. 1932.

4. Caldwell, G. W. (M.D.), and Dennett, R. H. (M.D.) The Clinical Value of Sunlight through Ultraviolet Transmitting Glass. Jour. Amer. Med. Assoc. 92: 2088-2090. 1929.

5. Chapters on Light. Illuminating Engineering Society, New York. 1924. (Second edition.)

6. Coblentz, W. W. Ultraviolet Radiation Useful for Therapeutic Purposes. Jour. Amer. Med. Assoc. 98:1082-1086. 1930.

7. Commery, E. W., and Webber, M. E. Conserving our Vision through Better Home Lighting. General Electric Co., Nela Park, Cleveland, Ohio. n.d.

8. Eddy, Lillian E. Home Lighting—A New Science. Practical Home Economics. 8:259-260. 1930.

9. Fleming, Wm. D. (Capt.) (1) The Anti-Rachitic Efficiency of Winter Sunlight of Washington, D. C. Military Surgeon. May, 1928. (Reprint.) (2) The Anti-Rachitic Efficiency of Skyshine in Washington, D. C. Military Surgeon. November, 1928. (Reprint.)

10. Gray, Greta. The Lighting of Nebraska Rural Homes by Kerosene and Gasoline Lamps. Agric. Expt. Sta. Bul. 225. Univ. of Nebraska, Lincoln, Neb. 1928.

11. Greenwood, Ernest. Modern Electric Service in the American Home. National Electric Light Assoc., New York. n.d.

12. Guide to Planning Electrical Wiring. The Society for Electrical Development, Inc., New York. 1930.

13. Harrison, Ward. Some "Don'ts" for the Designer of Art Moderne Lighting. Trans. Illum. Eng. Soc. 26:217-218. 1931.

14. Higbie, H. H., and Bull, H. S. How Glass Affects Your Daylighting. Trans. Illum. Eng. Soc. 26:219-257. 1931.

15. Home Lighting Course (4 lessons). Westinghouse Lamp Co., New York. 1931.

16. Home Lighting Lessons (15). Edison Lamp Works, General Electric Co., Nela Park, Cleveland, Ohio. 1930.

17. Hough, Walter. Collection of Heating and Lighting Utensils in the U. S. National Museum, Smithsonian Institution. U. S. Nat. Museum Bul. 141. Washington, D. C. 1928.

18. Kunerth, Wm. (1) Lighting for Country Homes and Village Communities. Eng. Expt. Sta. Bul. 55. Iowa State College, Ames, Iowa. 1919. (2) The Orientation of Buildings on the Basis of Sunlight. Iowa Academy of Sci. 31. Iowa State College, Ames, Iowa. 1924. (3) A Text Book of Illumination. John Wiley & Sons, Inc., New York. 1929. (4) Minimum Light Intensities Required for Reading. n.d.

19. Kunerth, Wm., and Miller, R. D. Variations of Intensities of the Visible and of the Ultraviolet in Sunlight and in Skylight. Paper presented before Illuminating Engineering Society, Pittsburgh, Pa. October, 1931.

20. Luckiesh, Matthew. (1) Artificial Light. Century Co., New York. 1920. (2) Lighting Fixtures and Lighting Effects. McGraw-Hill Book Co., Inc., New York. 1925. (3) Light and Health, Williams and Wilkins Co., Baltimore, Md. 1926. (4) Artificial Sunlight. D. Van Nostrand Co., New York. 1930. (5) Seeing. Williams and Wilkins Co., Baltimore, Md. 1931.

21. McDermott, L. H., and MacManus, C. J. The Photo-Electric Recording of Daylight. Illum. Eng. 24:41-44. 1932.

22. Measurement of Light. Bul. 104. Electrical Testing Laboratories, New York. 1928.

23. Monier-Williams, R. H. The Tallow Chandlers' Company and Their Craft. Illum. Eng. 24:5-7. 1932.

24. North Light. Textile Colorist 53:124. 1931.

25. Powell, A. L. Light for Ornament. Trans. Illum. Eng. Soc. 22:1039-1047. 1927.

26. Randall, W. C., and Martin, A. J. Daylighting in the Home. Trans. Illum. Eng. Soc. 26:275-291. 1931.

27. Report on Window Glass Substitutes. Council on Physical Therapy. Jour. Amer. Med. Assoc. 88:1562-1567. 1927.

28. Swinburn, J. The Early History of the Electric Light. Illum. Eng. 24:11-12. 1932.

29. Tang, Kwan Y. Visual Performance under Daylight, Incandescent, Mercury Vapor, and Their Mixtures. Trans. Illum. Eng. Soc. 26:258-274. 1931.

30. Thornton, Frank, Jr. New House Wiring Ideas. Elec. Installation Record. February, 1931.

31. Waldron, Kathryn. The Lighting of a Home under Various Color Conditions. Unpublished thesis. Iowa State College Library, Ames, Iowa. 1931.

32. Waugh, Sarai. Principles of Lighting the Home. Ladies' Home Jour. Leaflet 207. Curtis Publishing Co., Philadelphia, Pa. n.d.

33. Willis, B. What is a Lumen? Unpublished data. Iowa State College, Ames, Iowa.

ILLUSTRATIONS: Figs. 101, 104, 105, 109-113, General Electric Co.; 102, 103, Best Electric Co.; 106, William Kunerth.

CHAPTER XV

HOME PLUMBING

The need of a reliable supply of water and of sanitary means for disposal of waste is as old as man, but only since people have lived in congested areas has the problem become acute.

In cities and in many towns the water supply and frequently the sewage disposal are the business of the city engineer and, except from the service end, need not concern the individual householder. Unfortunately the rural home must itself take the responsibility. Whether the source be stream, lake, spring, or well, it is essential to keep water free from contamination, both from the surface of the ground and due to seepage through the soil.

Running water.—Running water is undoubtedly the most important labor-saving device in the home. The city supply is collected in large reservoirs, often many miles from where it is used, and is pumped by a central station to the separate homes under sufficient pressure to cause it to flow freely when a faucet is opened. If the rural home is to have running water the necessary pressure must be provided locally. It is commonly obtained by making use of gravity. The water is raised by a pump operated by hand, wind, gasoline engine, or electric motor to a small reservoir at the top of the house and flows down through the pipes to the faucets below. When running water is not possible, a hand pump at the sink at least brings water within easy reach.

Pumps.—Several varieties of pumps are available, a piston suction type or a combination suction and force pump at the well or kitchen sink, and a force pump to lift the water to the elevated tank. (Fig. 114.) The hand pump will deliver from 4 to 5 gallons of water a minute into the reservoir, if operated at 20 strokes per minute. The usual gasoline engine of stationary type for running a pump uses approximately one pint of gasoline per horsepower per hour. This system is only about 33 per cent efficient, and there is also a certain amount of friction in the pipes to be overcome, all of which must be taken into consideration in estimating the size of gasoline engine needed for any given installation. As has been noted (p. 47) there is a limit to the size of motor which may be operated on the home electric plant.

Windmill.—The most reliable and economical method for pumping water, however, is by the windmill, or air-motor, so called. It should be constructed of galvanized steel and should require oiling only once a year. The windmill is most efficient when the velocity of the wind ranges between 15 and 18 miles per hour, but will operate successfully in light winds of 8 to 10 miles per hour. United

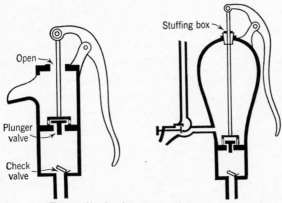

Fig. 114.—Suction pump. Force pump.

States Weather Bureau records indicate that there are few places where wind fails to attain this velocity for a large part of every day. With the exception of the cost of installation, there is almost no expense for operation or maintenance, and given the yearly oiling the windmill will run night and day with practically no attention for 20 to 30 years. A storage tank supplies the water needed during periods of calm.

Unfortunately, serious errors are frequently made in the installation of the windmill so that the expected efficiency and the service desired are not always obtained. In many cases too large a cylinder is installed, resulting in excessive strains on the pump and windmill mechanism, especially in brisk winds. Another common fault is a poorly constructed well platform. The platform is generally used as the foundation for the pump, and unless well built and carefully braced allows too great movement and vibration which cause unnecessary wear and loose pipe joints.

Plumbing.—Plumbing is no new art. Excavations in ancient Crete reveal extensive baths with the necessary connecting pipes, and many European towns have remains of old Roman baths, both public and private. In no country of the present day, however, is the bathroom so extensively found in the humble as well as in the wealthy home as in America.

Bathroom appliances.—Sanitary plumbing ware was first made in this country in 1871. It has been steadily improved in quality and design until bathroom fixtures and kitchen sinks of great variety and beauty are now available. The sink has been discussed in Chapter I on kitchen arrangement (p. 21). The appliances commonly found in the bathroom are lavatory, bath, and closet bowl and tank; also, more and more frequently, the combination or separate shower. The sitz bath and foot bath may occasionally be installed in the larger, more pretentious bathroom, but because of the extra cost and limited use are not usually found in the average home.

Materials.—Bathroom fixtures may be made from marble, vitrified china, porcelain, or enamelware. Since marble cannot be molded it is used only for flat surfaces, all curved or shaped surfaces being constructed of porcelain or vitreous china and fitted to the marble slab. The china is used for smaller pieces, not over 36 inches in length, which do not tend to warp out of shape during the drying and firing processes. China is all-clay, white throughout, and impervious to ordinary household acids and cleansers, possessing therefore highly durable and sanitary characteristics which make it especially desirable for the closet bowl. Porcelain fixtures, on the other hand, have a buff colored body under the clay and glaze coating. They are of greater thickness than the china pieces and are fired only once to avoid excessive shrinkage, which tends to leave undesirable cracks and blemishes. Because of their weight and because of the tendency of the surface to craze, porcelain fixtures are less commonly used than formerly, having been largely replaced by enamelware.

Enamelware.—Enamel plumbing fixtures are made in the same way as any other kind of enamelware (p. 29). They are somewhat less costly than fixtures of the other materials, but with care will last a long time. Processes perfected within the last ten years make it possible to render the enamel impervious to household stains and acids, so that sinks are frequently constructed of this ware.

Color.—All of the different materials may be obtained in a wide variety of colors. Fixtures of colored porcelain or vitreous china cost approximately 50 per cent more than the white, and colored enamels, 25 per cent more. Since there is a variation in degree and length of heating in the manufacture of pieces from the different materials, it is not possible to match colors exactly in porcelain and china and enamelware, but colors which harmonize may be used.

Bureau of Standards regulations.—All fixtures must pass a final inspection and test before they are packed. It is not possible to eliminate in the manufacturing process all the minute amounts of impurities which may occur in the day. These impurities may cause slight irregularities or imperfections, scarcely discernible to the untrained eye, which do not in any way impair the utility or sanitary characteristics of the piece. Several years ago (1926) a group of manufacturers of plumbing fixtures cooperated with the United States Bureau of Standards in setting up a code by which the different pieces might be graded. According to the code agreed upon fixtures are divided into "regular selection" and "culls." Some manufacturers also have a "special selection" group, which contains only the very superior pieces. The regulations specify the dimensions required for various parts of a fixture, and the number and kinds of blemishes which are allowed. All pieces shall carry the trade mark or name of the manufacturer in a permanent, visible place. It is usually stamped on before the glaze is applied. Vitreous china culls must be marked with two parallel lines cut through the glaze into the body of the fixture at specified points. The lines are filled with water-resistant red enamel or varnish to be clearly visible. The crates in which culls are shipped are marked with two dashes of red paint, which may be seen without opening. Porcelain culls are similarly marked with two dots instead of two lines.

Piping.—The kind of material selected for the water supply lines which connect the street main to the house fixtures depends upon the hardness of the water. Water of medium hardness is considered most desirable. Soft water corrodes wrought-iron and steel pipes, causing them to rust out in a comparatively few years, and when lead pipes are used, frequently results in lead poisoning. Hard waters, on the other hand, deposit minerals in the pipes and gradually fill them. Brass, of the variety known as "red," is suggested for use with soft water, and for all hot water connections; wrought-iron or galvanized steel of at least one inch diameter for hard waters, which, however, should be partially softened if possible.

In the northern states service pipes should be laid below the frost line, usually 5 feet or more; in southern states to a depth greater than that to which the heat from the sun will penetrate. The pipes should be protected against injury by a packing of earth or sand, free from sizable stones, and with a surrounding sleeve where the pipe passes through the foundation wall. Friction and back pressure may be reduced by keeping the lines of uniform size and free from all excessive twists and turns. The material used also influences the amount of friction, copper and brass offering less resistance to flow than the other metals. Rusting greatly increases friction. Inside the cellar wall a valve in the main pipe controls the water supply of the house.

Water softening.—Extremely hard water has so many undesirable characteristics that it is softened whenever possible. The common household method of softening is by the zeolite process. Hard water usually contains salts of magnesium and calcium. Zeolites are sodium silicates, the sodium being replaceable by the magnesium and calcium, which precipitate out as insoluble salts, leaving a comparatively soft water. When all the sodium has been used the zeolite is treated with common salt, sodium chloride, which sets free the calcium and magnesium from the zeolite, so that it may be used again in softening the water. After the system is installed, the only operating cost is for the sodium chloride, which is inexpensive.

"Brass goods."—The metal faucets, spouts, and wastes attached to or used with the fixtures are known as "brass goods." They are, as the name implies, of brass, commonly plated with nickel, but occasionally with gold or silver, and recently with chromium, which is especially desirable because of its resistance to scratches, and ease of cleaning. China and crystal-glass are also used for handles and knobs.

Instead of being exposed, fittings are sometimes concealed within the wall. This is a desirable arrangement, but may necessitate a utility closet in the wall to give access for repairs. Such fittings tend to cost somewhat more than the exposed type.

Faucets.—Faucets should have easily grasped handles and should not drip, but close tightly without unnecessary effort. The metal seats should be of durable material which will give long service, but which may be easily replaced if necessity arises. Spouts should be constructed to deliver a full steady flow at uniform pressure without spattering, and the pipes which connect the fittings to the water and

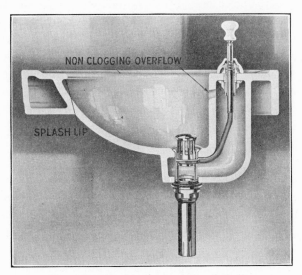

NON CLOGGING OVERFLOW

SPLASH LIP

FIG. 115.—Lavatory basin with splash lip.

waste mains should be of a sufficient size to keep the lines open. When the strainer plug in the waste pipe is removable, it is more easily cleaned. Valves should work easily and efficiently, opening or closing completely with a minimum of effort.

Lavatory.—The lavatory is made in a variety of shapes and sizes; the slab may be rectangular, square, oval, or round, with or without an apron and/or back, and be supported by two legs, a single pedestal-shaped leg, or be fastened to the wall with brackets. The bracket type is less expensive, conserves space, and permits easy cleaning of the floor beneath. Occasionally the lavatory is designed to fit into a corner. The basin, also of any shape preferred, is fitted into the slab. A splash lip on the basin prevents slopping over, when the water flows with force. (Fig. 115.) The faucets have one, two, or four-pronged handles, and are usually marked for hot and cold water. When there are small children in the family a self-closing faucet is an advantage, preventing waste and overflow accidents. Each faucet may have its own spout or there may be a combination spout to mix the hot and cold water to the desired temperature. The spout may overhang the basin or be an integral part of the basin. This latter type of construction is not recommended because of the possibility of the spout being submerged in dirty water which may then enter the supply system and cause contamination. The waste pipe is stopped with a pop-up, operated by the pull or push of a knob, or it may be closed less expensively with a rubber stopper attached to a chain. An overflow opening into the drain is usually provided.

Bath.—Baths may be all straight sided to provide maximum area or may have one sloping end to permit the bather to recline. The more expensive models are of porcelain enclosed in tile or built into a recess; the less expensive, of enamelware with a painted exterior, either on legs or on a shaped base. The tub on legs should be avoided wherever possible because of the difficulty of cleaning beneath it. The fittings may be exposed, or concealed in the wall; the spout, separate for hot and cold water or in combination, may be overhanging, integral with the tub, or projecting through the end of the tub; the waste may be either the pop-up or stopper and chain, the latter being preferable. Unless no other arrangement is possible the tub should not be placed beneath a window. Any one wishing to open the window must stretch across the tub; dust and dirt, blowing in from outside, settle in the tub; and any air leakage around the window causes an uncomfortable draft on the bather.

Shower.—The overhead shower, controlled by a mixing valve to give water of the desired temperature, is often placed above the tub in the smaller bathroom. The thermostatically controlled mixing valve is more expensive, but eliminates all danger of a sudden spray of very hot water which occasionally occurs with variation in line pressure, e.g., when a closet is flushed while the shower is operating, resulting in a serious accident. A shower, by doing away with the filling and emptying of the tub, cuts the bathing period in half. It does not take the place of the cleansing, relaxing tub bath, but it is refreshing and invigorating and is very popular with young people. When the shower head is pivoted on a ball joint the water is kept away from the face and hair. If a shower is not possible, a partial substitute is obtainable in the spray, which can be attached to the bath spout. With the shower protective curtains are essential. These may be of duck, or of any of the waterproofed materials, silk, cretonne, or chintz. Occasionally a shower panel of plate glass is used. When the shower is in a separate compartment there may be side sprays as well as the top shower.

Closets.—Since closets are more frequently cleaned with strong cleaning agents than other bathroom fixtures, it is essential that they

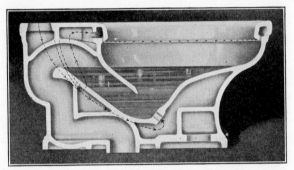

Fig. 116.—Siphon jet closet. Note the broad water surface.

be made of vitreous china, which is twice fired and impervious to the action of acids. The construction must provide a powerful flushing action without getting out of order.

Types of action. Siphon jet.—There are three types of action; the siphon jet, the reverse trap with or without the jet, and the wash down, also with or without the jet. Of these the siphon jet is considered the most desirable. When the tank valve is opened the water in the closet passes out of the jet at the bottom of the bowl, causing a siphon action which lowers the water level quickly and empties the bowl. Meanwhile the water from the tank flows in around the rim and cleanses the sides. This type of bowl has a deep water seal against the entrance of sewer gas, and a broad water surface which reduces the area exposed to soil. (Fig. 116.)

Reverse trap.—In the reverse trap type the water flushing through the jet and around the rim raises the level in the closet bowl sufficiently to force the water over the top of the passage wall and start the siphon action into the outlet pipe.

Wash down.—The wash down closet is simpler than the others in construction and, therefore, less expensive, but is not generally considered as efficient. The trap is at the front of the bowl. Action is started by water flushing around the rim and so raising the water level until it flows over the dam. (Fig. 117.)

The flush pipe from the tank enters the siphon jet closet at the top, the reverse trap and wash down types at the back. Closet bowls

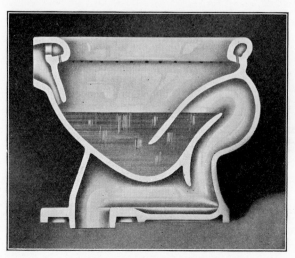

FIG. 117.—Washdown closet.

should not be too high; between 14 and 15 inches is considered the correct height for the most efficient action of the abdominal and intestinal muscles.

Tank.—The tank is an essential part of the closet, since it holds the water used for flushing, the level of the water being controlled by a float. The operating mechanism opens the flush valve, which is usually sealed by a rubber ball, and the float drops, then gradually lifts again as the tank fills to the level at which the stop is set. In some of the more recent tanks a leather seat washer attached to a "cage" is used instead of the rubber ball and this gives a much quieter action. "When the operating lever raises the disc from its seat, the inflowing water buoys the float, holding the disc open.

After the flush, the water in the cage drains away slowly, very gently lowering the float until the disc comes to its seat. It is the positive, slow-closing feature that makes operation so quiet."[1]

Some tanks have a flat shelf-like cover which is convenient for holding toilet articles, others the more common rimless and slightly curved top. The metal flush pipe, connecting the tank and closet bowl, is usually nickel plated, but may be covered with a china case, integral with the tank and closet, which adds greatly to the appearance, and is much more easily kept clean.

Accessories.—Among the useful accessories which may be included in the bathroom furnishings are towel bars, soap dishes, separate or built in, grab-rods to aid in getting in and out of the bath, medicine cabinets, mirrors, shelves, and dressing tables.

Bathroom.—It is no longer considered essential to have the bathroom square or oblong in shape, alcoves affording convenient locations for the tub or closet. Bathrooms are often smaller, too, since fixtures have become more compact, and it is frequently possible to convert an empty closet or an unused hall space into a bathroom, perhaps an extra one, which will eliminate the bath-line, which not rarely occurs when several members of a family wish a morning shower. Color in the bathroom is also a pleasing innovation, though a somewhat more costly one than the use of white. Inexpensive fixtures in color are not a wise investment.

Ready built bathrooms.—At the present time it is possible to buy unit panels to which are fastened the lavatory or bath, complete with the necessary fittings and accessories. The panels are attached to a steel frame with space between for the pipes, so that the fixtures may be added to an old house without disturbing the walls, all connections being made beneath the floor. Or, if preferred, the remaining panels to form a room may be purchased. The panels are insulated against vibration and noise.

Trap.—The waste pipe draining any plumbing fixture is equipped with a trap, which is a part of the pipe, between 2 and 4 inches in depth, bent into the form of an S or of a P. This trap, being filled with water, prevents any odors from the drainage system from leaking into the house. The P-shaped trap is used in pipes which drain horizontally through the wall, the S-trap in pipes draining

[1] Crane Company, Homes of Comfort. p. 65.

vertically through the floor. Too deep traps are to be avoided, since solids tend to deposit in them, and make frequent cleaning necessary, and clean traps are essential if sanitary conditions are to be maintained.

Venting.—Some type of venting is necessary when a plumbing system is installed in houses of more than one story. "This is a separate system of air piping, having a branch connection to the sewer side of each trap, which either admits or emits air as may be needed to protect the water seal."[2] When this equilibrium is disturbed the water which forms the seal in the traps is siphoned off, allowing noxious gases to enter. The circulating air also oxidizes the decomposing drainage and so hinders pipe corrosion. Circulation is brought about by the varying temperatures within and without the building, and also by the flow of water through the waste pipes.

Sewage disposal.—Where connection to a central sewage system is not possible, some local means of disposal must be provided. A cesspool is the common method, but the septic tank is considered more efficient and sanitary. The tank of reinforced poured concrete combines the work of settling and of partially digesting the solids, which tend to change to liquid and gases, leaving a residue of scum on the top and of sludge at the bottom of the tank. The bottom of the tank should have a hopper construction, or slant toward the inlet end to aid in the further digestion of the sludge. The tank effluent is absorbed by the subsoil or, partly clarified, is piped through tile fields or leaching trenches until it becomes purified through contact with the air after which it is spread over the land at a rate at which it will be absorbed.

The tank should have a water capacity equivalent to one day's sewage, which for the average home is approximately 60 gallons per person, with an extra allowance for settling and digestion. When water is used in abundance a 50 per cent larger volume must be allowed. The sludge in the settling chamber must be cleaned out fairly frequently, once a year or oftener, depending upon the amount of sewage received.

More satisfactory than the use of the septic tank alone is its connection to a dosing chamber. This chamber collects the effluent until sufficient in amount to start an automatic siphon, which causes a

[2] House Design, Construction and Equipment. p. 231.

large amount of liquid to flow at once over an extended portion of ground. The flow then stops until the dosing chamber is again full. This method allows a more thorough distribution of the sewage, and also affords free intervals for the ground to air and any waste material to oxidize before the next dosage. (Fig. 118.)

Value of hot water.—Hot water is essential in the home for the protection of health. Hot water is needed to insure clean hands, clean clothes, clean foods, and clean utensils. A hot water heater is, therefore, of primary importance.

Methods of heating. Waterfront.—In homes without central heat and even in many small homes with a furnace, water is com-

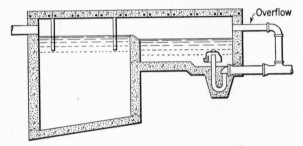

FIG. 118.—Septic tank with dosing chamber.

monly heated by means of a waterfront in the kitchen range, the water being stored in a nearby tank, usually of 30-gallon capacity. If the water is soft the tank should be of copper and the waterfront and connecting pipes of brass. Brass piping should not be used, however, with a galvanized storage tank, because of the tendency toward electrolytic action between the metals with resultant corrosion.

Furnace connection.—During the winter months it is usually more economical to heat water by connecting the storage tank to a pipe coil in the fire-box of the furnace, or indirectly by utilizing the heat of the hot water or steam system. For the summer the tank is cross-connected to a coal, oil, gas, or electric heater. The coal heater is similar in construction and method of heating to the waterfront or coil in the kitchen range. (Fig. 119.)

Gas water heaters.—Gas water heaters are of three general types: tank (non-automatic), automatic storage, and instantaneous.

Non-automatic heaters.—The non-automatic tank heater is the simplest type of water heater. The tank of sheet steel or of copper has a capacity of 30 gallons in the average family size. The burner, below the tank or in a side arm attachment, is of cast iron, and is lighted by hand. In the side arm heater the water to be heated passes through a helically wound copper coil above the burner and as it heats and expands, rises through a pipe to the top of the tank, and cold water from the bottom flows into the coil. Circulating in this way, the water is gradually heated throughout. Water is drawn from the top of the tank so that the hottest water is always obtained first.

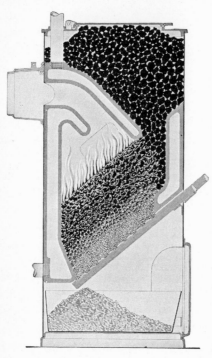

The other non-automatic type has the burner below the tank. Flues carry the hot combustion products up and around the tank to aid in heating the water. This type is now usually supplied with a two-way burner which allows either a large heat flame or a small heat flame, similar to the burner on some of the new model gas ranges. The simmering section of the burner burns continuously, and provides enough heat to give a tank of

Fig. 119.—Automatic water heater which uses coal for fuel.

140°F. water in 10 hours. This supplies sufficient hot water for ordinary daily household use. When a larger amount is needed for laundry, the large burner may be lighted.

Automatic storage heater.—In the automatic storage heater a well-insulated storage tank is connected to a circulating heater. By means of a thermostat in the tank the temperature of the water is held at a definite temperature. When it falls below this temperature, the gas is automatically turned on to the burner, and lighted from a pilot which burns continuously. Most automatic storage heaters have the burners below the storage tank, as in some non-automatic types; others have them on the side similar to the burner in the tank (non-automatic) heater.

Instantaneous heater.—The instantaneous water heater is so constructed that a very large heating unit is automatically turned on whenever a faucet is opened. This burner heats the water so rapidly that it may be drawn at once, the rate at which the water passes through the heating coil and, therefore, the temperature of the water being regulated by a thermostat. This type of heater may be very expensive to run if the consumer is careless in the use of hot water.

Thermal efficiency.—The tank heaters and automatic storage heaters usually have a thermal efficiency of about 70 per cent. The American Gas Association Laboratory's minimum requirement is for an efficiency of 65 per cent, with an hourly standby loss, in the case of the storage heaters, of less than 10 per cent. "The hourly standby loss is the percentage of the heat in the stored water (above room temperature) lost, which must be replaced by the main burner and pilot to maintain a uniform storage temperature."[3] Kerosene oil may be used in place of gas or coal in equipment similar to the appliances using these fuels.

Electric heaters.—Electricity may be used for hot water heaters, if the rate per kilowatthour is not prohibitive. So far the well-insulated storage tank type has proved the most satisfactory. Electric heaters are automatic, and eliminate flame and the need for flue connection.

Relief valve.—Hot water heaters should have a "relief" valve, so that if the burner is left ignited in the non-automatic types, or if anything goes wrong with the automatic appliance, and the water is heated sufficiently to change to steam, it may blow off into the drain without danger of an explosion.

Insulation.—Insulated water tanks and insulated supply pipes add to the efficiency of the system. A supply pipe covered with a one-inch thickness of asbestos insulation loses only about one-fifth as many British thermal units in radiation as the uninsulated pipe.

Care of heater.—Storage tanks should be fitted with a drain faucet to allow for emptying and cleaning. Hard water tends to

[3] Apmann, A. M. Domestic Gas Appliances. p. 116. (c) Courtesy, American Gas Journal.

deposit mineral scales in the tank and pipes, and the mineral corrodes the coils and greatly increases the heat required. When the temperature of the water is constantly maintained above that recommended by the manufacturer, such deposits are accelerated.

Temperature of water.—For general household requirements, water ranged in temperature from 130° to 160°F. is usually satisfactory. It is customary to heat the water to the higher temperature and cool it as used by mixing it with cold water.

Summary.

1. A reliable water supply and sanitary means for disposal of waste are primary necessities.
2. In the rural home running water may be made available by pumping the supply to an elevated storage tank. Pumps are operated by hand, gasoline engine, electric motor, or windmill. The windmill is the most satisfactory and economical method.
3. Modern plumbing tends to create desirable sanitary conditions by the use of:
   (*a*) Fixture materials impervious to moisture, stains, and crazing.
   (*b*) Pipes resistant to corrosion.
   (*c*) "Brass goods," tightly fitting and easily cleaned.
4. Lavatories should be of vitreous china or enamelware, with overhanging mixing faucet, and pop-up waste.
5. Bathtubs should be built in or have a pedestal base, have an overhanging mixing faucet, and chain and stopper for waste, and not be placed under a window.
6. Showers should have a thermostatically controlled mixing valve to avoid danger of scalding.
7. Closets should be of vitreous china, 14 or 15 inches high, have vigorous cleaning action and a broad water surface.
8. Each waste pipe should be supplied with a trap to prevent return of sewer gases.
9. A venting system, to maintain equal air pressure and circulation in the waste pipes, is necessary in all houses of more than one story.
10. Sewage disposal is best cared for by a central system or by a local septic tank connected to a dosing chamber. The tank should be cleaned at least once a year.
11. Hot water is essential for cleanliness and health.
12. Water may be heated in an attachment of the kitchen range or house heating system, or in a separate heater by the use of gas, oil, coal,

or electricity. Water of 130° to 160°F. is usually satisfactory for all household requirements.

References

1. A. G. A. Approval Requirements for Gas Water Heaters. American Gas Association Testing Laboratory, Cleveland, Ohio. 1931.
2. Babbitt, Harold E. Plumbing. McGraw-Hill Book Co., Inc., New York. 1928.
3. "Established 3500 B. C." Trenton Potteries Co., Trenton, N. J. 1925.
4. Harribine, Grace E., A Study of the Cost and Efficiency of Different Types of Fuel Used for Domestic Water Heating. Unpublished thesis. Iowa State College Library, Ames, Iowa. 1927.
5. Home of Comfort. Crane Company, Chicago, Illinois. 1929.
6. House Design, Construction and Equipment. Chap. IV. Plumbing and Sanitation. The President's Conf. on Home Building and Home Ownership, Washington, D. C. 1932.
7. Murphy, Lindon J. (1) Residential Sewage Treatment Plans. Bul. 93 (revised). 1932. (2) Water Softening for the Home. Bul. 105. 1930. (3) Water Supply for the Isolated Home. Bul. 114. 1933. Eng. Ext. Service, Iowa State College, Ames, Iowa.
8. Sanitary Sewage Disposal for the Farm Home. Agric. Eng. Sect., Iowa State College, Ames, Iowa. n.d.
9. Staple Vitreous China Plumbing Fixtures. Simplified Practice Recommendation 52. U. S. Bureau of Standards, Washington, D. C. 1927.
10. Staple Porcelain (All-Clay) Plumbing Fixtures. Commercial Standard CS4-29. U. S. Dept. Commerce, Bureau of Standards, Washington, D. C. 1929.
11. Warren, G. M. Farm Water Power. U. S. D. A. Farmers' Bul. 1658. Washington, D. C. 1931.

ILLUSTRATIONS: Figs. 114, 118, Engineering Extension Service, Iowa State College; 115-117, Crane Co., Chicago; 119, The Floyd-Wells Co., Royersford, Pa.

CHAPTER XVI

HEATING AND VENTILATION

HEATING

In all but tropical or semi-tropical regions some external source of warmth is a necessity during the cold months of the year, for the law that heat tends to flow from the warmer to the colder place holds good here as in other cases, and the heat loss from our bodies would be too great for life to survive the winter season in a cold climate. Even in semi-tropical countries a fire at night or in the early morning is often a welcome addition to the comforts of living.

It is a long cry from the early campfire, used for protection and light as well as for warmth, to the modern home heating plant. First the campfire itself was brought inside the tent or hut, but the smoke came, too, along with the warmth and was only effectively eliminated with the building of the fireplace and chimney. How inadequate the fireplace proved as a source of heat in severe weather is shown by the records of early days in New England which tell of water freezing a foot away from blazing logs on the hearth.

In 1744 Benjamin Franklin built a stove, called by his name, which was placed in the center of the room and radiated its heat in all directions. He regulated the combustion with dampers, and claimed that with one-fourth the fuel it heated his room twice as well as the fireplace. For many years Franklin stoves warmed the homes of the country, and a man's standing in the community may often have been based upon the number of such stoves which he possessed.

Methods of heating.—Stoves are still widely used for heat as well as for cooking even in America, although the people of the United States, more than those of other countries, have adopted the central heating system. The stove is a unit heater, commonly called a space heater. Space heaters are of many kinds and forms: an open charcoal brazier in Eastern lands, ornate stoves of porcelain in central and western Europe, the homely but efficient base burner in America.

Central heating systems.—The central system most frequently used in the home is warm air or hot water, although steam is sometimes used, especially in apartment houses.

Factors affecting size of plant. Inside temperature.—Regardless of type of system, certain preliminary investigations must be made to determine the size of plant required. The size obviously depends upon the maximum heat which the plant must furnish, a requirement influenced not only by the conditions which are to prevail within the home, but also by external weather conditions and by the construction of the house itself. It has been customary to determine the inside temperature at the "breathing line," which is a point 5 feet above the floor and 3 feet from an outside wall. In most houses, in which rooms are not over 10 feet high, this temperature varies from 65° to 72°F., depending upon whether the determination is made in kitchen, living room, or bath. With certain types of heating equipment, temperatures at floor or ceiling frequently vary considerably from this breathing line temperature, being too low on the floor, and too hot at the ceiling. Since so great a variation leads only to discomfort, an attempt is being made to have the temperature determined at not more than 30 inches above the floor, even 18 inches having been suggested.

Outside conditions.—Outside conditions in most sections of the country are variable, including both sunshine and cloudy weather, wind, rain, and snow. It is not necessary to consider the minimum temperature or the maximum wind velocity, since the minimum temperature may not occur every year, and at best is of short duration, and the same is true of the velocity of the wind. It is usually customary to take as the lowest temperature for the given location a temperature of 15°F. above the average minimum reported by the United States Weather Bureau for the previous ten years. Fifteen miles per hour may be taken as the average wind velocity.

Construction of house.—The effect of the construction of the house on heat requirement varies with the type of materials used, since heat transmission, and hence heat loss, differ with different materials. The age of the building, presence of cracks around doors and windows, method of ventilating by opening windows or doors, and exposed location all have an influence also. Wind increases loss of heat around doors and windows, especially on the sides exposed to the prevailing winds. It is a common observation that more heat is required on a windy day than on a calm one, even though the temperature may not be as low. Not only does the heat leak out, but cold filters in. Although a storm window is not essential if the house window is well fitting, tests show that when the house window fits loosely, the storm window may reduce the infiltration of cold air as much as 50 per cent.

As has been noted the amount of heat transmitted through the walls of a house depends upon the kinds of materials used in construction, including the amount of glass used in windows. The heat coefficient of various building materials has been determined experimentally and the tabulated results are available. In the use of such results it is usually preferable to consult a heating engineer who will be able to tell whether the added cost of the desired insulation will really result in sufficient saving in fuel to be worth while. Heat transmission occurs because of the difference between inside and outside temperatures. In the chapter on refrigeration it was learned that insulation hinders the flow of heat from a place of higher temperature to one of lower temperature. In the construction of the house, heat transfer may be greatly diminished by using insulating materials in partitions next to unheated spaces, as in floors above unheated cellars or in ceilings next to cold attics or the roof. Such insulation tends to produce more uniform temperatures throughout the rooms and also prevents condensation of moisture caused by the difference in temperatures, condensation which is most injurious to the building and its fittings. Tests show that plastering may reduce the heat leakage as much as 96 per cent, and a thick coat of cold water paint, 50 per cent. Heavy building paper placed between the sheathing and shingles also markedly reduces heat and cold transfer. In determining the effective heat loss and cold infiltration, it is customary to use the average wind velocity during the months of December, January, and February.

The interrelation of construction costs (including insulation and weatherstripping) and the cost of the heating plant and the fuel is discussed in some detail in Chapter III, Volume V, of the publications of the President's Conference on Home Building and Home Ownership.[1]

Central heating systems. Warm air.—Warm air heating systems are of the gravity type, in which circulation is maintained by the difference in the weight of the warm air leaving the furnace, and of the cooler air entering the furnace; or of the forced type, in which circulation is maintained by a fan. Most warm air systems used in homes are of the gravity type.

Parts of system. Casing. Leaders. Stacks.—The inner section of the furnace in which the fuel is burned is enclosed in a brick or sheet metal casing, through which the air circulates. The heated air passes from the sides or top of the casing into sheet metal pipes, known as leaders, the size of which depends upon the temperature desired in the air as it enters a room, but which should have a diameter of at least 8 inches. The tops of all leaders should leave the furnace casing at the same height and should have an upgrade of approximately one inch for each foot of length. The leaders open into vertical pipes in the walls, called stacks. Stacks should always be placed in inside walls and should be square or nearly square in shape. The stacks carrying the heated air to the upper floors should be not less than 70 per cent of the area of the leaders. All ducts should be insulated against wood or other inflammable materials.

Registers.—The stacks open into register boxes set in the floors or walls, and from these boxes the warm air passes through the register into the room. The register should have a minimum free area equal to the area of its leader, and this free area should be at least 70 per cent of the gross area of the register. The National Warm Air Heating Association specifies 175°F. as the desirable temperature of the air issuing from the register, when the leaders are 6 to 8 feet long. When leaders are longer than 8 feet they must be well covered with an insulating wrapping or so much heat will be lost in transit that the desired temperature will not be maintained. If the air is too hot it will tend to rise toward the ceiling, leaving the floor cold.

Recirculating ducts.—The air supply may be brought from the outside, or from within the house through what are known as recirculating ducts, or there may be a combination of the two methods.

[1] Pp. 122-125.

It requires approximately twice as much coal to heat the house if all the air is brought from outside. The recirculating duct method is, therefore, the more common, and to be efficient, the duct should have an area greater than the total area of the warm air pipes. Long ducts, particularly, must be of large size. A smooth inner surface and good pitch minimize the friction. The room opening of the duct is placed near to a source of cold air, i.e., close to a cold wall, under a window, or near a door. The furnace end of the duct must be below the bottom of the grate.

Grate.—There is a close interdependence between the efficiency of the furnace, the combustion rate, and the temperature maintained at the register. The grate must be large enough to burn the fuel, and the chimney must be properly constructed to produce a sufficient draft. Chimneys will be discussed in a later section (p. 298). Experiments carried on at the University of Illinois have shown that the number of British thermal units per total grate per hour may be nearly tripled by the use of an adequate fan. With the fan, too, the air may be of lower temperature, on account of increased circulation.

Hot water system.—In hot water systems, in which water circulates instead of air, a boiler takes the place of the furnace, the pipes are smaller, and the heat is passed on to the rooms by radiators. The circulation may be maintained by gravity, due to the difference in weight of the water in the return and outflow pipes, or the pressure actuating the flow may be produced by a pump. In systems using a pump the pressure is greater than in gravity systems, so that smaller pipes and radiators may be used, thereby reducing the installation cost. The cost of running the pump must be taken into consideration, however.

The hot water system may be the two-pipe type in which each radiator is connected directly to the boiler, and as a result all radiators are supplied with water of approximately the same temperature; or it may have but one pipe. In the latter type the water flows through several radiators before returning to the boiler, and is, therefore, cooler in each succeeding radiator. To offset this cooling, larger radiators must be used. The two-pipe type is further divided into the direct and reversed return systems. In the direct return system the water from the more distantly connected radiators follows a longer path in returning to the boiler, so that the radiator nearest to the boiler tends to receive more hot water than the others; in the reversed system all paths are of comparatively equal length.

Boiler.—The boiler selected will depend on the character of the load, the space available, and the kind of fuel to be used. It is well to choose one which may be adapted to any future change in fuel, is easy to clean and fire, and requires a minimum amount of attention. Boilers are made of cast iron or of steel. The cast iron types are usually sectional in form, of round horizontal sections with a circular grate or of rectangular vertical sections. Both types have a low water line and allow a maximum hot water pressure of about 30 pounds. The steel boiler has a water-jacketed fire-box, so that it is not necessary to protect the steel with brickwork. Another type, known as the "magazine feed boiler," is often used in the home, because of its fairly large fuel capacity, which lengthens the time between firings. It may be built of cast iron or steel, and is adapted for the burning of small sized anthracite. The coal is fed onto the grates from a hopper located above the fire-box, and the action continues until the supply is exhausted. Cast iron boilers resist corrosion to a greater extent than boilers of other materials.

All boilers should have a combustion chamber large enough to allow sufficient mixing of air with the gases to bring about complete combustion, and at the same time maintain a high enough temperature for burning to take place before the gases are cooled by contact with the boiler surfaces. The output of boilers is rated in British thermal units per hour.

Boiler rooms.—Boiler rooms should be centrally located and well lighted. A space at least 3 feet longer than the boiler fire-box should be left in front of the boiler for firing, stoking, ash removal, and cleaning. A 3-foot space on one side gives access to dampers, cleanouts, etc., and a similar space in the rear gives access to the chimney and other cleanouts. The ceiling of the boiler room is preferably not less than $3\frac{1}{2}$ feet above the normal water line of the boiler to allow for necessary piping. The outflow water pipe is at the top of the boiler, the return pipe at the bottom.

Expansion tank.—An expansion tank is usually necessary to allow for the expansion and contraction of the water in the system during heating and cooling. The tank may be open or closed. An open tank is placed above the highest radiator and allows expansion at atmospheric pressure; the closed tank is placed below the level of the radiators, and is under increased pressure when the water expands. Either location should prevent boiling in any radiator when the boiler is run at high speed on a very cold day. The tank should have a capacity equivalent to about 10 per cent of the capacity of the system, or twice the volume increase when the water is heated from its average to its maximum temperature. It should be protected against boiling or freezing. Occasionally the boiler pipes are connected to the water system and the expansion tank eliminated. Such a connection is separate from the usual cold water connection used to fill the boiler.

Piping.—The pipes leaving the boiler are known as risers. They should be pitched to allow gases to rise and provided with vents for the escape of the gas. Insulation should cover the pipes to keep in the heat. Uninsulated pipes may result in heat loss equivalent to a ton or more of coal. These losses in heat transmission are not losses like those from the top of the chimney, for they are in the house somewhere, but they may be sufficient to decrease to too great an extent the heat needed in the individual rooms. A valve in each pipe permits the entire system to be drained or only a section, as desired.

Radiator.—Radiator is the name given to an exposed heating unit in counter distinction to a unit enclosed in a wall or in a room cabinet, which is known as a convector. The term radiator is somewhat of a misnomer since less than 50 per cent of the heat from the radiator is emitted by radiation, the larger percentage of heat being transferred by conduction to the air in contact with the unit and then carried by convection currents throughout the room.

Types of radiators.—The tubular radiator is the type most commonly found in the home, although the wall type is used to advantage in certain rooms such as bathrooms, toilets, and basement rooms, the flat sections being hung singly or in multiple against the wall or ceiling. The long low tubular radiator gives more satisfactory heating results than the high one.

Location of radiators.—Radiators should be placed below or near the area of maximum heat loss. Beneath windows has been found to be an especially favorable location since the warm air rising from the radiator protects against drafts around the window, and the infiltering cold air is warmed as it passes over the radiator.

Painting on radiators.—Painting a radiator influences the amount of heat radiated, but has only a negligible effect on the convection loss. It is the outside coat which affects radiation, bright metallic paints greatly reducing the heat emission. Severns found that if the heating value of a radiator covered with dull black paint were considered 100 per cent, the comparative value of aluminum bronze was only 90.8 per cent, but that gray paint gave a heating value of 101.1 per cent. The effect of paint on tubular radiators is less noticeable, since much of the heat transfer is by convection rather than by radiation. With the open tank the water temperature in the radiator should not be above 170°F.; with the pressure tank the temperature may be as high as 220°F.

Convectors.—Convectors, or enclosed heating units, transfer the heat almost entirely by conduction to the surrounding air, from where it is circulated by convection currents. Frequently an ordinary radiator is enclosed. Such an enclosure may result in better heat distribution below the breathing line, giving lower temperatures at the ceiling where heat is not needed. On the other hand, if the enclosure or shield is not properly designed, the radiator may fail to heat the room adequately and it will be necessary to replace the radiator with one of larger size. Tests conducted by the Engineering Experiment Station of the University of Illinois, in which a cloth cover was placed over a radiator and extended 6 inches down the sides, gave unsatisfactory results, reducing the heat emitted.

Filling the system.—When the expansion tank is open, i.e., the water flows by gravity, the system is filled with water in the following manner; with all radiator air vents closed the valve connecting the boiler to the water supply line is partly opened. Then, starting with the radiators on the first floor, the air vents are opened one after another until all radiators are filled with water. Additional water is allowed to flow into the system until the level reached is approximately 1/3 of the gauge glass on the expansion tank. The opening of the radiator vents must be repeated after the boiler has been running for a few days, because water, before it has been boiled, always contains a certain amount of air, which tends to collect in the radiators.

Steam heating.—Systems of heating by steam use a boiler, piping, and radiators similar to those used in the hot water system. Steam flows to the radiator, where it condenses and the water flows back to the boiler. It is more satisfactory to have the system built for a low initial pressure—approximately one pound in a residence plant—and for a comparatively small pressure drop, not over 2 ounces for the entire home system. Such a system will operate under higher pressures without trouble, but when a system of high initial pressure and large pressure drop is operated at low pressure poor circulation results, often with noise in the pipes. A knocking noise, known as "water-hammer," also frequently occurs when the steam of high velocity opposes the condensate flowing in the opposite direction back to the boiler, or if water lies in the pipes or in the radiators. Radiators are usually controlled by air valves which may be throttled, or by an orifice varying the pressure.

Selection of heater.—In selecting a furnace choose one with adequate combustion space and adequate heat-exchanging surfaces if satisfactory heating results are to be obtained. It is not true economy to pay a low initial price and then have a high cost of operation in an effort to secure the desired heat.

Care of furnace and boiler.—The efficient service which any piece of equipment will render depends to a great extent upon the care which it receives. The heater is no exception. Inside passages and flues frequently become clogged with soot because of a poor draft, which causes too slow a rate of combustion and, hence, a smoky fire. Soot is an insulator and hinders the absorption of heat. Chimney sweeps seem to have gone out of fashion, and yet a yearly freeing of the chimney from deposits of soot and scale will increase the efficiency of the heating plant to a noticeable degree.

Since the furnace or boiler usually deteriorates more rapidly during the summer months of rest than when in use, it should be thoroughly cleaned, both flues and inside surfaces, shortly after the fire is out. The pipe connecting the furnace to the chimney may be removed with advantage to a dry place. The rusting of interior surfaces is minimized by spraying with lubricating oil, and machined parts, such as door and damper bearings, may be coated with oil or grease. The grate and ash-pit are also cleaned and if, in the case of the boiler, condensation tends to occur on either exterior or interior surfaces, the boiler should be drained. It is also well to loosen the nuts on the ends of the tie-rods which hold sectional boilers together. This decreases any tension which may be caused by corrosion. The doors to ash-pit, clean-out, and fire-box may be left open.

Before the hot water boiler is started in the fall, the system is drained, flushed to remove sediment and dirt, and then refilled as described on p. 295. All control devices should be tested, and if necessary, readjusted.

During the winter season when the furnace or boiler is in use, excess ashes should not be allowed to collect in the ash-pit, but should be removed daily. If ashes push up against the grate, they will tend to burn it out, or at least warp the grate bars.

Maintaining a fairly even rate of operation also tends to increase the life of the heater. The custom of allowing the furnace to run at greatly reduced speed during the night and then opening the drafts and forcing the fire in the morning to bring the house back to a comfortable temperature is bad for the heater, and a very doubtful means of economizing on fuel, for this morning forcing causes a serious over-load on the plant, thereby shortening its life, and fuel is frequently burned in large quantities so that excessive amounts of heat are carried up the chimney.

If properly fired, the grate may be shaken early in the morning, the draft opened, and the fire allowed to run for some time before adding fuel, even on cold winter mornings. Fresh coal tends to cool the fire and slow up the heating process. In mild weather the grate need not be shaken, but the draft may be opened and after the fire has burned up, the usual fuel added.

Factors affecting efficiency.—The efficiency of any furnace or boiler depends upon the completeness of combustion of the fuel, and this in turn depends to a large extent upon the amount of draft. The draft, produced by a difference between the air pressure in the system and that of the outside atmosphere, draws in the air which supports combustion and causes circulation of the gases. When secondary air is admitted above the fuel bed, it is usually not sufficiently mixed with the combustible gases before they have been cooled below their ignition temperatures, so that these gases pass off as smoke to the detriment of the outside air and with decreased heat in the system. Such conditions are more apt to occur when the coal is fine rather than in lumps. When lump coal is used, however, care must be taken not to allow an amount of air, in excess of what is needed to bring about complete combustion, to circulate, since useful heat is thereby carried up the chimney, which is used by most home plants to supply a natural draft. Some heat must escape to cause the difference in temperature necessary to produce the draft, but an excess should be avoided. When the natural draft is not sufficient a fan may be built into the chimney to aid the suction, or a forced draft may be produced by a fan below the fire-box.

Chimney.—According to the regulations of the National Board of Fire Underwriters a chimney should have only one opening for the boiler or furnace, and one smoke opening. The draft in the chimney is spiral in form, so that round or nearly square chimneys are most efficient. The clean-out must be air-tight. Chimneys with walls at least 8 inches thick may be left unlined if the inner bricks are of refractory clay; chimneys of less thickness must be lined with fire clay at least ¾ of an inch thick, smooth on the inside, without any cracks or crevices. No chimney shall have walls less than 3¾ inches thick. Outside chimneys are subject to greater heat losses than those on the inside, and should, accordingly, have thicker walls. Flue linings shall extend 4 inches below the bottom of the furnace openings and 4 inches above the chimney, and be capped with concrete, terra cotta, stone, or similar substances which, however, shall not reduce the area of the outlet to less than that of the flue. The chimney must be high enough so that wind will not strike the top at an angle above the horizontal. To avoid this chimneys shall extend 3 feet above flat roofs and 2 feet higher than any ridge pole within 30 feet. In general, chimneys under 35 feet in height do not give sufficient draft and are to be avoided, though chimneys of less height may prove satisfactory when there are no higher buildings in the near surroundings. Chimneys should be tested to be sure that they are smoke-tight.

Draft loss.—The amount and effectiveness of the draft depend not alone upon the chimney, but also upon the construction of the furnace or boiler and the character of the fuel. The draft is hindered by a thick bed of fine fuel which gives only small interstices through which the air may pass. Bituminous coal usually requires less draft because of the large openings between the coarse chunks of coal. A high percentage of ash and/or dirt with the coal also causes draft loss by slowing up combustion. Similarly, the flow of air may be impeded or accelerated by the type of grate and the presence of baffles and tubes in the boiler. It is well to test the amount of draft needed with any coal and rate of burning to give the most satisfactory results.

Fuels.—Fuels have been discussed in Chapter IV, from the point of view of their use in the kitchen range. When these same fuels are used in heating systems the problem is somewhat different and certain additional suggestions may be of value. It must always be kept in mind that "it is quite impossible to separate the fuel from the equipment in which it is burned."

Anthracite.—Anthracite burns uniformly with a short flame and little smoke and requires the minimum of attention between firings. With all except the smaller sizes the fuel bed should be fired deeply and evenly; with pea coal the glowing coals are pushed to one side or to the back and the new coal shoveled into the hollow thus made. Shake the grate before each firing to remove the ash and improve the draft. Never poke an anthracite fire; poking brings the ash to the surface where it melts and forms clinker.

Bituminous.—Bituminous and semi-bituminous coals are more easily ignited than the anthracites; they burn with a fairly long flame and some smoke which tends to deposit soot. Therefore, they require a good supply of secondary air after firing to aid in consuming the gases and reducing the smoke. The whole fuel bed is never fired at one time, but the fuel is pushed aside and the new coal added in the hollow. Some authorities suggest pushing the burning fuel to the back of the fire-box so that the gases given off from the new coal may pass over the glowing lumps and be ignited before reaching the flue. (Fig. 120.) In this way smoke is largely eliminated and the problem of temperature wastage through the chimney, a problem which is much more prevalent with bituminous than with anthracite coal, practically disappears. If the bed is fired as deeply as possible up to the level of the door or even higher at the back there will be a longer interval between firings. A deep fuel bed also improves the draft, for soft coal burns unevenly and tends to form holes in the bed, when fired in thin layers. These holes reduce the draft.

The bituminous coals are inclined to cake so that stoking is often necessary. This may be done any time from 20 minutes to one hour after firing, as seems advisable. In stoking, care must be taken not to bring the bar to the surface of the fuel bed, as the ash comes too, and forms clinker. Bituminous coal burns more rapidly than anthracite, and, therefore, requires less draft, but on the other hand, usually needs more attention. Best results are obtained if the fuel is

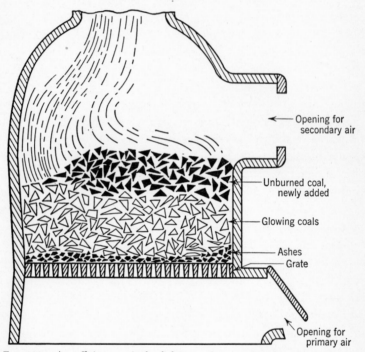

FIG. 120.—An efficient method of firing a furnace with bituminous coal.

added and the fire shaken at regular intervals. Too frequent shaking or poking will spoil any fire.

Quite recently a process has been developed for dust proofing coal by treating it with a calcium chloride spray. Coal so treated is entirely free from dust and dirt, without any increase in cost to the consumer, so that this most objectionable feature of coal usage has been eliminated.

Coke.—Coke burns more rapidly than the other varieties of coal and gives a hot fire with little or no ash so that a screen of refractory brick is necessary to protect the grate. The secondary air damper should be left partly open most of the time and all openings to the ash-pit kept closed. Keep the fuel bed deep and shake only slightly.

Stokers.—Although most furnaces are fired by hand, stokers are being used more and more widely because of their higher efficiency. They distribute the fuel evenly, regulate the air needed for complete combustion, and often remove ash. With stokers the temperature may be controlled to vary less than one degree in 24 hours, so that any satisfactory temperature may be uniformly maintained.

Stokers are not new. Though they have been used in apartment houses and homes only for the past few years, they have been employed for industrial purposes for a long time, several patents running back nearly 100 years.

Types.—Stokers are of two general types, the overfeed and underfeed. One overfeed stoker has a moving grate which carries a uniform layer of coal through the furnace at a rate of speed sufficient to allow complete combustion by the time the grate reaches the rear. No clinkers are formed since the fuel is not disturbed, and the ash is dumped over the back end into the pit. Another overfeed stoker has a "rocking" grate which breaks up the coal, allowing air to enter, but tends to form clinker. Both types have an arch over the front end of the stoker to aid in the ignition of the incoming fuel.

The underfeed types have a system of retorts below the fire bed into which the fuel is fed, and then raised to the bed. The gases are released as the fuel is raised, and mix with the air and burn. Since the efficient and complete burning of the fuel and hence the economy of operation depend upon the retort, its correct design is of prime importance. Blowers may be used to increase the draft. With a forced draft there are no ashes to handle, for the ash inherent in the coal fuses to a "doughnut" clinker, which may be taken out with tongs. With better grades of coal it is usually necessary to remove these clinkers only once a week, even in very cold weather, but if the coal is high in ash content or low in heat value it may be necessary to take out the clinkers every day during severe cold spells. The overfeed stokers need more height in the combustion chamber than the underfeed types, to allow the gases to oxidize. Coal may be fed intermittently or continuously.

Many stokers have large hoppers which are filled periodically by hand, either by the home owner, or the coal dealer, who offers complete heat service at a fixed rate per month. This service includes removal of ashes or clinkers. Some of the newer stokers used with anthracite coals convey the coal from the bin or bunker to the boiler, and remove the ashes in turn to a covered receptacle, the conveyer itself being under the cellar floor. With these types the storage compartments for both coal and ashes may be outside the home, an arrangement which eliminates all dust and dirt and provides the ultimate in performance.

Oil.—Specially designed oil burners are frequently used for house heating, or oil may be used with an attachment in place of coal in the boiler, although this method is not as efficient. Formerly only the first three grades of oil were burned in domestic heaters, but improvement in the form of the burner has made possible the use of the last three grades which are heavier and have a higher British thermal unit rating per gallon.

The oil is stored in tanks; in the cellar, when the tank is not over 275 gallons capacity, or buried outside, according to the regulations of the National Board of Fire Underwriters, when the capacity is from 550 to 1,500 gallons. The oil must be vaporized before it will burn, either by forcing it through a small orifice or by throwing it in a thin film from a rotating disc. The necessary air is usually supplied by a fan, preferably motor-driven.

The burner may be intermittent or what is known as the "high-low" type. With the intermittent type some means of ignition must be provided, either a gas pilot or an electric spark. The "off and on" burner is more satisfactory in mild weather, but the high-low type possesses the advantage on very cold days when the intermittent burner tends to produce more heat than the boiler can absorb. The temperature is usually controlled by a thermostat in one of the living rooms.

As a safeguard it is essential to have an automatic device to shut off the heat when the water falls below the safety line, also a device to protect against too hot water or too great steam pressure if the burner runs a long time. The direct flame should not impinge upon the boiler surface, which should be protected with a lining of fire brick. Burner flues should be cleaned at least once a year. The basement or boiler room should be open to the outside air; if necessary cut an inch from the bottom of the outer door.

Gas.—Gas may be used as the source of heat in either warm air furnaces or boilers. It is thermostatically controlled. In general automatic devices tend to save fuel but often give a higher temperature in the spring and fall than is necessary.

Space heaters.—In many parts of the South and Southwest, winters are not sufficiently severe to necessitate central heating plants; instead space heaters are used when needed, and stored in summer. They are often gas-fired because of the prevalence of natural gas in these regions, but electricity may be used.

Types.—Some space heaters look like cabinet radios. The burners are within a central drum around which the air circulates, the cool air entering at the bottom and the heated air leaving through the top. Other heaters are in the form of unit steam or hot water radiators with a separate chamber which may or may not be vented, in which the automatically controlled gas burns. Warm air radiators may be similarly heated.

Radiant heaters of iron, enamel, or brass have refractory bodies of fire clay which are heated by a Bunsen type flame. When the radiating surface is polished metal instead of fire clay, the flame is usually luminous. Gas logs of fire clay, constructed like radiant heaters, or the coal basket type may be used in the fireplace.

Electric heaters.—Electricity may be used in all types of space heaters instead of gas, and even in central systems where the cost is not prohibitive. It gives maximum efficiency and is clean, reliable, without the danger of flame or undesirable products of combustion, and is simply and accurately regulated.

Oil space heaters.—Portable kerosene-burning heaters have been used for years to provide extra heat before the central plant is started or on severe winter days. Recently an oil-burning heating stove has been placed on the market. It burns the heavier fuel oils in a specially constructed fire bowl without a wick, and may have flue connection. The gravity feed supplies the oil in sufficient quantities to keep the flame burning at a rate necessary to maintain the temperature indicated on the dial control. The heater is equipped with a reservoir large enough for approximately two days' supply and may be refueled without extinguishing the fire, or the heater may be connected to a tank outside the house and the oil-flow controlled by a valve. Some units have shutters on the sides which may be opened at various angles to direct the heat to any part of the room. This type of heater is especially useful in rural homes without central systems, since sufficient heat is given off by the one unit to keep several rooms comfortable except, perhaps, in very severe weather.

Unit furnaces.—Between the central plant with the furnace in the cellar and systems of pipes extending throughout the house and the unit heater are various types not falling definitely into either classification. One of these types is the pipeless furnace. It is located as near the center of the basement as possible, and has one large flue or register in the floor above, through which all the heat flows. Although fairly successful in heating the cottage or bungalow home it usually does not produce sufficient heat to warm second floor rooms to a comfortable degree in all kinds of weather, and the space directly above the furnace tends to be overheated.

Where the house has no cellar, a coal-burning unit-type of heater in one room may be connected to radiators in the other rooms and the whole house heated in this way, or the coal may be replaced with oil or gas, eliminating the labor and dirt of fueling and removal of ashes.

Recently a new heating unit, which combines the functions of kitchen range, hot water heater, and furnace, has been placed on the market. By the use of a small electric blower, warmed humidified air is forced through small insulated metal ducts to all the rooms. At the same time the hot water boiler is heated and the top surface and oven raised to cooking temperature. Forced-air draft insures complete combustion, and heat exchangers conserve the heat and increase the efficiency.

VENTILATION

Air is the first and most important essential for life. The average man consumes about 4 pounds of water and 3 pounds of food a day; he breathes in during that short period 34 pounds of air. The larger portion of the day is spent within the walls of some building, so that some means of obtaining a supply of fresh air is indispensable to well-being. Ventilation, however, is no longer the simple matter of opening a window and changing the air, but under the new term, "air conditioning" implies maintaining conditions suitable for comfort and health—in other words, supplying the necessary oxygen, heat, and moisture, and removing harmful odors, dust, and excessive moisture and heat. Although this conditioning is most successfully accomplished by mechanical means, the majority of homes still find it necessary to attempt to ventilate by natural methods.

Area per individual.—The amount of oxygen removed from the air in one hour by an adult is negligible, but sufficient heat and moisture may be given off to increase the temperature and humidity to an uncomfortable extent. Consequently the minimum area recommended for each occupant in a room is 50 square feet or 500 cubic feet of air space. At the same time windows or doors should be open wide enough to give unobstructed spaces equivalent to at least 5 per cent of the floor area. In an efficiently ventilated kitchen the air should be completely changed every 10 minutes.

Natural ventilation.—Natural ventilation is brought about by the wind and the difference in temperature within and without the house. Vertical outlets as side windows are not nearly as effective as chimneys, but when a window is opened in a room containing a fireplace a very satisfactory circulation of air results. Windows on only one side of a room do not permit cross ventilation, and skylights are effective only when used with a side wall opening. The distance between openings should be measured vertically, not horizontally, and should be as great as possible that the outlet and inlet air may vary in temperature sufficiently to bring about circulation. When there is no perceptible movement of air, artificial circulation may be brought about with a fan which will produce a cooling effect equivalent to several degrees' drop in temperature.

Air conditioning.—When the air is recirculated instead of being brought from outside the house, it should first be conditioned. Air conditioning is removing the dust and keeping the atmosphere at the temperature and percentage of humidity best suited to the requirements of the body. Relative humidity, or simply humidity, as the term is somewhat loosely used, is the ratio of the water vapor actually present in the air to the amount which would be in the same volume of air if it were saturated. It is expressed in percentage.

When the relative humidity is low the body easily rids itself of waste matter through perspiration, but with high humidity, perspiration will not flow freely and evaporate, unless the air is moving.

"Effective temperature."—Both excessive heat and cold and extreme or sudden temperature changes are harmful to the body processes. "Effective temperature" is a term used to denote a combination of humidity, temperature, and air movement which results in comfort. Experiments seem to indicate that this temperature is between 63° and 71° in the winter, with the optimum at 66°. The summer range is from 67° to 75° with an optimum of 71°. The optimum temperature may seem low, when first experienced after being warmer, but the body readily adapts to it. Age, health, and activity, however, will tend to influence the temperature desired. The relative humidity should be such that evaporation will occur at a rate which leaves the skin and clothing dry. A minimum of 30 per cent is advised for winter, and a maximum of 60 per cent in the summer.

Winter conditions.—Almost without exception houses are kept too dry in winter unless air conditioned, for the process of heating the air dries it, since warm air can hold a much larger proportion of moisture than can cold air. Dry air having a high affinity for water causes too much moisture to leave the skin and lungs, resulting in a sensation of coolness, and the desire for a higher external temperature. The heat then makes the person feel lazy, if not actually uncomfortable, and the mucous membranes tend to dry so that disease germs find ready access and colds or other respiratory infections result. An "effective temperature" of 65° gives a temperature of 69.5°F. and a relative humidity of 40 per cent. At an outside temperature of zero it may be necessary to evaporate as much as 24 gallons of water in 24 hours to maintain a humidity of 40 per cent. Each pound of water evaporated at 70°F. absorbs about 1053 B.t.u. from the room, thus lowering the temperature and at the same time making the room more comfortable for occupancy. This lower temperature does not necessarily mean less fuel consumption, for heat is required to evaporate the water. Results of tests by the American Society of Heating and Ventilating Engineers' Research Laboratory showed that no water pan in the hot air furnace tested evaporated sufficient water to maintain a 40 per cent humidity, nor were the water pans in the radiator shields more successful in a second series of tests, when the outside temperature was approximately 0°F. At the present time hot air furnaces may be supplied with a water tank which is automatically filled as the water evaporates, so that the humidity may be increased to the desired amount. The effectiveness of radiator pans may be improved by keeping them clean and filled with water. Growing plants in a room also help to humidify the air.

Fig. 121.—Air filter, clean when new, but dirty after a few months of use.

High indoor humidity causes frost to form on the windows, although double windows retard the tendency. Frost will form on single windows at a temperature of 25°F., when the humidity is only 30 per cent, but with double windows the humidity can reach 48 per cent, even at a temperature of 0°F., before frosting occurs.

Air conditioning equipment.—Air conditioning has as yet found a very limited application in the home, but it is being used more and more extensively in factories, theaters, department stores, apartment houses, hotels, and public buildings. Air conditioning appliances will automatically keep the air at the desired temperature and humidity. One type is in the form of an atomizer which sprays the moisture directly into the room. In the indirect method the air is filtered, washed, and warmed or cooled, depending upon the season, before it circulates. Refrigeration types of coils are frequently used for the cooling process. In winter, moisture may be added, and in summer removed. The air is cleaned by circulating it through filters, which remove a very high percentage of the dust. (Fig. 121.) The heating and ventilating systems may be combined by using a fan to blow the conditioned air into the ducts leading to the rooms. Equipment for humidifying must be included.

Mechanical humidifiers of the cabinet or console type are also used and are usually satisfactory. Some types are built to fit inside the pipes of the warm air furnace system. Small unit air conditioners which fit on the sill of any window of standard size and are operated by being plugged into an electric socket are advertised to ventilate, filter, cool or heat, humidify, and even silence undesirable outside noises, simply by the turn of a dial.

Summary.

1. Some external source of heat is essential during the cold months of the year.
2. The type and size of heating plant needed are determined by the location and construction of the home, the internal temperature desired, and the average outside weather conditions which prevail.
3. A fuel should be selected which will give the desired results in the particular heating plant, under the prevailing conditions of operation.
4. The efficiency of the plant depends upon:
   (*a*) Adequate supply of air to bring about complete combustion.
   (*b*) A chimney of proper design to maintain necessary draft.
   (*c*) Adequate heating exchange surfaces.
   (*d*) Even rate of operation, which increases life of heater and affords comfort to occupants.
   (*e*) Freedom from deposits of soot in flues or on surfaces.
   (*f*) Removal of ashes and/or clinker when coal is burned.
5. Stokers, by distributing the fuel evenly, regulating the air needed for combustion, and removing the ash, increase the efficiency of coal-fired heaters.
6. Space heaters may burn coal, gas, or electricity, depending upon availability and cost.

7. The object of ventilation, whether by natural or mechanical means, is to maintain conditions suitable for comfort and health.

8. Air conditioning equipment supplies clean air of the correct temperature and humidity both winter and summer.

References

1. A. G. A. Requirements. (1) House Piping and Appliance Installation. 1928. (2) Central House Heating Gas Appliances. 1930. (3) Space Heaters. 1931. American Gas Association, New York.

2. American Society of Heating and Ventilating Engineers Guide. 1932. 1933. Amer. Soc. Heat. and Vent. Eng., New York.

3. Baker, C. W. How to Improve the Hot-Air Furnace. Dept. Int., Bureau of Mines, Tech. Paper 208, Washington, D. C. 1918.

4. Barkley, J. F. Questions and Answers for the Home Fireman. U. S. Dept. Commerce, Bureau of Mines, Washington, D. C. 1933.

5. Breckenridge, L. P., and Flagg, S. B. Saving Fuel in Heating a House. Dept. Int., Bureau of Mines, Tech. Paper 97. Washington, D. C. 1917.

6. Heat and the Span of Life. Amer. Radiator Co., New York. 1928.

7. Heating and Ventilating. Heating and Ventilating Magazine Co., New York.

8. House Design, Construction and Equipment. President's Conf. on Home Building and Home Ownership. Washington, D. C. 1932.

9. How to Burn Soft Coal in the Heating Plant. Eng. Ext. Dept. Bul. 41. Iowa State College, Ames, Iowa. 1918.

10. How to Care for Your Home Plant. Amer. Radiator Co., New York. 1933.

11. Journal of the American Society of Heating and Ventilating Engineers. New York.

12. Kreisinger, H., Augustine, C. E., and Katz, S. H. Low-Rate Combustion in Fuel Beds of Hand Fired Furnaces. Dept. Int., Bureau of Mines, Tech. Paper 139. Washington, D. C. 1918.

13. Kreisinger, H., Augustine, C. E., and Ovitz, F. K. Combustion of Coal and Design of Furnaces. Dept. Int., Bureau of Mines, Bul. 135. Washington, D. C. 1917.

14. Langdon, H. H., and Dana, H. J. Fuel Economy in Domestic Automatic Heating. Eng. Bul. 39. Eng. Expt. Sta., State College of Washington, Pullman, Wash. 1932.

15. Nicholls, P., and Staples, C. W. Removal of Soot from Furnaces and Flues by the Use of Salts or Compounds. U. S. Dept. Commerce, Bureau of Mines, Bul. 360. Washington, D. C. 1932.

16. Nicholls, P., Flagg, S. B., and Augustine, C. E. Five Hundred Tests of Various Coals in House-Heating Boilers. Dept. of Com., Bureau of Mines, Bul. 276. Washington, D. C., 1928.

17. Romance of Air. Amer. Radiator and Standard Sanitary Corp., New York. 1933.

18. Safe Use and Storage of Gasoline and Kerosene on the Farm. U.S.D.A. Farmers' Bul. 1678. Washington, D. C. 1932.

19. Senner, A. H. The Domestic Oil Burner. U.S.D.A. Circ. 405 (revised). 1930.

20. Willard, A. C. Warm-Air Heating Plants. Ladies' Home Jour. Leaflet 205. Curtis Publishing Co., Philadelphia, Pa. 1929.

21. Willard, A. C., Kratz, A. P., and Day, V. S. (1) Investigation of Warm-Air

Furnaces and Heating Systems. Eng. Expt. Sta. Bul. 120. 1921. (2) The Research
Residence. Part IV. Eng. Expt. Sta. Bul. 189. 1929. Univ. of Illinois, Urbana, Ill.
22. Willard, A. C., Kratz, A. P., Fahnestock, M. K., and Konzo, S. Investigation of
Heating Rooms with Direct Steam Radiators Equipped with Enclosures and
Shields. Transactions, Amer. Soc. Heat. and Vent. Eng. 35:77-118. 1929.
23. Wood, T. D., and Hendricksen, E. M. Ventilation and Health. D. Appleton and
Co., New York. 1927.

ILLUSTRATIONS: Fig. 120, Engineering Extension Service, Iowa State College; 121,
The Fox Furnace Co., Elyria, Ohio.

INDEX

Numbers refer to pages

A

Absorption system, 182
Adsorption, 198
A. G. A. Approval Seal, 104
Air conditioning, 305
  equipment, 307
Aluminum, 26, 135
  saucepans, 136
Apartment kitchens, 9
Artificial light, history of, 238
Asbestos, 34

B

Back pressure, in electric cleaner, 231, 233
Baffle, range, 68
  refrigerator, 171
Bakelite, 32
Baking dishes, 146
Baking sheets, 146
Bath, 278
Bearings, 197
Beaters, electric, 131
  hand, 150
Bowls, 132, 153
Branch circuits, 44, 247, 248
"Brass goods," 276

C

Cake pans, 145
Can opener, 154
Can sealer, 161
Chimney, 298
Circuit breaker, 43, 247
Circular work center, 5
Clearing-away center, 3
Closed units, electric range, 61
Closet bowl, tank, 280
  types of, 279
Coal, 52, 299
  range, 107
Combustion of gas, 53, 95
Compression system, 178

Convectors, 295
Convenience outlets, 250
Cooking and serving center, 3
Cork, 35
Cutlery, forks, 159
  knives, 155
  spatula, 159
  spoons, 159

D

Daylight in home, 244
Defrosting, 189
Dirt in rugs, types of, 224
Drip coffee pot, 124, 162
Dryers, 212
Dusting tools, 234
Dutch oven, 138

E

Economical use, of electricity, 75
  of gas, 105
"Effective temperature," 306
Efficient use of oven, electric, 76, 77
  gas, 99
Egg cooker, electric, 130
  non-electric, 162
Electric circuit, 41, 248
Electric cleaner, back pressure in, 231, 233
  bag, 231, 233
  care of, 232
  dusting tools, 234
  fan, 230
  parts of, 226
  types, 226
Electric conductors, 39
Electric cookers, 120
Electric current, alternating, 40
  definition, 39
  direct, 40
  distribution main, 42
  generation, 39
  transmission of, 42
Electric home plants, 45
Electricity, cost of, 45, 46

Electric meter, 43
Electric range, broiler pan, 70
    care of, 78
    closed units, 61
    color, 56
    construction, 57
    heat indicator, 70
    installation of, 74
    open units, 59
    operation, 75
    oven, baffle, 68
        insulation, 66
        lining, 65
        units, 67
    selection of utensils for, 76
    size, 56
    switches, 72
    thermostat, 70
    time control, 72
    types, 56
    units, life of, 65
        speed of, 64
        wattage capacity, 63, 67
    vent, 70
    wiring of, 63
Eyesight conservation, 264

F

Fabrics, effect of washing, 200
Faucets, 277
Floor finishes, 16
Floor machines, electric, 234
Foot candle, 242
Fuels, anthracite, 52, 299
    bituminous, 52, 299
    coke, 300
    electricity, 53, 303
    gas, 53, 303
    gasoline, 53
    kerosene, 53, 303
    oil, 302
Fuse panel, 44, 247
Fuses, 43

G

Gas, bottled, 53, 85
    carburetted water, 53, 84
    chemical composition of, 86
    coal, 84
    heating value, 83
    history, 82
    meter, 88

Gas—(Continued)
    natural, 53, 84
    physics of, 83
Gasoline, 53, 110
    range, 109
Gas range, burners, 92
    care of, 103
    economy of use, 105
    flame, 96
    flue, 96
    insulation, 99
    oven, 98
        regulator, 100
    path of gas flow, 95
    top lighter, 102
    types, 91
Gas water heaters, automatic storage, 284
    instantaneous, 285
    non-automatic, 284
Gears, 196
Glare, 243, 253
Graters, 160

H

"Hard" flame, 97
Hard water, 198
Heat control, irons, 215
    ovens, 70, 100
Heat indicator, 70
Heating plant, boiler, 293
    care of, 296
    expansion tank, 293
    hot water, 292
    size of, 289
    space heaters, 303
    steam, 296
    unit furnaces, 304
    warm air, 291
Home plants, electric, 45
Hot plates, 122
Hot water heaters, care of, 285
    coal, 283
    electric, 285
    gas, 283
    insulation of, 285
    waterfront, 283
House heating, history of, 288
    methods, 288

I

Ice chamber, 171
Illuminometer, 242

Iron, characteristics of, 213
  cord, 214
  heat control, 215
  types, 213
Ironers, controls, 218
  heating of, 220
  history, 212
  shoe, 217
  types, 219
Ironing board, 216
Ironing temperature, 218

J

Juice extractors, 133, 161

K

Kerosene, 53, 113, 118
  range, 110
    care of, 117
    long-drum burner, 113
    ovens, 118
    short-drum burner, 111
Kettles, 136
Kitchen, apartment, 9
  artificial light in, 15
  clearance space, 7, 9, 23
  doors and windows, 12
  exposure, 15
  floor and wall finishes, 16
  moderately sized, 12
  pantry, 20
  planning desk, 23
  routing, 4
  rural, 11
  shape, 7
  sink, 21
  size, 8
  storage cabinets, 10, 17
  ventilation, 15
  work centers, 2
  working heights, 22
Knife sharpener, 154
Knives, 155

L

Lamps, A, 262
  care of, 263
  frosted, 261
  health, 266
  Mazda B, 261
  Mazda C, 261
  types, 258

Latent heat, 168
Lavatory, 277
Light, cove, 264
  decorative, 263
  intensity, 241
  measurement, 241, 242
  non-electric, 268
  panel, 264
  physics of, 240
  transmission, 243
Light fixtures, bathroom, 258
  bedroom, 258
  care of, 263
  central, 249
  dining room, 256
  entrance, 254
  hall, 255
  kitchen, 257
  living room, 255
  rehabilitation of, 258
  stair, 250
  types, 253
  wall, 250
Linoleum, 16, 36
Long-drum burner, 113
Lumen, 242

M

Materials used in equipment, aluminum,
    26
  asbestos, 34
  Bakelite, 32
  chromium, 31
  copper, 31
  cork, 35
  earthenware, 32
  glass, 32
  iron, 27
  linoleum, 36
  mica, 34
  Monel, 32
  nickel, 31
  porcelain enamel, 29
  rock wool, 34
  rubber tile, 37
  tin, 29
Measuring cups, 147
Measuring spoons, 148
Meter, electric, 43
  gas, 88
Mixing machines, 130
Molds, 161
Monel, 32

Motor, electric cleaner, 231
    ironer, 218
    refrigerator, 179
    washer, 207
Motor-driven agitator cleaner, 229
Motor-driven brush cleaner, 227
Muffin pans, 145

N

Name plate, 48
National Electric Code, 42, 246, 247

O

Ohm's law, application of, 48
Oil-burning refrigerator, 186
Open circuit, 48
Open units, 59
Operating efficiency, 54
Oven regulator, 70, 100

P

Pans, cake, 145
    muffin, 145
    roasting, 144
Percolator, 122
Piping, plumbing, 275
Porcelain enamel, 29, 274
Preparation center, 2
Pressure cooker, 140
Pumps, 272

R

Radiator, effect of painting, 295
    location, 294
    types, 294
Range, coal, 107
    electric, 56
    gas, 91
    gasoline, 109
    kerosene, 110
Recirculating ducts, 291
Red Seal Plan, 248
Refrigerant, ammonia, 192
    characteristics, 189
    methyl chloride, 191
    sulphur dioxide, 190
Refrigeration, absorption system, 182
    amount of ice needed, 175
    compression system, 178
    history, 165
    ice, 171

Refrigeration—(Continued)
    need for, 169
    physical principles of, 167
Refrigerator, automatic quick freezing, 181
    brine tank, 181
    care of, 192
    circulation in, 171, 172
    classification of ice types, 177
    coldest location, 172
    construction, 173
    conventional unit, 180
    defrosting, 189
    door, 176
    drain pipe, 177
    food space, 177
    gas burner, 186
    insulation, 174
    lining, 174
    location of food in, 172
    mechanical, 177
    oil-burning, 186
    rotary compressor, 180
    sealed-in unit, 180
    size, 188
    specifications for, 173
    thermostat, 181
Registers, 291
Regulations for bathroom fixtures, 275
Roasting pans, 144
Rock wool, 34
Rug structure, 224
Running water, 272
Rural kitchens, 11

S

Saucepans, 136
Sewage disposal, 282
Short circuit, 50
Short-drum burner, 111
Shower, 278
Sifters, 149
Sink, 21
Slicers, 161
Small equipment, classification, 120, 135
Soap, 199
"Soft" flame, 97
Soil, on clothing, 201
Spatula, 159
Specific heat, 167
Stain removal, 210
Steamer, 140
Stoker, 301
Storage cabinets, 17
Straight-air suction cleaner, 226

Strainers, 149
Surface tension, 198
Switch, light, 251
  range, 72

T

Table stoves, 121
Thermal efficiency, 54
Thermostat, range, 70
  refrigerator, 181
Time control, electric, 72
  gas, 102
Toaster, 124
Transformer, 41
Trap, 279, 281
Tricolator, 124, 162

V

Vent, electric range, 70
  gas range, 98
  plumbing, 282
Ventilation, air conditioning, 305
  importance of, 304
  natural, 305
  winter conditions, 306

W

Waffle iron, 127
Wall finishes, 16
Washing machines, care of, 210
  filling tub, 208
  gas attachment, 208
  materials, 207
  protective devices, 207
  types, 201
Washing process, 209
Washing time, 203
Water extractor, air-pressure, 206
  centrifugal, 205
  wringer, 204
Waterless cooker, 139
Water softening, 276
Windmill, 273
Wire, sizes, 46, 247
Wiring, adequate, 246, 248
  cost of, 268
  distribution center, 246
  symbols, 248
  systems, 247
Work centers, 2
Wringers, 204

Date Due

Nov 15 '44			
Nov 10 '49			
May 23 '50			
Dec 19 '52			
RESERVE			
OFF RES.			